Elementary Differential Equations

Elementary

Second Edition

Differential Equations

EARL D. RAINVILLE

Professor of Mathematics
The University of Michigan

The Macmillan Company · New York

Printed in the United States of America

Seventh Printing 1962

Library of Congress catalog card number: 58-5011

Chapters 1–17 appear under the title *A Short Course in Differential Equations,* Second Edition, © The Macmillan Company 1958.

Preface

The present edition of this book includes many topics not treated in the first edition.   Much of the new material is aimed at arousing, or increasing, the student's desire to continue his studies beyond the scope of this book.   In particular, Chapter 20 presents a short introduction to the Gamma and factorial functions, the hypergeometric and confluent hypergeometric equations, Bessel's equation, and the polynomials of Legendre, Hermite and Laguerre.   The sections on orthogonal polynomials in Chapter 24 were added for the same purpose.   A few other new topics appear at intervals throughout the book.

The number of exercises has been increased to almost 1600, nearly half of which are new.   Several changes, which I hope are improvements, have been made in the old text material.

As in the first edition, I have tried to exhibit both the techniques for obtaining solutions and the basic ideas and theory behind these techniques.   The numerous exercises have been constructed carefully with the aim of developing the student's skill and often of adding to his knowledge.   Definitions and statements of fact are made with care.

The material is arranged to permit great flexibility in the choice of topics for a semester course.   Except for Chapters 1, 2, 7–9, and 16–19, any chapter on ordinary differential equations (Chapters 1-22) can be omitted as a whole without interfering with the study of later chapters.   Parts of chapters can be omitted in many instances.

For a course which aims at reaching power series as rapidly as is consistent with some treatment of more elementary methods, a reasonable set of omissions would be Chapters 4, 6, 10, 15, Sections 53–56 of Chapter 11, the latter parts of Chapters 16, 17, plus whatever applications the instructor cares to omit.

This book has sufficient material for a year course, if the individual topics are taken up with the attention to detail that a full year course suggests.

Applications occupy about one fifth of the book. It is my belief that the student benefits more from the detailed study of a few applications than he does from a casual contact with numerous ones.

Chapters 1 through 17 of this book appear separately as *A Short Course in Differential Equations.* The shorter version is intended for courses which do not include any discussion of infinite series methods.

I am grateful for the comments and suggestions received from many of my colleagues here at Michigan and from instructors and students in other colleges and universities. It has not been feasible to include all the additional topics and expanded treatments requested, for such inclusion would have nearly doubled the size of the book.

I am pleased to acknowledge in particular the aid and encouragement I received from Professors C. A. Hutchinson, Jack R. Britton, and L. C. Snively of the University of Colorado, Professors William N. Huff and Fred Brafman of the University of Oklahoma, Professors R. V. Churchill, R. C. F. Bartels, G. E. Hay, and the late Donat K. Kazarinoff of the University of Michigan.

Certain acknowledgements made in the preface to the first edition are still pertinent in the present edition. I remain thus additionally indebted to Professors Britton, Churchill, Brafman, and Huff as well as to Dr. E. F. Ziegler, M.D., of Pasadena, to Professor Ross R. Middlemiss of Washington University, and to Drs. Alice and David Dickinson of The University of Massachusetts.

Earl D. Rainville

Ann Arbor, Michigan

Contents

Chapter 10: *Nonhomogeneous Equations: Operational Methods*

Chapter 11: *Variation of Parameters and Other Methods*

Chapter 12: *Applications*

Chapter 13: *Systems of Equations*

Chapter 14: *Electric Circuits and Networks*

Chapter 15: *The Existence of Solutions*

Chapter 16: *Equations of Order One and Higher Degree*

Chapter 17: *Special Equations of Order Two*

Chapter 18: *The Power Series Method*

Chapter 19: *Solutions Near Regular Singular Points*

Chapter 20: *Equations of Hypergeometric Type*

Chapter 21: *Additional Topics on Power Series Solutions*

Chapter 22: *Numerical Methods*

*E*lementary *D*ifferential *E*quations

Chapter 1

Definitions, Elimination of
Arbitrary Constants

1. Examples of differential equations. A differential equation is one which involves at least one derivative of an unknown function. As in equation (3) below, a derivative may be involved implicitly through the presence of differentials. Our aim is to solve differential equations; that is, to find the unknown function, or functions, which occur.

Differential equations arise frequently in physics, engineering, and chemistry and on occasion in such subjects as biology, physiology, and economics. The solution of differential equations plays an important role in the study of the motions of heavenly bodies such as planets and moons. Guided missiles and the huge modern rockets would probably have remained in the realm of science fiction but for the solution of certain differential equations. Without such equations there would indeed be mystery in the motion of an artificial satellite.

The following are examples of differential equations:

$$(1) \qquad \frac{dy}{dx} = \cos x,$$

$$(2) \qquad \frac{d^2y}{dx^2} + k^2y = 0,$$

$$(3) \qquad (x^2 + y^2)dx - 2xy \, dy = 0,$$

$$(4) \qquad \frac{\partial u}{\partial t} = h^2 \left(\frac{\partial^2 u}{\partial x^2} + \frac{\partial^2 u}{\partial y^2} \right),$$

$$(5) \qquad L\frac{d^2i}{dt^2} + R\frac{di}{dt} + \frac{1}{C}i = E\omega \cos \omega t,$$

$$(6) \qquad \frac{\partial^2 V}{\partial x^2} + \frac{\partial^2 V}{\partial y^2} = 0,$$

$$(7) \qquad \left(\frac{d^2 w}{dx^2}\right)^3 - xy\frac{dw}{dx} + w = 0,$$

$$(8) \qquad \frac{d^3 x}{dy^3} + x\frac{dx}{dy} - 4xy = 0,$$

$$(9) \qquad \frac{d^2 y}{dx^2} + 7\left(\frac{dy}{dx}\right)^3 - 8y = 0,$$

$$(10) \qquad \frac{d^2 y}{dt^2} + \frac{d^2 x}{dt^2} = x,$$

$$(11) \qquad x\frac{\partial f}{\partial x} + y\frac{\partial f}{\partial y} = nf.$$

When an equation involves one or more derivatives with respect to a particular variable, that variable is called an *independent* variable. A variable is called *dependent* if a derivative of that variable occurs in the equation.

In the equation

$$(5) \qquad L\frac{d^2 i}{dt^2} + R\frac{di}{dt} + \frac{1}{C}i = E\omega \cos \omega t$$

i is the dependent variable, t the independent variable, and $L, R, C, E,$ and ω are called parameters. The equation

$$(6) \qquad \frac{\partial^2 V}{\partial x^2} + \frac{\partial^2 V}{\partial y^2} = 0$$

has one dependent variable V and two independent variables.

Since the equation

$$(3) \qquad (x^2 + y^2)dx - 2xy\, dy = 0$$

may be written

$$x^2 + y^2 - 2xy\frac{dy}{dx} = 0$$

or

$$(x^2 + y^2)\frac{dx}{dy} - 2xy = 0$$

we may consider either variable to be dependent, the other being the independent one.

ORAL EXERCISE

Identify the independent variables, the dependent variables, and the parameters in the equations of this section.

2. Definitions. A relation defining an explicit function is called a solution of a differential equation if it satisfies that equation in the ordinary sense of checking upon direct substitution. For example, let us verify that

$$y = e^{2x}$$

is a solution of the equation

$$(1) \qquad \frac{d^2y}{dx^2} + \frac{dy}{dx} - 6y = 0.$$

We substitute our tentative solution into the left member of equation (1) and find that

$$\frac{d^2y}{dx^2} + \frac{dy}{dx} - 6y = 4e^{2x} + 2e^{2x} - 6e^{2x} \equiv 0,$$

which completes the desired verification.

Consider, however, the differential equation

$$(2) \qquad (4x^3 - y^3)dx + (2y - 3xy^2)dy = 0$$

and the relation

$$(3) \qquad x^4 - xy^3 + y^2 = c,$$

in which c is a constant. It is surely not convenient to solve equation (3) for either x or y. But differentiation of both members of (3) produces

$$4x^3\,dx - y^3\,dx - 3xy^2\,dy + 2y\,dy = 0,$$

which is merely a rearrangement of (2). If x and y are related by equation (3), then x, y, dx, and dy are related by (2). Therefore we wish to call the relation (3) a solution of equation (2). This suggests the broader definition of the term solution which we now state.

Any relation, free from derivatives, which involves one or more of the variables and which is consistent with the differential equation will be called a solution of the equation.

An equation involving partial derivatives is called a *partial differential equation;* one involving ordinary derivatives is called an *ordinary differential equation.*

The *order* of a differential equation is the order of the highest-ordered derivative appearing in the equation.   For instance,

$$(4) \qquad \frac{d^2y}{dx^2} + 2b\left(\frac{dy}{dx}\right)^3 + y = 0$$

is an equation of "order two."   It is also referred to as a "second-order equation."

The *degree* of an ordinary differential equation is its algebraic degree in the highest-ordered derivative present in the equation.

The equation

$$\left(\frac{d^2y}{dx^2}\right)^3 + \frac{d^2y}{dx^2}\left(\frac{dy}{dx}\right)^4 - x^7y = \sin x$$

is of degree three because in so far as the second derivative alone is concerned the equation is a cubic.   Equation (4) is of degree one.

Any equation of the form

$$(5) \qquad M(x,\ y)dx + N(x,\ y)dy = 0$$

is of order one and degree one.   All the equations which we shall solve in the second chapter may be written in the form (5).

A very important concept is that of the linearity or nonlinearity of a differential equation.   An equation is said to be *linear* if each term of the equation is either linear in all the dependent variables and their various derivatives or does not contain any of them.   Otherwise the equation is said to be *nonlinear.*   Such a term as $y\dfrac{dy}{dx}$ is of degree two in y and its derivative together and is therefore nonlinear. Every linear equation is of degree one, but not every equation of degree one is linear.   Note that equation (4) above is nonlinear.

The equation

$$x^2y'' + xy' + (x^2 - n^2)y = 4x^3$$

is linear in y.   The manner in which the independent variable enters the equation has nothing to do with the property of linearity.

ORAL EXERCISES

For each of the following state whether the equation is ordinary or partial, linear or nonlinear, and give its order and degree.

1. $\dfrac{d^2x}{dt^2} + k^2x = 0.$

2. $\dfrac{\partial^2 w}{\partial t^2} = a^2 \dfrac{\partial^2 w}{\partial x^2}.$

3. $(x^2 + y^2)dx + 2xy\,dy = 0.$

4. $y' + P(x)y = Q(x).$

5. $y''' - 3y' + 2y = 0.$

6. $yy'' = x.$

7. $\dfrac{\partial^2 u}{\partial x^2} + \dfrac{\partial^2 u}{\partial y^2} + \dfrac{\partial^2 u}{\partial z^2} = 0.$

8. $\dfrac{d^4y}{dx^4} = w(x).$

9. $x\dfrac{d^2y}{dt^2} - y\dfrac{d^2x}{dt^2} = c_1.$

10. $L\dfrac{di}{dt} + Ri = E.$

11. $(x + y)dx + (3x^2 - 1)dy = 0.$

12. $x(y'')^3 + (y')^4 - y = 0.$

13. $\left(\dfrac{d^3w}{dx^3}\right)^2 - 2\left(\dfrac{dw}{dx}\right)^4 + yw = 0.$

14. $\dfrac{dy}{dx} = 1 - xy + y^2.$

15. $y'' + 2y' - 8y = x^2 + \cos x.$

16. $a\,da + b\,db = 0.$

3. The elimination of arbitrary constants. In practice, differential equations arise in many ways, some of which we shall encounter later. There is one way of arriving at a differential equation which is useful in that it gives us a feeling for the kinds of solutions to be expected. In this section we shall start with a relation (the solution) involving arbitrary constants and, by elimination of those arbitrary constants, come to a differential equation satisfied by the original relation. In a sense we start with the answer and find the problem.

Methods for the elimination of arbitrary constants vary with the way in which the constants enter the given relation. A method which is efficient for one problem may be very poor for another. One fact persists throughout. Since each differentiation yields a new relation, the number of derivatives which need be used is the same as the number of arbitrary constants to be eliminated. We shall in each case determine the differential equation which is:

(a) Of order equal to the number of arbitrary constants in the given relation;

(b) Consistent with that relation;

(c) Free from arbitrary constants.

EXAMPLE (a): Eliminate* the arbitrary constants c_1 and c_2 from the relation

(1) $$y = c_1 e^{-2x} + c_2 e^{3x}.$$

Since two constants are to be eliminated, we obtain the two derivatives,

(2) $$y' = -2c_1 e^{-2x} + 3c_2 e^{3x},$$

(3) $$y'' = 4c_1 e^{-2x} + 9c_2 e^{3x}.$$

The elimination of c_1 from equations (2) and (3) yields

$$y'' + 2y' = 15c_2 e^{3x};$$

the elimination of c_1 from equations (1) and (2) yields

$$y' + 2y = 5c_2 e^{3x}.$$

Hence

$$y'' + 2y' = 3(y' + 2y),$$

or

$$y'' - y' - 6y = 0.$$

Another method for obtaining the differential equation in this example proceeds as follows. We know from a theorem in elementary algebra that the three equations (1), (2), and (3) considered as equations in the two unknowns c_1 and c_2 can have solutions only if

(4) $$\begin{vmatrix} -y & e^{-2x} & e^{3x} \\ -y' & -2e^{-2x} & 3e^{3x} \\ -y'' & 4e^{-2x} & 9e^{3x} \end{vmatrix} = 0.$$

Since e^{-2x} and e^{3x} cannot be zero, equation (4) may be rewritten, with the factors e^{-2x} and e^{3x} removed, as

$$\begin{vmatrix} y & 1 & 1 \\ y' & -2 & 3 \\ y'' & 4 & 9 \end{vmatrix} = 0$$

---

* By differentiations and pertinent legitimate mathematical procedures. Elimination by erasure, for instance, is not permitted.

from which the differential equation

$$y'' - y' - 6y = 0$$

follows immediately.

This latter method has the advantage of making it easy to see that the elimination of the constants $c_1, c_2, \cdots, c_n$ from a relation of the form

$$y = c_1 e^{m_1 x} + c_2 e^{m_2 x} + \cdots + c_n e^{m_n x}$$

will always lead to a linear differential equation

$$a_0 \frac{d^n y}{dx^n} + a_1 \frac{d^{n-1} y}{dx^{n-1}} + \cdots + a_{n-1} \frac{dy}{dx} + a_n y = 0,$$

in which the coefficients $a_0, a_1, \cdots, a_n$ are constants. The study of such differential equations will receive much of our attention in this course.

EXAMPLE (b): Eliminate the constant a from the equation

$$(x - a)^2 + y^2 = a^2.$$

Direct differentiation of the relation yields

$$2(x - a) + 2yy' = 0,$$

from which

$$a = x + yy'.$$

Therefore, using the original equation, we find that

$$(yy')^2 + y^2 = (x + yy')^2,$$

or

$$y^2 = x^2 + 2xyy',$$

which may be written in the form

$$(x^2 - y^2)dx + 2xy\, dy = 0.$$

Another method will be used on the equation of this example as an illustration of a device which is frequently helpful. The method is based upon the isolation of an arbitrary constant.

The equation

$$(x - a)^2 + y^2 = a^2$$

may be put in the form

$$x^2 + y^2 - 2ax = 0,$$

or

$$\frac{x^2 + y^2}{x} = 2a.$$

Then differentiation of both members leads to

$$\frac{x(2x\,dx + 2y\,dy) - (x^2 + y^2)dx}{x^2} = 0,$$

or

$$(x^2 - y^2)dx + 2xy\,dy = 0,$$

as desired.

EXAMPLE (c): Eliminate B and α from the relation

(5) $$x = B \cos(\omega t + \alpha),$$

in which ω is a parameter (not to be eliminated).

First we obtain two derivatives of x with respect to t:

(6) $$\frac{dx}{dt} = -\omega B \sin(\omega t + \alpha),$$

(7) $$\frac{d^2x}{dt^2} = -\omega^2 B \cos(\omega t + \alpha).$$

Comparison of equations (5) and (7) shows at once that

$$\frac{d^2x}{dt^2} + \omega^2 x = 0.$$

EXAMPLE (d): Eliminate c from the equation

$$cxy + c^2x + 4 = 0.$$

At once we get

$$c(y + xy') + c^2 = 0.$$

Since $c \neq 0$,

$$c = -(y + xy')$$

and substitution into the original equation leads us to the result

$$x^3(y')^2 + x^2yy' + 4 = 0.$$

EXERCISES

In each of the following eliminate the arbitrary constants.

1. $x \sin y + x^2 y = c$.   ANS. $(\sin y + 2xy)dx + (x \cos y + x^2)dy = 0$.

2. $3x^2 - xy^2 = c$.   ANS. $(6x - y^2)dx - 2xy \, dy = 0$.

3. $xy^2 - 1 = cy$.   ANS. $y^3 \, dx + (xy^2 + 1)dy = 0$.

4. $cx^2 + x + y^2 = 0$.   ANS. $(x + 2y^2)dx - 2xy \, dy = 0$.

5. $x = A \sin (\omega t + \beta)$: ω a parameter, not to be eliminated.

$$\text{ANS.} \quad \frac{d^2x}{dt^2} + \omega^2 x = 0.$$

6. $x = c_1 \cos \omega t + c_2 \sin \omega t$; ω a parameter.   ANS. $\dfrac{d^2x}{dt^2} + \omega^2 x = 0$.

7. $y = cx + c^2 + 1$.   ANS. $y = xy' + (y')^2 + 1$.

8. $y = mx + \dfrac{h}{m}$; h a parameter, m to be eliminated.

$$\text{ANS.} \quad y = xy' + \frac{h}{y'}.$$

9. $y^2 = 4ax$.   ANS. $2x \, dy - y \, dx = 0$.

10. $y = ax^2 + bx + c$.   ANS. $y''' = 0$.

11. $y = c_1 + c_2 e^{3x}$.   ANS. $y'' - 3y' = 0$.

12. $y = 4 + c_1 e^{3x}$.   ANS. $y' - 3y = -12$.

13. $y = c_1 + c_2 e^{-4x}$.   ANS. $y'' + 4y' = 0$.

14. $y = c_1 e^x + c_2 e^{-x}$.   ANS. $y'' - y = 0$.

15. $y = x + c_1 e^x + c_2 e^{-x}$.   ANS. $y'' - y = -x$.

16. $y = c_1 e^{2x} + c_2 e^{3x}$.   ANS. $y'' - 5y' + 6y = 0$.

17. $y = x^2 + c_1 e^{2x} + c_2 e^{3x}$.   ANS. $y'' - 5y' + 6y = 6x^2 - 10x + 2$.

18. $y = c_1 e^x + c_2 x e^x$.   ANS. $y'' - 2y' + y = 0$.

19. $y = A e^{2x} + B x e^{2x}$.   ANS. $y'' - 4y' + 4y = 0$.

20. $y = c_1 e^{2x} \cos 3x + c_2 e^{2x} \sin 3x$.   ANS. $y'' - 4y' + 13y = 0$.

21. $y = c_1 e^{ax} \cos bx + c_2 e^{ax} \sin bx$; a and b are parameters.

$$\text{ANS.} \quad y'' - 2ay' + (a^2 + b^2)y = 0.$$

22. $y = c_1 x + c_2 e^x$.   ANS. $(x - 1)y'' - xy' + y = 0$.

23. $y = c_1 x^2 + c_2 e^{-x}$.   ANS. $x(x + 2)y'' + (x^2 - 2)y' - 2(x + 1)y = 0$.

4. Families of curves.   A relation involving a parameter, as well as one or both of the coordinates of a point in a plane, represents a family of curves, one curve corresponding to each value of the parameter.   For instance, the equation

$$(1) \qquad (x - c)^2 + (y - c)^2 = 2c^2,$$

or

$$(2) \qquad x^2 + y^2 - 2c(x + y) = 0,$$

may be interpreted as the equation of a family of circles, each having its center on the line $y = x$ and each passing through the origin. Figure 1 shows several elements, or members, of this family.

If the constant c in equation (1) or in equation (2) is treated as an arbitrary constant and eliminated as in the preceding section, the result is called the *differential equation of the family* (1). In this

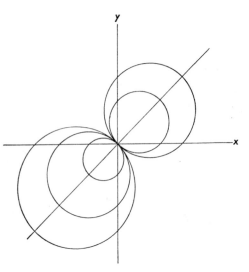

FIGURE 1

example the elimination of c is easily performed by isolating c, then differentiating the equation with respect to x. Thus, from

$$\frac{x^2 + y^2}{x + y} = 2c$$

we find that

$$\frac{(x + y)(2x\,dx + 2y\,dy) - (x^2 + y^2)(dx + dy)}{(x + y)^2} = 0.$$

Therefore

(3) $\qquad (x^2 + 2xy - y^2)dx - (x^2 - 2xy - y^2)dy = 0$

is the differential equation of the family of circles (1).

Note that equation (3) associates with each point (x, y) in the plane a definite slope

$$(4) \qquad \frac{dy}{dx} = \frac{x^2 + 2xy - y^2}{x^2 - 2xy - y^2},$$

except where the denominator on the right in (4) vanishes. An examination of the method which was used to get (4) from (1) shows that at any point (x, y) equation (4) gives the slope of that curve of the family (1) which passes through the point in question.

A simple and convenient check is now revealed. When the

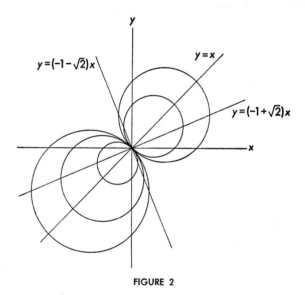

FIGURE 2

denominator on the right of equation (4) vanishes, the curve passing through that point must have a vertical tangent. From

$$x^2 - 2xy - y^2 = 0$$

we see that

$$(5) \qquad y = (\sqrt{2} - 1)x$$

or

$$(6) \qquad y = -(\sqrt{2} + 1)x.$$

In Figure 2 the straight lines (5) and (6) appear along with the family (1). It is seen that the lines (5) and (6) cut the members of the family of circles in precisely those points of vertical tangency.

For a two-parameter family of curves the differential equation will be of second order, and such a simple geometric interpretation is not available.

EXAMPLE (a): Find the differential equation of the family of parabolas (Figure 3) with vertex at the origin and focus on the y-axis.

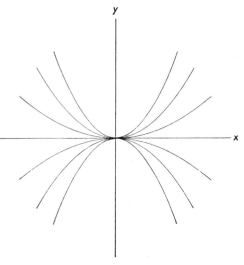

FIGURE 3

From analytic geometry we find the equation of this family of parabolas to be

(7) $$x^2 = 4ay.$$

Then from

$$\frac{x^2}{y} = 4a$$

the a may be eliminated by differentiation. Thus it follows that

(8) $$2xy\,dx - x^2\,dy = 0.$$

We may write the differential equation of the family (7) as

(9) $$2y\,dx - x\,dy = 0$$

because $x = 0$ is still a solution of (9), so that nothing was lost in removing the factor x from the left member of (8).

EXAMPLE (b): Find the differential equation of the family of circles (Figure 4) with centers on the y-axis.

Since a member of the family of circles of this example may have its center anywhere on the y-axis and its radius of any magnitude, we are dealing with the two-parameter family

(10) $$x^2 + (y - b)^2 = r^2.$$

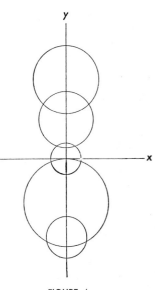

We shall eliminate both b and r and arrive, of course, at a second-order differential equation for the family (10).

At once
$$x + (y - b)y' = 0,$$

from which

$$\frac{x + yy'}{y'} = b.$$

Then

$$\frac{y'[1 + yy'' + (y')^2] - y''(x + yy')}{(y')^2} = 0,$$

so that the desired differential equation is

$$xy'' - (y')^3 - y' = 0.$$

FIGURE 4

EXERCISES

In each exercise obtain the differential equation of the family of plane curves described and sketch several representative members of the family.

1. Straight lines through the origin.   ANS. $y\,dx - x\,dy = 0.$
2. Straight lines through the fixed point (h, k).   The h and k are not to be eliminated.   ANS. $(y - k)dx - (x - h)dy = 0.$

3. Straight lines with slope and y-intercept equal.

ANS. $y\,dx - (x+1)dy = 0$.

4. Straight lines with slope and x-intercept equal.   ANS. $(y')^2 = xy' - y$.

5. Straight lines with algebraic sum of the intercepts fixed as k.

ANS. $(xy' - y)(y' - 1) + ky' = 0$.

6. Straight lines at a fixed distance p from the origin.

ANS. $(xy' - y)^2 = p^2[1 + (y')^2]$.

7. Circles with center at the origin.   ANS. $x\,dx + y\,dy = 0$.

8. Circles with center on the x-axis.   ANS. $yy'' + (y')^2 + 1 = 0$.

9. Circles with fixed radius r and tangent to the x-axis.

ANS. $(y \pm r)^2(y')^2 + y^2 \pm 2ry = 0$.

10. Circles tangent to the x-axis.

ANS. $[1 + (y')^2]^3 = [yy'' + 1 + (y')^2]^2$.

11. Circles with center on the line $y = -x$, and passing through the origin.

ANS. $(x^2 - 2xy - y^2)dx + (x^2 + 2xy - y^2)dy = 0$.

12. Circles of radius unity.   Use the fact that the radius of curvature is one.

ANS. $(y'')^2 = [1 + (y')^2]^3$.

13. All circles.   Use the curvature.   ANS. $y'''[1 + (y')^2] = 3y'(y'')^2$.

14. Parabolas with vertex on the x-axis, with axis parallel to the y-axis, and with distance from focus to vertex fixed as a.   ANS. $a(y')^2 = y$.

15. Parabolas with vertex on the y-axis, with axis parallel to the x-axis, and with distance from focus to vertex fixed as a.   ANS. $x(y')^2 = a$.

16. Parabolas with axis parallel to the y-axis and with distance from vertex to focus fixed as a.   ANS. $2ay'' = 1$.

17. Parabolas with axis parallel to the x-axis and with distance from vertex to focus fixed as a.   ANS. $2ay'' + (y')^3 = 0$.

18. Work Ex. 17, using differentiation with respect to y.   ANS. $2a\dfrac{d^2x}{dy^2} = 1$.

19. Use the fact that

$$\frac{d^2x}{dy^2} = \frac{d}{dy}\left(\frac{dx}{dy}\right) = \frac{dx}{dy}\frac{d}{dx}\left(\frac{dx}{dy}\right) = \frac{dx}{dy}\frac{d}{dx}\left(\frac{dy}{dx}\right)^{-1} = -y''/(y')^3$$

to prove that the answers to Exs. 17 and 18 are equivalent.

20. Parabolas with vertex and focus on the x-axis.   ANS. $yy'' + (y')^2 = 0$.

21. Parabolas with axis parallel to the x-axis.   ANS. $y'y''' - 3(y'')^2 = 0$.

22. Central conics with center at the origin and vertices on the coordinate axes.   ANS. $xyy'' + x(y')^2 - yy' = 0$

23. The confocal central conics

$$\frac{x^2}{a^2 + \lambda} + \frac{y^2}{b^2 + \lambda} = 1$$

with a and b held fixed.   ANS. $(xy' - y)(yy' + x) = (a^2 - b^2)y'$.

24. The cubics $cy^2 = x(x - a)^2$ with a held fixed.   First write

$$\ln c + 2 \ln y = \ln x + 2 \ln (x - a),$$

then differentiate.   ANS. $2x(x - a)y' = (3x - a)y.$

25. The quartics $c^2y^2 = x^3(x - a)$ with a held fixed.

ANS. $2x(x - a)y' = (4x - 3a)y.$

26. The cubics of Ex. 24 with c held fixed and a to be eliminated.

ANS. $c(2xy' - y)^2 = 4x^3.$

27. The quartics of Ex. 25 with c held fixed and a to be eliminated.

ANS. $c^2y(2xy' - 3y) = x^4.$

28. The strophoids $y^2 = \dfrac{x^2(a + x)}{a - x}.$

ANS. $(x^4 - 4x^2y^2 - y^4)dx + 4x^3y\,dy = 0.$

29. The cissoids $y^2 = \dfrac{x^3}{a - x}.$ ANS. $2x^3y' = y(y^2 + 3x^2).$

30. The trisectrices of Maclaurin $y^2(a + x) = x^2(3a - x).$

ANS. $(3x^4 - 6x^2y^2 - y^4)dx + 8x^3y\,dy = 0.$

31. Circles through the intersections of the circle $x^2 + y^2 = 1$ and the line $y = x.$ Use the "$u + kv$" form; that is, the equation

$$x^2 + y^2 - 1 + k(y - x) = 0.$$

ANS. $(x^2 - 2xy - y^2 + 1)dx + (x^2 + 2xy - y^2 - 1)dy = 0.$

32. Circles through the fixed points $(a, 0)$ and $(-a, 0).$ Use the method of Ex. 31.   ANS. $2xy\,dx + (y^2 + a^2 - x^2)dy = 0.$

33. The circles $r = 2a(\sin \theta - \cos \theta).$

ANS. $(\cos \theta - \sin \theta)dr + r(\cos \theta + \sin \theta)d\theta = 0.$

34. The cardioids $r = a(1 - \sin \theta).$

ANS. $(1 - \sin \theta)dr + r \cos \theta\,d\theta = 0.$

35. The cissoids $r = a \sin \theta \tan \theta.$ (See Ex. 29.)

ANS. $\sin \theta \cos \theta\,dr - r(1 + \cos^2 \theta)d\theta = 0.$

36. The strophoids $r = a(\sec \theta + \tan \theta).$ ANS. $\dfrac{dr}{d\theta} = r \sec \theta.$

37. The trisectrices of Maclaurin $r = a(4 \cos \theta - \sec \theta).$ (See Ex. 30.)

ANS. $\cos \theta(4 \cos^2 \theta - 1)dr + r \sin \theta(4 \cos^2 \theta + 1)d\theta = 0.$

Chapter 2

Equations of the First Order and First Degree

5. General solutions of ordinary differential equations. An ordinary differential equation of the nth order has, in general, a solution containing n arbitrary constants.* We shall call such a solution the general solution. Other terms frequently used are complete solution, complete primitive, and complete integral.

6. Separation of variables. The general equation of the first order and first degree is

$$(1) \qquad M\ dx + N\ dy = 0,$$

where M and N may be functions of both x and y. Some equations of the type (1) are so simple that they can be put in the form

$$(2) \qquad A(x)dx + B(y)dy = 0;$$

that is, the variables can be separated. Then the solution can be written down at once. For it is only a matter of finding a function F whose total differential is the left member of (2). Then $F = c$, where c is an arbitrary constant, is the desired result.

EXAMPLE (a): Solve the equation

$$(3) \qquad 2(y + 3)dx - xy\ dy = 0.$$

Separation of the variables leads to

$$\frac{2dx}{x} - \frac{y\ dy}{y + 3} = 0,$$

---

* A proof and a precise statement appear, for example, in E. L. Ince, *Ordinary Differential Equations*, London, Longmans, Green and Co., 1927.

or

$$(4) \qquad \frac{2dx}{x} - \left[1 - \frac{3}{y+3}\right]dy = 0.$$

Hence we could write the solution as

$$(5) \qquad 2\ln x - y + 3\ln(y+3) = c.$$

Although (5) is a correct solution, the presence of two logarithmic terms suggests that we put the arbitrary constant in logarithmic form also. Thus, directly from (4) we may write the solution in the form

$$(6) \qquad 2\ln x - y + 3\ln(y+3) + \ln c_1 = 0,$$

where c_1 is an arbitrary constant different from the c of (5).

From (6) we get

$$y = 2\ln x + 3\ln(y+3) + \ln c_1,$$

from which it follows that

$$(7) \qquad e^y = c_1 x^2 (y+3)^3,$$

which is more compact than (5).

Of course, (5) can be transformed into (7) quite easily. From (5)

$$y + c = 2\ln x + 3\ln(y+3),$$

or

$$e^{y+c} = x^2(y+3)^3.$$

Now we put

$$e^c = \frac{1}{c_1}$$

and arrive at (7).

The problem of changing one form of solution into another form is one which arises frequently when two or more persons solve the same differential equation and a check on the results is desired. Unless the use to which the solution will be put is known there is little reason for preference for one form over another, except for considerations of compactness, symmetry, and other esthetic qualities. It is essentially a matter of individual inclination. See Section 7 below for further remarks on the form of the solution.

EXAMPLE (b): Solve the equation

$$(8) \qquad (1 + y^2)dx + (1 + x^2)dy = 0$$

together with the "boundary condition": when $x = 0$, $y = -1$.

From the differential equation we get

$$\frac{dx}{1 + x^2} + \frac{dy}{1 + y^2} = 0$$

from which it follows at once that

$$(9) \qquad \text{Arctan } x + \text{Arctan } y = c.$$

In the solution (9), each "Arctan" stands for the principal value of the inverse tangent and is subject to the restriction

$$-\tfrac{1}{2}\pi < \textbf{Arctan } x < \tfrac{1}{2}\pi.$$

The boundary condition that when $x = 0$, $y = -1$ permits us to determine the value of c which must be used to obtain the particular solution which is desired here. Since Arctan $0 = 0$ and Arctan $(-1) = -\pi/4$, the solution of the boundary value problem is

$$(10) \qquad \text{Arctan } x + \text{Arctan } y = -\pi/4.$$

Suppose next that we wish to sketch the curve (10). Resorting to a device of trigonometry we take the tangent of each side of (10). Since tan (Arctan x) $= x$ and

$$\tan (A + B) = \frac{\tan A + \tan B}{1 - \tan A \tan B},$$

we are led to the equation

$$\frac{x + y}{1 - xy} = -1,$$

or

$$(11) \qquad xy - x - y - 1 = 0.$$

Now (11) is the equation of an equilateral hyperbola with asymptotes $x = 1$ and $y = 1$. But if we turn to (10) we see from

$$\text{Arctan } x = -\pi/4 - \text{Arctan } y$$

that, since $(-\text{Arctan } y) < \pi/2$,

$$\text{Arctan } x < \pi/4.$$

Hence $x < 1$ and equation (10) represents only one branch of the hyperbola (11). In Figure 5 the solid curve is the graph of equation (10); the solid curve together with the dotted curve is the graph of equation (11).

Each branch of the hyperbola (11) is a solution of the differential equation, one branch for $x < 1$, the other for $x > 1$. In this problem we were forced onto the left branch, equation (10), by the boundary condition that $y = -1$ when $x = 0$.

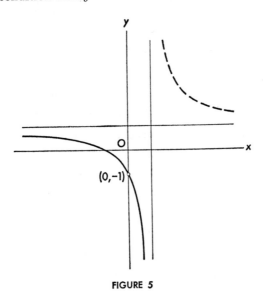

FIGURE 5

One distinction between the solutions (10) and (11) can be seen by noting that a computing machine, given the differential equation (8) and seeking a solution which passes through the point $(0, -1)$, would draw only the left branch of the curve in Figure 5. The barrier (asymptote) at $x = 1$ would prevent the machine from learning of the existence of the other branch of the hyperbola (11).

7. On the form of solutions.   Consider the equation

(1) $$2x(y + 1)dx - y\, dy = 0.$$

Separating the variables in equation (1), we obtain

(2) $$2x\, dx = \left(1 - \frac{1}{y + 1}\right) dy.$$

Therefore the general solution of equation (1) is

(3) $$x^2 = y - \ln (y + 1) + c.$$

Suppose, however, that we wish to solve a boundary value problem consisting of the differential equation (1) together with the condition that when $x = 0$, $y = -2$. Putting $y = -2$ into the right member of equation (3) would lead to the use of $\ln (-1)$. Since (-1) has no real logarithm, we prefer to avoid this complication. Hence we seek other forms for the general solution of equation (1).

Since

$$d \ln (-y - 1) = \frac{-dy}{-y - 1} = \frac{dy}{y + 1},$$

it is possible to write the general solution of equation (2) in the form

(4) $$x^2 = y - \ln (-y - 1) + c_1.$$

Substituting $x = 0$ and $y = -2$ into equation (4) causes no trouble. It leads us to the equation

$$0 = -2 - \ln (1) + c_1,$$

from which we find $c_1 = 2$.   Thus the desired solution of the boundary value problem is

$$x^2 = y + 2 - \ln (-y - 1), \quad \text{for } y < -1.$$

It can be seen that the solution (3) is useful for the range $y > -1$, while the solution (4) is useful for $y < -1$.   In at least two ways it is possible to write a solution combining the advantages of (3) with those of (4).

Since

$$d \ln [c_2(y + 1)] = \frac{c_2\, dy}{c_2(y + 1)} = \frac{dy}{y + 1},$$

the general solution of equation (1) may be written in the form

$$(5) \qquad x^2 = y - \ln [c_2(y + 1)].$$

In adjusting the solution (5) to our immediate purpose, we place $x = 0$, $y = -2$ and find that

$$0 = -2 - \ln (-c_2),$$

so that $\ln (-c_2) = -2$, or $c_2 = -e^{-2}$. Hence the desired solution is

$$x^2 = y - \ln [-e^{-2}(y + 1)],$$

or

$$x^2 = y + 2 - \ln [-(y + 1)].$$

In equation (5), c_2 will turn out to be negative when a boundary condition requires that $y < -1$ and positive when it is required that $y > -1$.

From equation (5) it is not difficult to obtain the relation

$$(6) \qquad (y + 1)e^{x^2} = c_3 e^y$$

as another form of the solution of the differential equation (1).

In this book we shall usually leave solutions in forms similar to (5) or (6) above. Whenever an answer such as equation (3) is given, it is implied that the user will adjust its form to his particular purpose. The result should be verified by direct appeal to the differential equation so that the validity of the transition from one solution to another does not enter the argument.

EXERCISES

In Exs. 1–24 obtain the general solution.

1. $(1 - x)y' = y^2$.   ANS. $y \ln [c(1 - x)] = 1$.
2. $\sin x \sin y \, dx + \cos x \cos y \, dy = 0$.   ANS. $\sin y = c \cos x$.
3. $xy^3 \, dx + e^{x^2} \, dy = 0$.   ANS. $e^{-x^2} + y^{-2} = c$.
4. $2y \, dx = 3x \, dy$.   ANS. $x^2 = cy^3$.
5. $my \, dx = nx \, dy$.   ANS. $x^m = cy^n$.
6. $y' = xy^2$.   ANS. $y(x^2 + c) + 2 = 0$.
7. $\dfrac{dV}{dP} = \dfrac{-V}{P}$.   ANS. $PV = C$.

8. $ye^{2x} dx = (4 + e^{2x})dy.$ ANS. $c^2y^2 = 4 + e^{2x}.$

9. $dr = b(\cos \theta \, dr + r \sin \theta \, d\theta).$ ANS. $r = c(1 - b \cos \theta).$

10. $xy \, dx - (x + 2)dy = 0.$ ANS. $e^x = cy(x + 2)^2.$

11. $x^2 \, dx + y(x - 1)dy = 0.$ ANS. $(x + 1)^2 + y^2 + 2 \ln [c(x - 1)] = 0.$

12. $(xy + x)dx = (x^2y^2 + x^2 + y^2 + 1)dy.$

  ANS. $\ln (x^2 + 1) = y^2 - 2y + 4 \ln [c(y + 1)].$

13. $x \cos^2 y \, dx + \tan y \, dy = 0.$ ANS. $x^2 + \tan^2 y = c^2.$

14. $xy^3 \, dx + (y + 1)e^{-x} dy = 0.$ ANS. $e^x(x - 1) = \dfrac{1}{y} + \dfrac{1}{2y^2} + c.$

15. $\dfrac{d\theta}{dz} = z(1 - z^2) \sec^2 \theta.$ ANS. $2\theta + \sin 2\theta = c - (1 - z^2)^2.$

16. $\dfrac{dx}{dt} = \sin^2 x \cos^3 t.$ ANS. $3 \cot x + 3 \sin t - \sin^3 t + c = 0.$

17. $\alpha \, d\beta + \beta \, d\alpha + \alpha\beta(d\alpha + d\beta) = 0.$ ANS. $\alpha\beta = ce^{-(\alpha+\beta)}.$

18. $\cos y \, dx = x \, dy.$ ANS. $x = c(\sec y + \tan y).$

19. $(1 + \ln x)dx + (1 + \ln y)dy = 0.$ ANS. $x \ln x + y \ln y = c.$

20. $x \, dx - \sqrt{a^2 - x^2} \, dy = 0.$

  ANS. $y - c = -\sqrt{a^2 - x^2}$, the lower half of the circle $x^2 + (y - c)^2 = a^2.$

21. $x \, dx + \sqrt{a^2 - x^2} \, dy = 0.$

  ANS. $y - c = \sqrt{a^2 - x^2}$, the upper half of the circle $x^2 + (y - c)^2 = a^2.$

22. $a^2 \, dx = x \sqrt{x^2 - a^2} \, dy.$ ANS. $x = a \sec \dfrac{y + c}{a}.$

23. $y \, dx = (e^{3x} + 1)dy.$ ANS. $y^3(1 + e^{-3x}) = c^3.$

24. $y \ln x \ln y \, dx + dy = 0.$ ANS. $x \ln x + \ln \ln y = x + c.$

In Exs. 25–30 obtain the particular solution satisfying the boundary condition indicated.

25. $xyy' - y^2 = 1$; when $x = 2$, $y = 1$. ANS. $x^2 - 2y^2 = 2.$

26. $\dfrac{dr}{dt} = -2rt$; when $t = 0$, $r = r_0$. ANS. $r = r_0e^{-t^2}.$

27. $xy^2 \, dx + e^x \, dy = 0$; when $x \to \infty$, $y \to \frac{1}{2}$.

  ANS. $y = e^x/(2e^x - x - 1).$

28. $(2a^2 - r^2)dr = r^3 \sin \theta \, d\theta$; when $\theta = 0$, $r = a$.

  ANS. $a^2 + r^2 \ln \dfrac{r}{a} = r^2 \cos \theta.$

29. $y' = xe^{-y-x^2}$; when $x = 0$, $y = 0$. ANS. $2e^y = 3 - e^{-x^2}.$

30. $v \dfrac{dv}{dx} = g$; when $x = x_0$, $v = v_0$. ANS. $v^2 - v_0^2 = 2g(x - x_0).$

8. Homogeneous functions. Polynomials in which all terms are of the same degree, such as

$$x^2 - 3xy + 4y^2,$$
(1)
$$x^3 + y^3,$$
$$x^4y + 7y^5,$$

are called *homogeneous* polynomials. We wish now to extend that concept of homogeneity so that it will apply to functions other than polynomials.

If we assign a physical dimension, say length, to each variable x and y in the polynomials in (1), then each polynomial itself also has a physical dimension, length to some power. This suggests the desired generalization. If, when certain variables are thought of as lengths, a function has physical dimension length to the kth power, then we shall call that function homogeneous of degree k in those variables. For example, the function

$$x^3 e^{x/y} - 4y^2 \sqrt{x^2 + y^2}$$

is of dimension (length)^3 when x and y are lengths. Therefore that function is said to be homogeneous of degree 3 in x and y.

We permit the degree k to be any number. The function $\sqrt{x + 4y}$ is called homogeneous of degree $\frac{1}{2}$ in x and y. The function

$$\frac{x}{\sqrt{x^2 + y^2}}$$

is homogeneous of degree zero in x and y.

A formal definition of homogeneity follows: *The function $f(x, y)$ is said to be homogeneous of degree k in x and y if, and only if,*

$$f(\lambda x, \lambda y) = \lambda^k f(x, y).$$
(2)

The definition is easily extended to functions of more than two variables.

For the function

$$f(x, y) = x^3 e^{x/y} - 4y^2 \sqrt{x^2 + y^2}$$

considered above, the formal definition of homogeneity leads us to consider

$$f(\lambda x, \lambda y) = \lambda^3 x^3 e^{\lambda x/(\lambda y)} - 4\lambda^2 y^2 \sqrt{\lambda^2 x^2 + \lambda^2 y^2}.$$

But we see at once that

$$f(\lambda x, \lambda y) = \lambda^3 f(x, y);$$

hence $f(x, y)$ is homogeneous of degree 3 in x and y, as stated previously.

The following theorems prove useful in the next section.

THEOREM 1:   *If $M(x, y)$ and $N(x, y)$ are both homogeneous and of the same degree, the function $\dfrac{M(x, y)}{N(x, y)}$ is homogeneous of degree zero.*

THEOREM 2:   *If $f(x, y)$ is homogeneous of degree zero in x and y, $f(x, y)$ is a function of $\dfrac{y}{x}$ alone.*

Proof of Theorem 1 is left to the student.

Proof of Theorem 2: Let us put $y = vx$.   Then Theorem 2 states that if $f(x, y)$ is homogeneous of degree zero, $f(x, y)$ is a function of v alone.   Now

$$(3)\qquad f(x, y) = f(x, vx) = x^0 f(1, v) = f(1, v),$$

in which the x is now playing the role taken by λ in the definition (2) above.   By (3), $f(x, y)$ depends on v alone as stated in Theorem 2.

ORAL EXERCISES

Determine in each exercise whether the function is homogeneous or not.   If it is homogeneous, state the degree of the function.

1. $x^2 - 2xy - y^2$.

2. $x^3 - 4x^2 + y^3$.

3. $3x + \sqrt{x^2 - y^2}$.

4. $\dfrac{3x + 2y}{\sqrt{x^2 + y^2}}$.

5. $(x^3 - y^3)e^{x/y} + (x^2 + 4y^2)^{3/2}$.

6. $\sqrt{x + y}$.

7. $x \sin \dfrac{y}{x} - y \sin \dfrac{x}{y}$.

8. $3x^2 - \dfrac{x^3}{y} \operatorname{Arctan} \dfrac{x}{y}$.

9. e^x.

10. $\ln x$.

11. $e^{x/y}$.

12. $\ln (x/y)$.

13. $x \tan (y/x)$.

14. $x \ln x - y \ln y$.

15. $xe^x \tan (y/x)$.

16. $x \ln x - x \ln y$.

17. $\dfrac{x - y}{x^2 + y^2}$.

18. $\dfrac{a^2 - 2x^2}{(a^2 - x^2)^{3/2}}$.

9. Equations with homogeneous coefficients. Suppose the coefficients M and N in an equation of the first order and first degree,

$$(1) \qquad M(x, y)dx + N(x, y)dy = 0,$$

are both homogeneous functions and are of the *same degree* in x and y. By Theorems 1 and 2 of Section 8, the ratio M/N is a function of y/x alone. Hence equation (1) may be put in the form

$$(2) \qquad \frac{dy}{dx} + g\left(\frac{y}{x}\right) = 0.$$

This suggests the introduction of a new variable v by putting $y = vx$. Then (2) becomes

$$(3) \qquad x\frac{dv}{dx} + v + g(v) = 0,$$

in which the variables are separable. We can obtain the solution of (3) by the method of Section 6, insert y/x for v, and thus arrive at the solution of (1). We have shown that the substitution $y = vx$ will transform equation (1) into an equation, in v and x, in which the variables are separable.

The above method of attack would have been equally successful had we used $x = vy$ to obtain from (1) an equation in y and v. See Example (b) below.

EXAMPLE (a): Solve the equation

$$(4) \qquad (x^2 - xy + y^2)dx - xy\,dy = 0.$$

Since the coefficients in (4) are both homogeneous and of degree two in x and y, let us put $y = vx$. Then (4) becomes

$$(x^2 - x^2v + x^2v^2)dx - x^2v(v\ dx + x\ dv) = 0,$$

from which the factor x^2 should be removed at once. That done, we have to solve

$$(1 - v + v^2)dx - v(v\ dx + x\ dv) = 0,$$

or

$$(1 - v)dx - xv\ dv = 0.$$

Hence we separate variables to get

$$\frac{dx}{x} + \frac{v\ dv}{v - 1} = 0.$$

Then from

$$\frac{dx}{x} + \left[1 + \frac{1}{v - 1}\right]dv = 0$$

the solution is seen to be

$$\ln x + v + \ln (v - 1) = \ln c,$$

or

$$x(v - 1)e^v = c.$$

In terms of the original variables the solution is

$$x\left(\frac{y}{x} - 1\right)e^{y/x} = c,$$

or

$$(y - x)e^{y/x} = c.$$

EXAMPLE (b): Solve the equation

(5) $$xy\ dx + (x^2 + y^2)dy = 0.$$

Again the coefficients in the equation are homogeneous and of degree two. We could use $y = vx$, but the relative simplicity of the dx term in (5) suggests that we put

$$x = vy.$$

Then $dx = v\ dy + y\ dv$, and equation (5) is replaced by

$$vy^2(v\ dy + y\ dv) + (v^2y^2 + y^2)dy = 0,$$

or

$$v(v\,dy + y\,dv) + (v^2 + 1)dy = 0.$$

Hence we need to solve

(6)
$$vy\,dv + (2v^2 + 1)dy = 0,$$

which leads at once to

$$\ln(2v^2 + 1) + 4\ln y = \ln c,$$

or

$$y^4(2v^2 + 1) = c.$$

Thus the desired solution is]

$$y^4\left(\frac{2x^2}{y^2} + 1\right) = c;$$

that is,

(7)
$$y^2(2x^2 + y^2) = c.$$

Since the left member of the solution (7) cannot be negative, we may, for symmetry's sake, change the arbitrary constant to $c_1{}^4$, writing

$$y^2(2x^2 + y^2) = c_1{}^4.$$

It is worth while for the student to attack equation (5) using $y = vx$. That method leads directly to the equation

$$(v^3 + 2v)dx + x(v^2 + 1)dv = 0$$

which, though not difficult to solve, is not quite as simple as (6) above.

Frequently in equations with homogeneous coefficients it is quite immaterial whether one uses $y = vx$ or $x = vy$.

EXERCISES

In Exs. 1–21 obtain the general solution.

1. $(x - 2y)dx + (2x + y)dy = 0.$
      ANS. $\ln(x^2 + y^2) + 4\,\text{Arctan}\,(y/x) = c.$

2. $xy\,dx - (x^2 + 2y^2)dy = 0.$
      ANS. $x^2 = 4y^2\ln(y/c).$

3. $2(2x^2 + y^2)dx - xy\,dy = 0.$
      ANS. $x^4 = c^2(4x^2 + y^2).$

4. $(2x^2 + xy - 2y^2)dx = (x^2 - 4xy)dy$.

     ANS.   Arctan $(y/x) = 2 \ln [(x^2 + y^2)/(cx)]$.

5. $(x^2 + 2y^2)dx - xy\, dy = 0$.   ANS. $x^4 = c^2(x^2 + y^2)$.

6. $(x - y)(4x + y)dx + x(5x - y)dy = 0$.

     ANS. $x(y + x)^2 = c(y - 2x)$.

7. $(5v - u)du + (3v - 7u)dv = 0$.   ANS. $(3v + u)^2 = c(v - u)$.

8. $(x^2 + 2xy - 4y^2)dx - (x^2 - 8xy - 4y^2)dy = 0$.

     ANS. $x^2 + 4y^2 = c(x + y)$.

9. $(x^2 + y^2)dx - xy\, dy = 0$.   ANS. $y^2 = 2x^2 \ln (x/c)$.

10. $x(x^2 + y^2)^2(y\, dx - x\, dy) + y^6\, dy = 0$.

     ANS. $(x^2 + y^2)^3 = 6y^6 \ln (c/y)$.

11. $(x^2 + y^2)dx + xy\, dy = 0$.   ANS. $x^2(x^2 + 2y^2) = c^4$.

12. $xy\, dx - (x + 2y)^2\, dy = 0$.   ANS. $y^3(x + y) = ce^{x/y}$.

13. $v^2\, dx + x(x + v)dv = 0$.   ANS. $xv^2 = c(x + 2v)$.

14. $[x \csc (y/x) - y]dx + x\, dy = 0$.   ANS. $\ln (x/c) = \cos (y/x)$.

15. $x\, dx + \sin^2 (y/x)[y\, dx - x\, dy] = 0$.

     ANS. $4x \ln (x/c) - 2y + x \sin (2y/x) = 0$.

16. $(x - y \ln y + y \ln x)dx + x(\ln y - \ln x)dy = 0$.

     ANS. $(x - y) \ln x + y \ln y = cx + y$.

17. $[x - y \operatorname{Arctan} (y/x)]dx + x \operatorname{Arctan} (y/x)dy = 0$.

     ANS. $2y \operatorname{Arctan} (y/x) = x \ln [c^2(x^2 + y^2)/x^4]$.

18. $y^2\, dy = x(x\, dy - y\, dx)e^{x/y}$.   ANS. $y \ln (y/c) = (y - x)e^{x/y}$.

19. $t(s^2 + t^2)ds - s(s^2 - t^2)dt = 0$.   ANS. $s^2 = -2t^2 \ln (cst)$.

20. $y\, dx = (x + \sqrt{y^2 - x^2})dy$.   ANS. $\operatorname{Arcsin} (x/y) = \ln (y/c)$.

21. $(3x^2 - 2xy + 3y^2)dx = 4xy\, dy$.   ANS. $(y - x)(y + 3x)^3 = cx^3$.

22. Prove that, with the aid of the substitution $y = vx$, you can solve any equation of the form

$$y^n f(x)dx + H(x, y)(y\, dx - x\, dy) = 0,$$

where $H(x, y)$ is homogeneous in x and y.

In Exs. 23–35 find the particular solution indicated.

23. $(x - y)dx + (3x + y)dy = 0$; when $x = 2$, $y = -1$.

     ANS. $2(x + 2y) + (x + y) \ln (x + y) = 0$.

24. $(y - \sqrt{x^2 + y^2})dx - x\, dy = 0$; when $x = \sqrt{3}$, $y = 1$.

     ANS. $x^2 = 9 - 6y$.

25. $(y + \sqrt{x^2 + y^2})dx - x\, dy = 0$; when $x = \sqrt{3}$, $y = 1$.

     ANS. $x^2 = 2y + 1$.

26. $[x \cos^2 (y/x) - y]dx + x\, dy = 0$; when $x = 1$, $y = \pi/4$.

     ANS. $\tan (y/x) = \ln (e/x)$.

27. $(y^2 + 7xy + 16x^2)dx + x^2\, dy = 0$; when $x = 1$, $y = 1$.

     ANS. $x - y = 5(y + 4x) \ln x$.

28. $y^2\, dx + (x^2 + 3xy + 4y^2)dy = 0$; when $x = 2$, $y = 1$.

     ANS. $4(2y + x) \ln y = 2y - x$.

29. $xy\,dx + 2(x^2 + 2y^2)dy = 0$; when $x = 0$, $y = 1$.

ANS. $y^4(3x^2 + 4y^2) = 4$.

30. $y(2x^2 - xy + y^2)dx - x^2(2x - y)dy = 0$; when $x = 1$, $y = \frac{1}{2}$.

ANS. $y^2 \ln x = 2y^2 + xy - x^2$.

31. $y(9x - 2y)dx - x(6x - y)dy = 0$; when $x = 1$, $y = 1$.

ANS. $3x^3 - x^2y - 2y^2 = 0$.

32. $y(x^2 + y^2)dx + x(3x^2 - 5y^2)dy = 0$; when $x = 2$, $y = 1$.

ANS. $2y^5 - 2x^2y^3 + 3x = 0$.

33. $(16x + 5y)dx + (3x + y)dy = 0$; the curve to pass through the point $(1, -3)$.   ANS. $y + 3x = (y + 4x) \ln (y + 4x)$.

34. $v(3x + 2v)dx - x^2\,dv = 0$; when $x = 1$, $v = 2$.

ANS. $2x^3 + 2x^2v - 3v = 0$

35. $(3x^2 - 2y^2)y' = 2xy$; when $x = 0$, $y = -1$.   ANS. $x^2 = 2y^2(y + 1)$.

10. Exact equations. In Section 6 it was noticed that when an equation can be put in the form

$$A(x)dx + B(y)dy = 0,$$

the general solution may be determined by integration; that is, by finding a function whose differential is $A(x)dx + B(y)dy$.

That idea can be extended to some equations of the form

$$(1) \qquad M(x, y)dx + N(x, y)dy = 0$$

in which separation of variables may not be possible. Suppose that a function $F(x, y)$ can be found which has for its total differential the expression $M\,dx + N\,dy$; that is,

$$(2) \qquad dF = M\,dx + N\,dy.$$

Then certainly

$$(3) \qquad F(x, y) = c$$

is the general solution of (1). For, from (3) it follows that

$$dF = 0,$$

or, in view of (2),

$$M\,dx + N\,dy = 0,$$

as desired.

Two things, then, are needed: first, to find out under what conditions on M and N a function F exists such that its total differential is exactly $M\,dx + N\,dy$; second, if those conditions are satisfied, actually to determine the function F.   If there exists a function F such that $M\,dx + N\,dy$ is exactly the total differential of F, we call equation (1) an *exact equation*.

If the equation

$$(1) \qquad\qquad M\,dx + N\,dy = 0$$

is exact, then by definition F exists such that

$$dF = M\,dx + N\,dy.$$

But, from calculus,

$$dF = \frac{\partial F}{\partial x}\,dx + \frac{\partial F}{\partial y}\,dy,$$

so

$$M = \frac{\partial F}{\partial x}, \quad N = \frac{\partial F}{\partial y}.$$

These two equations lead to

$$\frac{\partial M}{\partial y} = \frac{\partial^2 F}{\partial y \partial x} \text{ and } \frac{\partial N}{\partial x} = \frac{\partial^2 F}{\partial x \partial y}.$$

Again from calculus

$$\frac{\partial^2 F}{\partial y \partial x} = \frac{\partial^2 F}{\partial x \partial y},$$

provided these partial derivatives are continuous.   Therefore, if (1) is an exact equation, then

$$(4) \qquad\qquad \frac{\partial M}{\partial y} = \frac{\partial N}{\partial x}.$$

Thus, for (1) to be exact it is necessary that (4) be satisfied.

Let us now show that if condition (4) is satisfied, then (1) is an exact equation.   Let $\varphi(x, y)$ be a function for which

$$\frac{\partial \varphi}{\partial x} = M.$$

The function φ is the result of integrating $M\,dx$ with respect to x while holding y constant.   Now

$$\frac{\partial^2 \varphi}{\partial y \partial x} = \frac{\partial M}{\partial y};$$

hence, if (4) is satisfied, then also

(5) $$\frac{\partial^2\varphi}{\partial x\partial y} = \frac{\partial N}{\partial x}.$$

Let us integrate both sides of this last equation with respect to x, holding y fixed. In the integration with respect to x the "arbitrary constant" may be any function of y. Let us call it $B'(y)$, for ease in indicating its integral. Then integration of (5) with respect to x yields

(6) $$\frac{\partial\varphi}{\partial y} = N + B'(y).$$

Now a function F can be exhibited, namely,

$$F = \varphi(x, y) - B(y),$$

for which

$$
\begin{aligned}
dF &= \frac{\partial\varphi}{\partial x}\,dx + \frac{\partial\varphi}{\partial y}\,dy - B'(y)dy \\
&= M\,dx + [N + B'(y)]dy - B'(y)dy \\
&= M\,dx + N\,dy.
\end{aligned}
$$

Hence, equation (1) is exact. We have completed a proof of the theorem stated below.

THEOREM: *If M, N, $\dfrac{\partial M}{\partial y}$, and $\dfrac{\partial N}{\partial x}$ are continuous functions of x and y, then a necessary and sufficient condition that*

(1) $$M\,dx + N\,dy = 0$$

be an exact equation is that

(4) $$\frac{\partial M}{\partial y} = \frac{\partial N}{\partial x}.$$

Furthermore, the proof contains the germ of a method for obtaining the solution, a method used in Examples (a) and (b) below. It will be found, however, that with a little practice the solutions of very many exact equations can be written down by inspection. See Examples (c) and (d). No matter what method is used the result should be checked by differentiation.

EXAMPLE (a): Solve the equation

$$(7) \qquad 3x(xy - 2)dx + (x^3 + 2y)dy = 0.$$

First, from the fact that

$$\frac{\partial M}{\partial y} = 3x^2 \text{ and } \frac{\partial N}{\partial x} = 3x^2,$$

we conclude that equation (7) is exact. Therefore, its solution is $F = c$, where

$$(8) \qquad \frac{\partial F}{\partial x} = M = 3x^2y - 6x,$$

and

$$(9) \qquad \frac{\partial F}{\partial y} = N = x^3 + 2y.$$

Let us attempt to determine F from equation (8). Integration of both sides of (8) with respect to x, holding y constant, yields

$$(10) \qquad F = x^3y - 3x^2 + T(y),$$

where the usual arbitrary constant in indefinite integration is now necessarily a function $T(y)$, as yet unknown. In order to determine $T(y)$, we use the fact that the function F of equation (10) must also satisfy equation (9). Hence

$$x^3 + T'(y) = x^3 + 2y,$$

so that

$$T'(y) = 2y.$$

No arbitrary constant is needed in obtaining $T(y)$, since one is being introduced on the right in the solution $F = c$. Then

$$T(y) = y^2,$$

and from (10)

$$F = x^3y - 3x^2 + y^2.$$

Finally, the solution of equation (7) is seen to be

$$x^3y - 3x^2 + y^2 = c,$$

a result which is easily checked by differentiation.

EXAMPLE (b): Solve the equation

(11) $(2x^3 - xy^2 - 2y + 3)dx - (x^2y + 2x)dy = 0.$

Here

$$\frac{\partial M}{\partial y} = -2xy - 2 = \frac{\partial N}{\partial x}$$

so that the equation (11) is exact.

The solution of (11) is $F = c$, where

(12) $\frac{\partial F}{\partial x} = 2x^3 - xy^2 - 2y + 3$

and

(13) $\frac{\partial F}{\partial y} = -x^2y - 2x.$

Because (13) is simpler than (12), and for variety's sake, let us start the determination of F from equation (13).

At once, from (13)

$$F = -\tfrac{1}{2}x^2y^2 - 2xy + Q(x),$$

where $Q(x)$ will be determined from (12). The latter yields

$$-xy^2 - 2y + Q'(x) = 2x^3 - xy^2 - 2y + 3,$$

or

$$Q'(x) = 2x^3 + 3.$$

Therefore

$$Q(x) = \tfrac{1}{2}x^4 + 3x,$$

and the desired solution of (11) is

$$-\tfrac{1}{2}x^2y^2 - 2xy + \tfrac{1}{2}x^4 + 3x = \tfrac{1}{2}c,$$

or

$$x^4 - x^2y^2 - 4xy + 6x = c.$$

EXAMPLE (c): Solve the equation of Example (a) by inspection. Suppose that we have tested

(7) $3x(xy - 2)dx + (x^3 + 2y)dy = 0$

and found that it is exact. Then we may write down the general solution by inspection; that is, by careful observation of the left member of (7), we shall find a function of which it is the total differential.

First, the term $3x^2y\ dx$ suggests the differential of x^3y. Hence we search (7) for the necessary companion term $x^3\ dy$ and group the two terms. Any term such as $-6x\ dx$, which contains only one variable, is an exact differential as it stands. Thus we are led to rewrite equation (7) as

$$(3x^2y\ dx + x^3\ dy) - 6x\ dx + 2y\ dy = 0,$$

from which the general solution

$$x^3y - 3x^2 + y^2 = c$$

is evident.

EXAMPLE (d): Solve the equation

$$(11) \qquad (2x^3 - xy^2 - 2y + 3)dx - (x^2y + 2x)dy = 0$$

of Example (b) by inspection.

The grouping

$$2x^3\ dx - (xy^2\ dx + x^2y\ dy) - (2y\ dx + 2x\ dy) + 3dx = 0$$

leads at once to the result

$$\tfrac{1}{2}x^4 - \tfrac{1}{2}x^2y^2 - 2xy + 3x = \tfrac{1}{2}c,$$

or

$$x^4 - x^2y^2 - 4xy + 6x = c.$$

EXERCISES

Test each of the following equations for exactness and solve the equation. Those of the equations which are not exact may, of course, be solved by methods of the preceding sections.

1. $(x + y)dx + (x - y)dy = 0.$ ANS. $x^2 + 2xy - y^2 = c.$
2. $(6x + y^2)dx + y(2x - 3y)dy = 0.$ ANS. $3x^2 + xy^2 - y^3 = c.$
3. $(2xy - 3x^2)dx + (x^2 + y)dy = 0.$ ANS. $x^2y - x^3 + \tfrac{1}{2}y^2 = c.$
4. $(y^2 - 2xy + 6x)dx - (x^2 - 2xy + 2)dy = 0.$
      ANS. $xy^2 - x^2y + 3x^2 - 2y = c.$
5. $(2xy - y)dx + (x^2 + x)dy = 0.$ ANS. $y(x + 1)^3 = cx.$

6. $v(2uv^2 - 3)du + (3u^2v^2 - 3u + 4v)dv = 0.$
           ANS. $v(u^2v^2 - 3u + 2v) = c.$

7. $(\cos 2y - 3x^2y^2)dx + (\cos 2y - 2x \sin 2y - 2x^3y)dy = 0.$
           ANS. $\frac{1}{2} \sin 2y + x \cos 2y - x^3y^2 = c.$

8. $(1 + y^2)dx + (x^2y + y)dy = 0.$ ANS. $2 \text{ Arctan } x + \ln (1 + y^2) = c.$

9. $(1 + y^2 + xy^2)dx + (x^2y + y + 2xy)dy = 0.$
           ANS. $2x + y^2(1 + x)^2 = c.$

10. $(w^3 + wz^2 - z)dw + (z^3 + w^2z - w)dz = 0.$
           ANS. $(w^2 + z^2)^2 = 4wz + c.$

11. $(2xy - \tan y)dx + (x^2 - x \sec^2 y)dy = 0.$ ANS. $x^2y - x \tan y = c.$

12. $(\cos x \cos y - \cot x)dx - \sin x \sin y \, dy = 0.$
           ANS. $\sin x \cos y = \ln (c \sin x).$

13. $(r + \sin \theta - \cos \theta)dr + r(\sin \theta + \cos \theta)d\theta = 0.$
           ANS. $r^2 + 2r(\sin \theta - \cos \theta) = c.$

14. $x(3xy - 4y^3 + 6)dx + (x^3 - 6x^2y^2 - 1)dy = 0.$
           ANS. $x^3y - 2x^2y^3 + 3x^2 - y = c.$

15. $(\sin \theta - 2r \cos^2 \theta)dr + r \cos \theta(2r \sin \theta + 1)d\theta = 0.$
           ANS. $r \sin \theta - r^2 \cos^2 \theta = c.$

16. $[2x + y \cos (xy)]dx + x \cos (xy)dy = 0.$ ANS. $x^2 + \sin (xy) = c.$

17. $2xy \, dx + (y^2 + x^2)dy = 0.$ ANS. $y(3x^2 + y^2) = c.$

18. $2xy \, dx + (y^2 - x^2)dy = 0.$ ANS. $x^2 + y^2 = cy.$

19. $[2xy \cos (x^2) - 2xy + 1]dx + [\sin (x^2) - x^2]dy = 0.$
           ANS. $y[\sin (x^2) - x^2] = c - x.$

20. $(2x - 3y)dx + (2y - 3x)dy = 0.$ ANS. $x^2 + y^2 - 3xy = c.$

21. Do Ex. 20 by a second method.

22. $(xy^2 + y - x)dx + x(xy + 1)dy = 0.$ ANS. $x^2y^2 + 2xy - x^2 = c.$

23. $3y(x^2 - 1)dx + (x^3 + 8y - 3x)dy = 0;$ when $x = 0,\ y = 1.$
           ANS. $xy(x^2 - 3) = 4(1 - y^2).$

24. $(1 - xy)^{-2} dx + [y^2 + x^2(1 - xy)^{-2}]dy = 0;$ when $x = 4,\ y = 1.$
           ANS. $xy^4 - y^3 + 3xy - 3x - 3 = 0.$

25. $(ye^{xy} - 2y^3)dx + (xe^{xy} - 6xy^2 - 2y)dy = 0;$ when $x = 0,\ y = 2.$
           ANS. $e^{xy} = 2xy^3 + y^2 - 3.$

11. Integrating factors. It is natural when an equation is not exact to attempt to make it exact by the introduction of an appropriate factor, which is then called an integrating factor. An important application of integrating factors appears in Section 12. In Section 19 there is some discussion of tests for the determination of integrating factors.

At present we are concerned with those equations which are simple enough to enable us to find integrating factors by inspection. The ability to do this depends largely upon recognition of certain common exact differentials and upon experience.

Below are four exact differentials which occur frequently:

$$(1) \qquad d(xy) = x\,dy + y\,dx,$$

$$(2) \qquad d\left(\frac{x}{y}\right) = \frac{y\,dx - x\,dy}{y^2},$$

$$(3) \qquad d\left(\frac{y}{x}\right) = \frac{x\,dy - y\,dx}{x^2},$$

$$(4) \qquad d\left(\operatorname{Arctan}\frac{y}{x}\right) = \frac{x\,dy - y\,dx}{x^2 + y^2}.$$

Note the homogeneity of the coefficients of dx and dy in each of these differentials.

A differential involving only one variable, one such as $x^{-2}\,dx$, is an exact differential.

EXAMPLE (a): Solve the equation

$$(5) \qquad y\,dx + (x + x^3y^2)dy = 0.$$

Let us group the terms of like degree, writing the equation in the form

$$(y\,dx + x\,dy) + x^3y^2\,dy = 0.$$

Now the combination $(y\,dx + x\,dy)$ attracts attention, so we rewrite the equation, obtaining

$$(6) \qquad d(xy) + x^3y^2\,dy = 0.$$

Since the differential of xy is present in equation (6), any factor which is a function of the product xy will not disturb the integrability of that term. But the other term contains the differential dy, hence should contain a function of y alone. Therefore, let us divide by $(xy)^3$ and write

$$\frac{d(xy)}{(xy)^3} + \frac{dy}{y} = 0.$$

The equation above is integrable as it stands. Its solution is

$$-\frac{1}{2x^2y^2} + \ln y = -\ln c,$$

or

$$2x^2y^2 \ln (cy) = 1.$$

EXAMPLE (b): Solve the equation

(7) $$y(x^3 - y)dx - x(x^3 + y)dy = 0.$$

Let us regroup the terms of (7) to obtain

(8) $$x^3(y\,dx - x\,dy) - y(y\,dx + x\,dy) = 0.$$

Recalling that

$$d\left(\frac{x}{y}\right) = \frac{y\,dx - x\,dy}{y^2},$$

we divide the terms of equation (8) throughout by y^2 to get

(9) $$x^3 d\left(\frac{x}{y}\right) - \frac{d(xy)}{y} = 0.$$

Equation (9) will be made exact by introducing a factor, if it can be found, to make the coefficient of $d(x/y)$ a function of (x/y) and the coefficient of $d(xy)$ a function of (xy). Some skill in obtaining such factors can be developed with a little practice. When a factor can be found by inspection, that method is frequently the most rapid one.

There is a straightforward attack on equation (9) which has its good points. Assume that the integrating factor desired is $x^k y^n$, where k and n are to be determined. Applying that factor, we obtain

(10) $$x^{k+3}y^n d\left(\frac{x}{y}\right) - x^k y^{n-1} d(xy) = 0.$$

Since the coefficient of $d(x/y)$ is to be a function of the ratio (x/y), the exponents of x and y in that coefficient must be numerically equal, but of opposite sign. That is,

(11) $$k + 3 = -n.$$

In a similar manner from the coefficient of $d(xy)$ it follows that we must put

(12) $$k = n - 1.$$

From equations (11) and (12) we conclude that $k = -2, n = -1$. The desired integrating factor is $x^{-2}y^{-1}$ and (10) becomes

$$\frac{x}{y} d\left(\frac{x}{y}\right) - \frac{d(xy)}{x^2y^2} = 0$$

of which the solution is

$$\tfrac{1}{2}\left(\frac{x}{y}\right)^2 + \frac{1}{xy} = \frac{c}{2}.$$

Finally, we may write the desired solution of equation (7) as

$$x^3 + 2y = cxy^2.$$

EXAMPLE (c): Solve the equation

$$3x^2y\, dx + (y^4 - x^3)dy = 0.$$

Since two terms in the coefficients of dx and dy are of degree three and the other coefficient is not of degree three, let us regroup the terms to get

$$(3x^2y\, dx - x^3\, dy) + y^4\, dy = 0,$$

or

$$yd(x^3) - x^3\, dy + y^4\, dy = 0.$$

The form of the first two terms now suggests the numerator in the differential of a quotient, as in

$$d\left(\frac{u}{v}\right) = \frac{v\, du - u\, dv}{v^2}.$$

Therefore we divide each term of our equation by y^2 and obtain

$$\frac{yd(x^3) - x^3\, dy}{y^2} + y^2\, dy = 0,$$

or

$$d\left(\frac{x^3}{y}\right) + y^2\, dy = 0.$$

Hence the solution of the original equation is

$$\frac{x^3}{y} + \frac{y^3}{3} = \frac{c}{3},$$

or

$$3x^3 + y^4 = cy.$$

EXERCISES

Find the general solution except when the exercise indicates otherwise.

1. $y(2xy + 1)dx - x\,dy = 0.$ ANS. $x(xy + 1) = cy.$
2. $y(y^3 - x)dx + x(y^3 + x)dy = 0.$ ANS. $2xy^3 - x^2 = cy^2.$
3. $(x^3y^3 + 1)dx + x^4y^2\,dy = 0.$ ANS. $x^3y^3 = -3\ln(cx).$
4. $2t\,ds + s(2 + s^2t)dt = 0.$ ANS. $1 + s^2t = cs^2t^2.$
5. $y(x^4 - y^2)dx + x(x^4 + y^2)dy = 0.$ ANS. $y(3x^4 + y^2) = cx^3.$
6. $y(y^2 + 1)dx + x(y^2 - 1)dy = 0.$ ANS. $x(y^2 + 1) = cy.$
7. Do Ex. 6 by a second method.
8. $y(x^3 - y^5)dx - x(x^3 + y^5)dy = 0.$ ANS. $x^4 = y^4(c + 4xy).$
9. $y(x^2 - y^2 + 1)dx - x(x^2 - y^2 - 1)dy = 0.$
     ANS. $x^2 + cxy + y^2 = 1.$
10. $(x^3 + xy^2 + y)dx + (y^3 + x^2y + x)dy = 0.$
     ANS. $(x^2 + y^2)^2 = c - 4xy.$
11. $y(x^2 + y^2 - 1)dx + x(x^2 + y^2 + 1)dy = 0.$
     ANS. $xy + \text{Arctan}\,(y/x) = c.$
12. $(x^3 + xy^2 - y)dx + (y^3 + x^2y + x)dy = 0.$
     ANS. $2\,\text{Arctan}\,(y/x) = c - x^2 - y^2.$
13. $y(x^3e^{xy} - y)dx + x(y + x^3e^{xy})dy = 0.$ ANS. $2x^2e^{xy} + y^2 = cx^2.$
14. $xy(y^2 + 1)dx + (x^2y^2 - 2)dy = 0;$ when $x = 1,\, y = 1.$
     ANS. $x^2(y^2 + 1) = 2 + 4\ln y.$
15. $y^2(1 - x^2)dx + x(x^2y + 2x + y)dy = 0.$ ANS. $x^2y + x + y = cxy^2.$
16. $y(x^2y^2 - 1)dx + x(x^2y^2 + 1)dy = 0.$ ANS. $x^2y^2 = 2\ln(cx/y).$
17. $x^4y' = -x^3y - \csc(xy).$ ANS. $2x^2\cos(xy) = cx^2 - 1.$
18. $[1 + y\tan(xy)]dx + x\tan(xy)dy = 0.$ ANS. $\cos(xy) = ce^x.$
19. $y(x^2y^2 - m)dx + x(x^2y^2 + n)dy = 0.$ ANS. $x^2y^2 = 2\ln(cx^m/y^n).$
20. $x(x^2 - y^2 - x)dx - y(x^2 - y^2)dy = 0;$ when $x = 2,\, y = 0.$
     ANS. $3(x^2 - y^2)^2 = 4(x^3 + 4).$
21. $y(x^2 + y)dx + x(x^2 - 2y)dy = 0;$ when $x = 1,\, y = 2.$
     ANS. $x^2y - y^2 + 2x = 0.$
22. $y(x^3y^3 + 2x^2 - y)dx + x^3(xy^3 - 2)dy = 0;$ when $x = 1,\, y = 1.$
     ANS. $x^3y^3 + 4x^2 - 7xy + 2y = 0.$
23. $y(2 - 3xy)dx - x\,dy = 0.$ ANS. $x^2(1 - xy) = cy.$
24. $y(2x + y^2)dx + x(y^2 - x)dy = 0.$ ANS. $x(x + y^2) = cy.$
25. $y\,dx + 2(y^4 - x)dy = 0.$ ANS. $y^4 + x = cy^2.$
26. $y(3x^3 - x + y)dx + x^2(1 - x^2)dy = 0.$ ANS. $y\ln(cx) = x(1 - x^2).$
27. $2x^5y' = y(3x^4 + y^2).$ ANS. $x^4 = y^2(1 + cx).$
28. $(x^ny^{n+1} + ay)dx + (x^{n+1}y^n + bx)dy = 0.$
     ANS.   If $n \neq 0,\ x^ny^n = n\ln(cx^{-a}y^{-b}).$
           If $n = 0,\ xy = c_1x^{-a}y^{-b}.$
29. $(x^{n+1}y^n + ay)dx + (x^ny^{n+1} + ax)dy = 0.$
     ANS.   If $n \neq 1,\ (n - 1)(xy)^{n-1}(x^2 + y^2 - c) = 2a.$
           If $n = 1,\ x^2 + y^2 - c = -2a\ln(xy).$

12. The linear equation of order one. An important equation for which an integrating factor can always be determined in a straightforward manner is the linear equation of the first order.

An equation which is linear and of order one in the dependent variable y must by definition (page 4) be of the form

$$(1) \qquad A(x)dy + B(x)y\,dx = C(x)dx.$$

By dividing each member of equation (1) by $A(x)$, we obtain

$$(2) \qquad \boldsymbol{dy + P(x)y\,dx = Q(x)dx,}$$

which we choose as the standard form for the linear equation of order one.

For the moment, suppose that there exists for equation (2) an integrating factor $v(x)$, a function of x alone. Then

$$(3) \qquad v\,dy + vP(x)y\,dx = vQ(x)dx$$

must be an exact equation. But (3) is easily put in the form

$$M\,dx + N\,dy = 0$$

with

$$M = vPy - vQ,$$

and

$$N = v,$$

in which v, P, and Q are functions of x alone.

Therefore, if equation (3) is to be exact, it follows from the requirement $\dfrac{\partial M}{\partial y} = \dfrac{\partial N}{\partial x}$ that v must satisfy the equation

$$(4) \qquad vP = \frac{dv}{dx}.$$

From (4) v may be obtained readily, for

$$P\,dx = \frac{dv}{v},$$

so that

$$\ln v = \int P\,dx,$$

or

$$(5) \qquad v = e^{\int P \, dx}.$$

That is, if the equation (2) has an integrating factor independent of y, then that factor must be as given by equation (5).

It remains to be shown that the v given by equation (5) is actually an integrating factor of

$$(2) \qquad dy + P(x)y \, dx = Q(x)dx.$$

Let us apply the factor throughout (2), obtaining

$$(6) \qquad e^{\int P \, dx} \, dy + Pe^{\int P \, dx}y \, dx = Qe^{\int P \, dx} \, dx.$$

The left member of (6) is the differential of the product

$$ye^{\int P \, dx};$$

the right member of (6) is an exact differential since it is independent of y. Hence equation (6) is exact, which is what we wished to show.

Of course one integrating factor is sufficient. Hence we may use in the exponent $(\int P \, dx)$ any function whose differential is $P \, dx$.

With an integrating factor at hand we can lay down the following rule for integrating any linear equation of order one:

(a) Put the equation into standard form:

$$dy + Py \, dx = Q \, dx;$$

(b) Obtain the integrating factor $e^{\int P \, dx}$;

(c) Apply the integrating factor to the equation in its standard form;

(d) Solve the resultant exact equation.

Note, in integrating the exact equation, that *the integral of the left member is always the product of the dependent variable and the integrating factor used.*

EXAMPLE (a): Solve the equation

$$2(y - 4x^2)dx + x \, dy = 0.$$

The equation is linear in y. When put in standard form it becomes

$$(7) \qquad dy + \frac{2}{x} y \, dx = 8x \, dx.$$

Then an integrating factor is

$$e^{\int \frac{2dx}{x}} = e^{2 \ln x} = (e^{\ln x})^2 = x^2.$$

Next we apply the integrating factor to (7), thus obtaining the exact equation

$$(8) \qquad x^2 \, dy + 2xy \, dx = 8x^3 \, dx.$$

The solution of (8) is

$$(9) \qquad x^2 y = 2x^4 + c$$

and should be checked, particularly since verification of the result is so easy.

From (9) we get (8) by differentiation. Then the original differential equation follows from (8) by a simple adjustment. Hence (9) is a solution of the original equation.

EXAMPLE (b): Solve the equation

$$y \, dx + (3x - xy + 2)dy = 0.$$

Since the product $y \, dy$ occurs here, the equation is not linear in y. It is, however, linear in x. Therefore we arrange the terms as in

$$y \, dx + (3 - y)x \, dy = -2 \, dy$$

and pass to the standard form,

$$(10) \qquad dx + \left(\frac{3}{y} - 1 \right) x \, dy = -\frac{2}{y} \, dy.$$

Now

$$\int \left(\frac{3}{y} - 1 \right) dy = 3 \ln y - y + c_1,$$

so that an integrating factor for equation (10) is

$$e^{3 \ln y - y} = e^{3 \ln y} \cdot e^{-y} = (e^{\ln y})^3 \cdot e^{-y} = y^3 e^{-y}.$$

Application of this integrating factor to equation (10) leads to the exact equation

$$y^3e^{-y}\,dx + y^2(3-y)e^{-y}x\,dy = -2y^2e^{-y}\,dy,$$

from which we get

$$xy^3e^{-y} = -2\int y^2e^{-y}\,dy$$
$$= 2y^2e^{-y} + 4ye^{-y} + 4e^{-y} + c.$$

Thus we may write the solution as

$$xy^3 = 2y^2 + 4y + 4 + ce^y.$$

EXERCISES

In Exs. 1–25 find the general solution.

1. $(x^4 + 2y)dx - x\,dy = 0.$ ANS. $2y = x^4 + cx^2.$

2. $(3xy + 3y - 4)dx + (x+1)^2\,dy = 0.$
ANS. $y = 2(x+1)^{-1} + c(x+1)^{-3}.$

3. $y' = \csc x - y\cot x.$ ANS. $y\sin x = x + c.$

4. $t\dfrac{dx}{dt} = 6te^{2t} + x(2t - 1).$ ANS. $xt = (3t^2 + c)e^{2t}.$

5. $dy = (x - 3y)dx.$ ANS. $9y = 3x - 1 + ce^{-3x}.$

6. $(3x - 1)y' = 6y - 10(3x - 1)^{1/3}.$
ANS. $y = 2(3x-1)^{1/3} + c(3x-1)^2.$

7. $(y-2)dx + (3x - y)dy = 0.$ ANS. $12x = 3y + 2 + c(y-2)^{-3}.$

8. $(2xy + x^2 + x^4)dx - (1 + x^2)dy = 0.$
ANS. $y = (1 + x^2)(c + x - \text{Arctan } x).$

9. $y' = x - 2xy.$ Solve by two methods. ANS. $2y = 1 + ce^{-x^2}.$

10. $(y - \cos^2 x)dx + \cos x\,dy = 0.$
ANS. $y(\sec x + \tan x) = c + x - \cos x.$

11. $y' = x - 2y\cot 2x.$ ANS. $4y\sin 2x = c + \sin 2x - 2x\cos 2x.$

12. $(y - x + xy\cot x)dx + x\,dy = 0.$
ANS. $xy\sin x = c + \sin x - x\cos x.$

13. $\dfrac{dy}{dx} - my = c_1e^{mx},$ where c_1 and m are constants.
ANS. $y = (c_1x + c_2)e^{mx}.$

14. $\dfrac{dy}{dx} - m_2y = c_1e^{m_1x},$ where c_1, m_1, m_2 are constants and $m_1 \neq m_2.$
ANS. $y = c_3e^{m_1x} + c_2e^{m_2x},$ where $c_3 = c_1/(m_1 - m_2).$

15. $v\,dx + (2x + 1 - vx)dv = 0.$ ANS. $xv^2 = v + 1 + ce^v.$

16. $x(x^2 + 1)y' + 2y = (x^2 + 1)^3.$ ANS. $x^2y = \tfrac{1}{4}(x^2 + 1)^3 + c(x^2 + 1).$

17. $2x(y - x^2)dx + dy = 0$.   ANS. $y = x^2 - 1 + ce^{-x^2}$.

18. $(1 + xy)dx - (1 + x^2)dy = 0$.   ANS. $y = x + c(1 + x^2)^{1/2}$.

19. $2y\,dx = (x^2 - 1)(dx - dy)$.

          ANS. $(x - 1)y = (x + 1)[c + x - 2\ln(x + 1)]$.

20. $dx - (1 + 2x\tan y)dy = 0$.   ANS. $2x\cos^2 y = y + c + \sin y\cos y$.

21. $(1 + \cos x)y' = \sin x(\sin x + \sin x\cos x - y)$.

          ANS. $y = (1 + \cos x)(c + x - \sin x)$.

22. $y' = 1 + 3y\tan x$.   ANS. $3y\cos^3 x = c + 3\sin x - \sin^3 x$.

23. $(x^2 + a^2)dy = 2x[(x^2 + a^2)^2 + 3y]dx$; a is constant.

          ANS. $y = (x^2 + a^2)^2[c(x^2 + a^2) - 1]$.

24. $(x + a)y' = bx - ny$; a, b, n are constants with $n \neq 0$, $n \neq -1$.

          ANS. $n(n + 1)y = b(nx - a) + c(x + a)^{-n}$.

25. Solve the equation of Ex. 24 for the exceptional cases $n = 0$ and $n = -1$.

          ANS.   If $n = 0$, $y = bx + c - ab\ln(x + a)$.

                  If $n = -1$, $y = ab + c(x + a) + b(x + a)\ln(x + a)$.

26. In the standard form $dy + Py\,dx = Q\,dx$ put $y = vw$, thus obtaining

$$w(dv + Pv\,dx) + v\,dw = Q\,dx.$$

Then, by first choosing v so that

$$dv + Pv\,dx = 0$$

and later determining w, show how to complete the solution of

$$dy + Py\,dx = Q\,dx.$$

In Exs. 27–33 find the particular solution indicated.

27. $(2x + 3)y' = y + (2x + 3)^{1/2}$; when $x = -1$, $y = 0$.

          ANS. $2y = (2x + 3)^{1/2}\ln(2x + 3)$.

28. $y' = x^3 - 2xy$; when $x = 1$, $y = 1$.   ANS. $2y = x^2 - 1 + 2e^{1-x^2}$.

29. $L\dfrac{di}{dt} + Ri = E$, where L, R, and E are constants; when $t = 0$, $i = 0$.

          ANS. $i = \dfrac{E}{R}(1 - e^{-Rt/L})$

30. $L\dfrac{di}{dt} + Ri = E\sin\omega t$; when $t = 0$, $i = 0$.

          ANS.   Let $Z^2 = R^2 + \omega^2 L^2$.   Then
          $i = EZ^{-2}(R\sin\omega t - \omega L\cos\omega t + \omega Le^{-Rt/L})$.

31. Find that solution of $y' = 2(2x - y)$ which passes through the point $(0, -1)$.   ANS. $y = 2x - 1$.

32. Find that solution of $y' = 2(2x - y)$ which passes through the point $(0, 1)$.   ANS. $y = 2x - 1 + 2e^{-2x}$.

33. $(1 + t^2)ds + 2t[st^2 - 3(1 + t^2)^2]dt = 0$; when $t = 0$, $s = 2$.

          ANS. $s = (1 + t^2)(3 - e^{-t^2})$.

MISCELLANEOUS EXERCISES

In each exercise find the general solution unless the statement of the exercise stipulates otherwise.

1. $y' = e^{x+y}$.   ANS. $e^x + e^{-y} = c$.

2. $(x + y)dx + x\,dy = 0$.   ANS. $x(x + 2y) = c$.

3. $y^2\,dx - x(2x + 3y)dy = 0$.   ANS. $y^2(x + y) = cx$.

4. $(x^2 + 1)dx + x^2 y^2\,dy = 0$.   ANS. $xy^3 = 3(1 + cx - x^2)$.

5. $(x^3 + y^3)dx + y^2(3x + ky)dy = 0$; k is constant.
     ANS. $ky^4 + 4xy^3 + x^4 = c$.

6. $xy' = x^2 y^2 + 2y$.   ANS. $4x^2 = y(c - x^4)$.

7. $\dfrac{dy}{dx} - \cos x = \cos x \tan^2 y$.   ANS. $2 \sin x = y + \sin y \cos y + c$.

8. $\cos x \dfrac{dy}{dx} = 1 - y - \sin x$.   ANS. $y(1 + \sin x) = (x + c)\cos x$.

9. $\sin \theta \dfrac{dr}{d\theta} = -1 - 2r \cos \theta$.   ANS. $r \sin^2 \theta = c + \cos \theta$.

10. $y(x + 3y)dx + x^2\,dy = 0$.   ANS. $x^2 y = c(2x + 3y)$.

11. $\dfrac{dy}{dx} = \sec^2 x \sec^3 y$.   ANS. $3 \tan x + c = 3 \sin y - \sin^3 y$.

12. $y(2x^3 - x^2 y + y^3)dx - x(2x^3 + y^3)dy = 0$.
     ANS. $2x^2 y \ln (cx) = 4x^3 - y^3$.

13. $xy' = y(1 + 2xy)$.   ANS. $x(1 + xy) = cy$.

14. $xy\,dx + \sqrt{1 + x^2}\,dy = 0$.   ANS. $\ln (cy) = -\sqrt{x^2 + 1}$.

15. $[x - y \cot (y/x)]dx + x \cot (y/x)dy = 0$. Solve by two methods.
     ANS. $x \sin (y/x) = c$.

16. $y(x^2 + y^2)dx + x(3x^2 - 5y^2)dy = 0$; when $x = 2$, $y = 1$.
     ANS. $2y^5 - 2x^2 y^3 + 3x = 0$.

17. $y' + ay = b$; a and b are constants. Solve by two methods.
     ANS. $y = b/a + ce^{-ax}$.

18. $(x - y)dx - (x + y)dy = 0$. Solve by two methods.
     ANS. $x^2 - 2xy - y^2 = c$.

19. $\dfrac{dx}{dt} = \cos x \cos^2 t$.   ANS. $4 \ln (\sec x + \tan x) = 2t + \sin 2t + c$.

20. $(\sin y - y \sin x)dx + (\cos x + x \cos y)dy = 0$.
     ANS. $x \sin y + y \cos x = c$.

21. $(1 + 4xy - 4x^2 y)dx + (x^2 - x^3)dy = 0$; when $x = 2$, $y = \frac{1}{4}$.
     ANS. $2x^4 y = x^2 + 2x + 2 \ln (x - 1)$.

22. $(3 - 2xy)dx = \left(x^2 + \dfrac{1}{y^2} + \dfrac{1}{y}\right) dy$.
     ANS. $x^2 y - 3x - y^{-1} + \ln y = c$.

23. $[3x(y - 1) + y + 2]dx + x\,dy = 0$.   ANS. $xy = x - 1 + ce^{-3x}$.

24. $xy(dx - dy) = x^2\,dy + y^2\,dx.$ ANS. $x = y\ln(cxy).$

25. $a^2(dy - dx) = x^2\,dy + y^2\,dx;\ a$ is constant.

ANS. $2\,\mathrm{Arctan}\,(y/a) = \ln\,[c(x + a)/(x - a)].$

26. $(y - \sin^2 x)dx + \sin x\,dy = 0.$

ANS. $y(\csc x - \cot x) = x + c - \sin x.$

27. $(x - y)dx + (3x + y)dy = 0;$ when $x = 2,\ y = -1.$

ANS. $2(x + 2y) + (x + y)\ln(x + y) = 0.$

28. $y\,dx = (2x + 1)(dx - dy).$ ANS. $3y = (2x + 1) + c(2x + 1)^{-1/2}.$

In solving Exs. 29–33, recall that the principal value Arcsin x of the inverse sine function is restricted as follows:

$$-\tfrac{1}{2}\pi \le \mathbf{Arcsin}\ x \le \tfrac{1}{2}\pi.$$

29. $\sqrt{1 - y^2}\,dx + \sqrt{1 - x^2}\,dy = 0.$

ANS.   Arcsin x + Arcsin $y = c$, or a part of the ellipse $x^2 + 2c_1xy + y^2 + c_1{}^2 - 1 = 0$, where $c_1 = \cos c$.

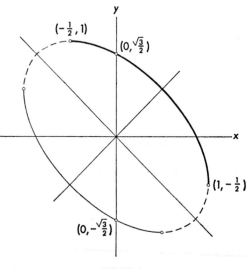

FIGURE 6

30. Solve the equation of Ex. 29 with the added condition that when $x = 0$, $y = \sqrt{3}/2.$

ANS.   Arcsin x + Arcsin $y = \pi/3$, or that arc of the ellipse $x^2 + xy + y^2 = 3/4$, which is indicated by a heavy solid line in Figure 6.

31. Solve the equation of Ex. 29 with the added condition that when $x = 0$, $y = -\sqrt{3}/2$.

  ANS. Arcsin x + Arcsin $y = -\pi/3$, or that arc of the ellipse $x^2 + xy + y^2 = 3/4$, which is indicated by a light solid line in Figure 6.

32. Show that after the answers to Exs. 30 and 31 have been deleted the remaining arcs of the ellipse

$$x^2 + xy + y^2 = 3/4$$

are not solutions of the differential equation

$$\sqrt{1 - y^2}\, dx + \sqrt{1 - x^2}\, dy = 0.$$

For this purpose consider the sign of the slope of the curve.

33. For the equation

$$\sqrt{1 - y^2}\, dx - \sqrt{1 - x^2}\, dy = 0$$

state and solve four problems analogous to Exs. 29–32 above.

34. $v\, du = (e^v + 2uv - 2u)dv.$ ANS. $v^2 u = ce^{2v} - (v + 1)e^v.$

35. $y(ye^{xy} + 1)dx + (xye^{xy} + e^{xy} + x)dy = 0$; when $x = 0$, $y = 1$.

  ANS. $ye^{xy} = 1 - xy.$

36. $y^2\, dx - (xy + 2)dy = 0.$ ANS. $xy = cy^2 - 1.$

37. $(x^2 - 2xy - y^2)dx - (x^2 + 2xy - y^2)dy = 0.$

  ANS. $(x + y)(x^2 - 4xy + y^2) = c^3.$

38. $y^2\, dx + (xy + y^2 - 1)dy = 0$; when $x = -1$, $y = 1$.

  ANS. $y^2 + 2xy + 1 = 2 \ln y.$

39. $y(y^2 - 3x^2)dx + x^3\, dy = 0.$ ANS. $2x^6 = y^2(x^4 + c).$

40. $y' = \cos x - y \sec x$; when $x = 0$, $y = 1$.

  ANS. $y(1 + \sin x) = \cos x(x + 2 - \cos x).$

41. Find that solution of $y' = 3x + y$ which passes through the point $(-1,0)$.   ANS. $y = -3(x + 1).$

42. Find that solution of $y' = 3x + y$ which passes through the point $(-1,1)$.   ANS. $y = -3(x + 1) + e^{x+1}.$

43. $y' = y \tan x + \cos x.$ ANS. $2y = \sin x + (x + c) \sec x.$

44. $(x^2 - 1 + 2y)dx + (1 - x^2)dy = 0$; when $x = 2$, $y = 1$.

  ANS. $(x + 1)y = (x - 1)[x + 1 + 2 \ln (x - 1)].$

45. $(x^3 - 3xy^2)dx + (y^3 - 3x^2y)dy = 0.$ ANS. $x^4 - 6x^2y^2 + y^4 = c.$

46. $(1 - x^2)y' = 1 - xy - 3x^2 + 2x^4.$ ANS. $y = x - x^3 + c(1 - x^2)^{1/2}.$

47. $(y^2 + y)dx - (y^2 + 2xy + x)dy = 0$; when $x = 3$, $y = 1$.

  ANS. $2y^2 + y = x.$

48. $(y^3 - x^3)dx = xy(x\, dx + y\, dy).$

  ANS. $2x^2 \ln (x + y) = cx^2 + 2xy - y^2.$

49. $y(x^2y^2 + x^2 + y^2)dx + x(x^2 + y^2 - x^2y^2)dy = 0.$

  ANS. $xy \text{ Arctan } (y/x) = cxy - 1.$

Chapter 3

Elementary Applications

13. Velocity of escape from the earth. Many physical problems involve differential equations of order one and degree one.

First consider the problem of determining the velocity of a particle projected in a radial direction outward from the earth and acted upon by only one force, the gravitational attraction of the earth.

We shall assume an initial velocity in a radial direction so that the motion of the particle takes place entirely on a line through the center of the earth.

According to the Newtonian law of gravitation the acceleration of the particle will be inversely proportional to the square of the distance from the particle to the center of the earth. Let r be that variable distance, and let R be the radius of the earth. If t represents time, v the velocity of the particle, a its acceleration, and k the constant of proportionality in the Newtonian law, then

$$a = \frac{dv}{dt} = \frac{k}{r^2}.$$

The acceleration is negative because the velocity is decreasing. Hence the constant k is negative. When $r = R$, then $a = -g$, the acceleration at the surface of the earth. Thus

$$-g = \frac{k}{R^2},$$

from which

$$a = -\frac{gR^2}{r^2}.$$

We wish to express the acceleration in terms of the velocity and

48

the distance. We have $a = \dfrac{dv}{dt}$ and $v = \dfrac{dr}{dt}$. Hence

$$a = \frac{dv}{dt} = \frac{dr}{dt}\frac{dv}{dr} = v\frac{dv}{dr},$$

so that the differential equation for the velocity is now seen to be

(1) $$v\frac{dv}{dr} = -\frac{gR^2}{r^2}.$$

The method of separation of variables applies to equation (1) and leads at once to the solution

$$v^2 = \frac{2gR^2}{r} + C.$$

Suppose the particle leaves the earth's surface with the velocity v_0. Then $v = v_0$ when $r = R$, from which the constant C is easily determined to be

$$C = v_0{}^2 - 2gR.$$

Thus a particle projected in a radial direction outward from the earth's surface with an initial velocity v_0 will travel with a velocity v given by the equation

(2) $$v^2 = \frac{2gR^2}{r} + v_0{}^2 - 2gR.$$

It is of considerable interest to determine whether the particle will escape from the earth. Now at the surface of the earth, at $r = R$, the velocity is positive, $v = v_0$. An examination of the right member of equation (2) shows that the velocity of the particle will remain positive if, and only if,

(3) $$v_0{}^2 - 2gR \geqq 0.$$

For, if the inequality (3) is satisfied, the velocity given by equation (2) will remain positive, since it cannot vanish, is continuous, and is positive at $r = R$. On the other hand, if the inequality (3) is not satisfied, then $v_0{}^2 - 2gR < 0$ and there will be a critical value of r

for which the right member of equation (2) is zero. That is, the particle would stop, the velocity would change from positive to negative, and the particle would return to the earth.

A particle projected from the earth with a velocity v_0 such that $v_0 \geqq \sqrt{2gR}$ will escape from the earth. Hence, the minimum such velocity of projection,

$$(4) \qquad\qquad v_e = \sqrt{2gR},$$

is called the *velocity of escape.*

The radius of the earth is approximately $R = 3960$ miles. The acceleration of gravity at the surface of the earth is approximately $g = 32.16$ feet per second per second, or $g = 6.09(10)^{-3}$ miles per second per second. For the earth the velocity of escape is easily found to be $v_e = 6.95$ miles per second.

Of course, the gravitational pull of other celestial bodies, the moon, the sun, Mars, Venus, etc., has been neglected in the idealized problem treated here. It is not difficult to see that such approximations are justified, since we are interested in only the critical initial velocity v_e. Whether the particle actually recedes from the earth forever or becomes, for instance, a satellite of some heavenly body, is of no consequence in the present problem.

If in this study we happen to be thinking of the particle as an idealization of a ballistic type rocket, then other elements must be considered. Air resistance in the first few miles may not be negligible. Methods for disposing of such difficulties are not suitable topics for discussion here.

It must be realized that the formula $v_e = \sqrt{2gR}$ applies equally well for the velocity of escape from the other members of the solar system, so long as R and g are given their appropriate values.

14. Newton's law of cooling. Experiment has shown that under certain conditions a good approximation to the temperature of an object can be obtained by using Newton's law of cooling: The temperature of a body changes at a rate which is proportional to the difference in temperature between the outside medium and the body itself.

Suppose, for instance, that a thermometer, which has been at the reading 70°F inside a house, is placed outside where the air tempera-

ture is 10°F. Three minutes later it is found that the thermometer
reading is 25°F. We wish to predict the thermometer reading at
various later times.

Let u (°F) represent the temperature of the thermometer at time
t (min), the time being measured from the instant the thermometer is
placed outside. We are given that when $t = 0$, $u = 70$ and when
$t = 3$, $u = 25$.

According to Newton's law the time rate of change of temperature, du/dt, is proportional to the temperature difference $(u - 10)$.
Since the thermometer temperature is decreasing, it is convenient
to choose $(-k)$ as the constant of proportionality. Thus the u is
to be determined from the differential equation

$$(1) \qquad \frac{du}{dt} = -k(u - 10),$$

together with the conditions

$$(2) \qquad\qquad \text{when } t = 0,\ u = 70$$

and

$$(3) \qquad\qquad \text{when } t = 3,\ u = 25.$$

We need to know the thermometer reading at two different times
because there are two constants to be determined, the k in equation
(1) and the "arbitrary" constant which occurs in the solution of the
differential equation (1).

From equation (1) it follows at once that

$$u = 10 + Ce^{-kt}.$$

Then condition (2) yields $70 = 10 + C$ from which $C = 60$, so that
we have

$$(4) \qquad\qquad u = 10 + 60e^{-kt}.$$

The value of k will be determined now by using the condition (3).
Putting $t = 3$ and $u = 25$ into equation (4) we get

$$25 = 10 + 60e^{-3k},$$

from which $e^{-3k} = \frac{1}{4}$, so that $k = \frac{1}{3} \ln 4$.

Thus the temperature u is given by the equation

(5) $$u = 10 + 60e^{-(t/3)\ln 4}.$$

Since $\ln 4 = 1.39$, equation (5) may be replaced by

(6) $$u = 10 + 60e^{-0.46t},$$

which is convenient when a table of values of e^{-x} is available.

Suppose the thermometer can be read only to the nearest degree and that we wish to know when the reading will first reach 10°F. Then we need to find the smallest t such that

$$60e^{-0.46t} < 0.5.$$

The result, to the nearest minute, is $t = 10$.

15. Simple chemical conversion. It is known from the results of chemical experimentation that, in certain reactions in which a substance A is being converted into another substance, the time rate of change of the amount x of unconverted substance is proportional to x.

Let the amount of unconverted substance be known at some specified time; that is, let $x = x_0$ at $t = 0$. Then the amount x at any time $t > 0$ is determined by the differential equation

(1) $$\frac{dx}{dt} = -kx$$

together with the condition that $x = x_0$ when $t = 0$. Since the amount x is decreasing as time increases, the constant of proportionality in equation (1) is taken to be $(-k)$.

From equation (1) it follows that

$$x = Ce^{-kt}.$$

But $x = x_0$ when $t = 0$. Hence $C = x_0$. Thus we have the result

(2) $$x = x_0 e^{-kt}.$$

Let us now add another condition which will enable us to determine k. Suppose it is known that at the end of half a minute, at

$t = 30$ (sec), two-thirds of the original amount x_0 has already been converted. Let us determine how much unconverted substance remains at $t = 60$ (sec).

When two-thirds of the substance has been converted, one-third remains unconverted. Hence $x = x_0/3$ when $t = 30$. Equation (2) now yields the relation

$$x_0/3 = x_0 e^{-30k}$$

from which k is easily found to be $(1/30) \ln 3$. Then with t measured in seconds, the amount of unconverted substance is given by the equation

$$(3) \qquad x = x_0 e^{-(t/30) \ln 3}.$$

At $t = 60$,

$$x = x_0 e^{-2 \ln 3} = x_0(3)^{-2} = x_0/9.$$

Hence one-ninth of the original amount of substance A remains unconverted at the end of one minute.

EXERCISES

1. The radius of the moon is roughly 1080 miles. The acceleration of gravity at the surface of the moon is about $0.165g$, where g is the acceleration of gravity at the surface of the earth. Determine the velocity of escape for the moon.   ANS.   1.5 mi/sec.

2. Determine to two significant figures the velocity of escape for each of the celestial bodies listed below. The data given are rough and g may be taken to be $6.1(10)^{-3}$ mi/sec².

	Accel. of gravity at surface	Radius in miles	Ans. in mi/sec
Venus	$0.85g$	3,800	6.3
Mars	$0.38g$	2,100	3.1
Jupiter	$2.6g$	43,000	37
Sun	$28g$	432,000	380
Ganymede	$0.12g$	1,780	1.6

3. A thermometer reading 18°F is brought into a room the temperature of which is 70°F. One minute later the thermometer reading is 31°F.

Determine the temperature reading as a function of time and in particular, find the temperature reading five minutes after the thermometer is first brought into the room.

ANS. $u = 70 - 52e^{-0.29t}$; when $t = 5$, $u = 58$.

4. A thermometer reading 75°F is taken out where the temperature is 20°F. The reading is 30°F four minutes later. Find (a) the thermometer reading seven minutes after the thermometer was brought outside, and (b) the time taken for the reading to drop from 75°F to within a half degree of the air temperature.   ANS. (a) 23°F; (b) 11.5 min.

5. At 1:00 P.M. a thermometer reading 70°F is taken outside where the air temperature is −10°F, ten below zero. At 1:02 P.M. the reading is 26°F. At 1:05 P.M. the thermometer is taken back indoors where the air is at 70°F. What is the thermometer reading at 1:09 P.M.?

ANS. 56°F.

6. At 9 A.M. a thermometer reading 70°F is taken outdoors where the temperature is 15°F. At 9:05 A.M. the thermometer reading is 45°F. At 9:10 A.M. the thermometer is taken back indoors where the temperature is fixed at 70°F. Find (a) the reading at 9:20 A.M. and (b) when the reading, to the nearest degree, will show the correct (70°F) indoor temperature.   ANS. (a) 58°F; (b) 9:46 A.M.

7. At 2:00 P.M. a thermometer reading 80°F is taken outside where the air temperature is 20°F. At 2:03 P.M. the temperature reading yielded by the thermometer is 42°F. Later the thermometer is brought inside where the air is at 80°F. At 2:10 P.M. the reading is 71°F. When was the thermometer brought indoors?   ANS. At 2:05 P.M.

8. Suppose that a chemical reaction proceeds according to the law given in Section 15 above. If half the substance A has been converted at the end of ten seconds, find when nine-tenths of the substance will have been converted.   ANS. 33 sec.

9. The conversion of a substance B follows the law used in Section 15 above. If only a fourth of the substance has been converted at the end of ten seconds find when nine-tenths of the substance will have been converted.   ANS. 80 sec.

10. For a substance C the time rate of conversion is proportional to the square of the amount x of unconverted substance. Let k be the numerical value of the constant of proportionality and let the amount of unconverted substance be x_0 at time $t = 0$. Determine x for all $t \geqq 0$.   ANS. $x = x_0/(1 + x_0kt)$.

11. Two substances, A and B, are being converted into a single compound C. In the laboratory it has been shown that, for these substances, the following law of conversion holds: the time rate of change of the amount x of compound C is proportional to the product of the amounts of unconverted substances A and B. Assume the units of measure so chosen that one unit of the compound C is formed from the combination of one unit of A together with one unit of B. If at time $t = 0$ there are a units

of substance A, b units of substance B, and none of the compound C present, show that the law of conversion may be expressed by the equation

$$\frac{dx}{dt} = k(a - x)(b - x).$$

Solve this equation with the given initial condition.

ANS. If $b \neq a$, $x = ab[e^{(b-a)kt} - 1]/[be^{(b-a)kt} - a]$;
if $b = a$, $x = a^2kt/(akt + 1.)$

12. In the solution of Ex. 11 above assume that $k > 0$ and investigate the behavior of x as $t \to \infty$. ANS. If $b \geqq a$, $x \to a$; if $b \leqq a$, $x \to b$.

13. Radium decomposes at a rate proportional to the quantity of radium present. Suppose that it is found that in 25 years approximately 1.1 per cent of a certain quantity of radium has decomposed. Determine approximately how long it will take for one-half the original amount of radium to decompose. ANS. 1600 years.

14. A certain radioactive substance has a half-life of 38 hours. Find how long it takes for 90% of the radioactivity to be dissipated.
ANS. 126 hrs.

15. A bacterial population B is known to have a rate of growth proportional to B itself. If between noon and 2 P.M. the population triples, at what time, no controls being exerted, should B become 100 times what it was at noon? ANS. About 8:22 P.M.

16. In the motion of an object through a certain medium (air at certain pressures is an example) the medium furnishes a resisting force proportional to the square of the velocity of the moving object. Suppose a body falls, due to the action of gravity, through such a medium. Let t represent time, v represent velocity, positive downward. Let g be the usual constant acceleration of gravity and let w be the weight of the body. Use Newton's law, force equals mass times acceleration, to conclude that the differential equation of the motion is

$$\frac{w}{g}\frac{dv}{dt} = w - kv^2,$$

where kv^2 is the magnitude of the resisting force furnished by the medium.

17. Solve the differential equation of Ex. 16 with the initial condition that $v = v_0$ when $t = 0$. Introduce the constant $a^2 = w/k$ to simplify the formulas. ANS. $(a + v)/(a - v) = (a + v_0)e^{2gt/a}/(a - v_0)$.

18. Obtain the dimensions, in some consistent set of units, of the variables and parameters of Exs. 16–17 above.

ANS. t in sec g in ft/sec^2
v in ft/sec k in (lb)(sec^2)/(ft^2)
w in lb a in ft/sec.

19. There are mediums which resist motion through them with a force proportional to the first power of the velocity. For such a medium state and solve problems analogous to Exs. 16–18 above, except that for convenience a constant $b = w/k$ may be introduced to replace the a^2 of Ex. 17. Show that b has the dimensions of a velocity.

ANS. $v = b + (v_0 - b)e^{-at/b}$.

FIGURE 7

20. Figure 7 shows a weight, w pounds, sliding down an inclined plane which makes an angle α with the horizontal. Assume that no force other than gravity is acting on the weight; that is, there is no friction, no air resistance, etc. At time $t = 0$, let $x = x_0$ and let the initial velocity be v_0. Determine x for $t > 0$.

ANS. $x = \frac{1}{2}gt^2 \sin \alpha + v_0t + x_0$.

21. A long, very smooth board is inclined at an angle of 10° with the horizontal. A weight starts from rest ten feet from the bottom of the board and slides downward under the action of gravity alone. Find how long it will take the weight to reach the bottom of the board and determine the terminal speed.

ANS. 1.9 sec and 10.5 ft/sec.

22. Add to the conditions of Ex. 20 above a retarding force of magnitude kv, where v is the velocity. Determine v and x under the assumption that the weight starts from rest with $x = x_0$. Use the notation $a = kg/w$.

ANS. $v = a^{-1}g \sin \alpha (1 - e^{-at})$;
$x = x_0 + a^{-2}g \sin \alpha (-1 + e^{-at} + at)$.

Chapter 4

Additional Topics on Equations of the First Order and First Degree

16. Substitution suggested by the equation. An equation of the form

$$M\,dx + N\,dy = 0$$

may not yield at once (or at all) to the methods of Chapter 2. Even then the usefulness of those methods is not exhausted. It may be possible by some change of variables to transform the equation into one of a type which we know how to solve.

A natural source of suggestions for useful transformations is the differential equation itself. If a particular function of one or both variables stands out in the equation, then it is worth while to examine the equation after that function has been introduced as a new variable. For instance, in the equation

$$(1) \qquad (x + 2y - 1)dx + 3(x + 2y)dy = 0$$

the combination $(x + 2y)$ occurs twice and so attracts attention. Hence we put

$$x + 2y = v$$

and, since no other function of x and y stands out, we retain either x or y for the other variable. The solution is completed in Example (a) below.

In the equation

$$(2) \qquad (1 + 3x \sin y)dx - x^2 \cos y\,dy = 0$$

the presence of both $\sin y$ and its differential $\cos y\,dy$, together with the fact that y appears in the equation in no other manner, leads us to put $\sin y = w$ and to obtain the differential equation in w and x. See Example (b) below.

EXAMPLE (a): Solve the equation

$$(1) \qquad (x + 2y - 1)dx + 3(x + 2y)dy = 0.$$

As suggested above, put

$$x + 2y = v.$$

Then

$$dx = dv - 2dy$$

and equation (1) becomes

$$(v - 1)(dv - 2dy) + 3v\,dy = 0,$$

or

$$(v - 1)dv + (v + 2)dy = 0.$$

Now the variables can be separated. From the equation in the form

$$\frac{v - 1}{v + 2}\,dv + dy = 0,$$

we get

$$\left[1 - \frac{3}{v + 2}\right]dv + dy = 0$$

and then

$$v - 3\ln(v + 2) + y + c = 0.$$

But $v = x + 2y$, so our final result is

$$x + 3y + c = 3\ln(x + 2y + 2).$$

EXAMPLE (b): Solve the equation

$$(2) \qquad (1 + 3x\sin y)dx - x^2\cos y\,dy = 0.$$

Put $\sin y = w$. Then $\cos y\,dy = dw$ and (2) becomes

$$(1 + 3xw)dx - x^2\,dw = 0,$$

an equation linear in w.   From the standard form

$$dw - \frac{3}{x} w \, dx = \frac{dx}{x^2}$$

an integrating factor is seen to be

$$e^{-3 \ln x} = x^{-3}.$$

Application of the integrating factor yields the exact equation

$$x^{-3} \, dw - 3x^{-4}w \, dx = x^{-5} \, dx,$$

from which we get

$$x^{-3}w = -\tfrac{1}{4}x^{-4} + \tfrac{1}{4}c,$$

or

$$4xw = cx^4 - 1.$$

Hence (2) has the solution

$$4x \sin y = cx^4 - 1.$$

17. Bernoulli's equation.   A well-known equation which fits into the category of Section 16 is Bernoulli's equation

$$(1) \qquad\qquad y' + P(x)y = Q(x)y^n.$$

If $n = 1$ in (1), the variables are separable, so we concentrate on the case $n \neq 1$.   Equation (1) may be put in the form

$$(2) \qquad\qquad y^{-n} \, dy + Py^{-n+1} \, dx = Q \, dx.$$

But the differential of y^{-n+1} is $(1 - n)y^{-n} \, dy$, so that equation (2) may be simplified by putting

$$y^{-n+1} = z,$$

from which

$$(1 - n)y^{-n} \, dy = dz.$$

Thus the equation in z and x is

$$dz + (1 - n)Pz \, dx = (1 - n)Q \, dx,$$

a linear equation in standard form.   Hence any Bernoulli equation can be solved with the aid of the above change of dependent variable (unless $n = 1$, when no substitution is needed).

EXAMPLE (a): Solve the equation

$$(3) \qquad y(6y^2 - x - 1)dx + 2x\, dy = 0.$$

First let us group the terms according to powers of y, writing

$$2x\, dy - y(x + 1)dx + 6y^3\, dx = 0.$$

Now it can be seen that the equation is a Bernoulli equation, since it involves only terms containing respectively dy, y, and y^n ($n = 3$ here). Therefore we divide throughout by y^3, obtaining

$$2xy^{-3}\, dy - y^{-2}(x + 1)dx = -6dx.$$

The equation above is linear in y^{-2}, so we put $y^{-2} = v$, obtain $dv = -2y^{-3}\, dy$, and need to solve the equation

$$x\, dv + v(x + 1)dx = 6dx,$$

or

$$(4) \qquad dv + v(1 + x^{-1})dx = 6x^{-1}\, dx.$$

Since

$$e^{x + \ln x} = xe^x$$

is an integrating factor for (4), the equation

$$xe^x\, dv + ve^x(x + 1)dx = 6e^x\, dx$$

is exact. Its solution

$$xve^x = 6e^x + c,$$

together with $v = y^{-2}$ leads us to the final result

$$y^2(6 + ce^{-x}) = x.$$

EXAMPLE (b): Solve the equation

$$(5) \qquad 6y^2\, dx - x(2x^3 + y)dy = 0.$$

This is a Bernoulli equation with x as the dependent variable, so it can be treated in the manner used in Example (a). That method of attack is left for the exercises.

Equation (5) can equally well be treated as follows. Note that if each member of (5) be multiplied by x^2 then the equation becomes

(6) $$6y^2x^2\,dx - x^3(2x^3 + y)dy = 0.$$

In (6) the variable x appears only in the combinations x^3 and its differential $3x^2\,dx$. Hence a reasonable choice for a new variable is $w = x^3$. The equation in w and y is

$$2y^2\,dw - w(2w + y)dy = 0,$$

an equation with coefficients homogeneous of degree two in y and w. The further change of variable $w = zy$ leads to the equation

$$2y\,dz - z(2z - 1)dy = 0,$$

or

$$\frac{4dz}{2z - 1} - \frac{2dz}{z} - \frac{dy}{y} = 0.$$

Therefore we have

$$2\ln(2z - 1) - 2\ln z - \ln y = \ln c,$$

or

$$(2z - 1)^2 = cyz^2.$$

But $z = w/y = x^3/y$, so that the solution we seek is

$$(2x^3 - y)^2 = cyx^6.$$

EXERCISES

In Exs. 1–22 obtain the general solution.

1. $(3x - 2y + 1)dx + (3x - 2y + 3)dy = 0.$
   ANS. $5(x + y + c) = 2\ln(15x - 10y + 11).$

2. $\sin y(x + \sin y)dx + 2x^2\cos y\,dy = 0.$
   ANS. $x^3\sin^2 y = c(3x + \sin y)^2.$

3. $\dfrac{dy}{dx} = (9x + 4y + 1)^2.$
   ANS. $3\tan(6x + c) = 2(9x + 4y + 1).$

4. $y' = y - xy^3e^{-2x}.$
   ANS. $e^{2x} = y^2(x^2 + c).$

5. $\dfrac{dy}{dx} = \sin(x + y).$
   ANS. $x + c = \tan(x + y) - \sec(x + y).$

6. $xy\,dx + (x^2 - 3y)dy = 0.$
   ANS. $x^2y^2 = 2y^3 + c.$

7. $(3\tan x - 2\cos y)\sec^2 x\,dx + \tan x \sin y\,dy = 0.$
   ANS. $\cos y \tan^2 x = \tan^3 x + c.$

8. $(x + 2y - 1)dx + (2x + 4y - 3)dy = 0.$ Solve by two methods.
   ANS. $(x + 2y - 1)^2 = 2y + c.$

9. Solve the equation

$$6y^2\, dx - x(2x^3 + y)dy = 0$$

of Example (b) above by treating it as a Bernoulli equation in the dependent variable x.

10. $2x^3y' = y(y^2 + 3x^2)$. Solve by two methods.

ANS. $y^2(c - x) = x^3$.

11. $(3 \sin y - 5x)dx + 2x^2 \cot y\, dy = 0$.

ANS. $x^3(\sin y - x)^2 = c \sin^2 y$.

12. $y' = 1 + 6xe^{x-y}$.

ANS. $e^{y-x} = 3x^2 + c$.

13. $y\, dx + x(3xy - 2)dy = 0$.

ANS. $y^2 = x(y^3 + c)$.

14. $xy' = y - y^3 \cos x$. Solve by two methods.

ANS. $x^2 = 2y^2(x \sin x + \cos x + c)$.

15. $2y\, dx + x(x^2 \ln y - 1)dy = 0$.   ANS. $y(1 + x^2 - x^2 \ln y) = cx^2$.

16. $\cos y \sin 2x\, dx + (\cos^2 y - \cos^2 x)dy = 0$.

ANS. $\cos^2 x(1 + \sin y) = \cos y(y + c - \cos y)$.

17. $(ke^{2v} - u)du = 2e^{2v}(e^{2v} + ku)dv$.

ANS. $2k$ Arctan $(ue^{-2v}) = \ln\,[c(u^2 + e^{4v})]$.

18. $y' \tan x \sin 2y = \sin^2 x + \cos^2 y$. ANS. $(\sin^2 x + 3 \cos^2 y) \sin x = c$.

19. $(x + 2y - 1)dx - (x + 2y - 5)dy = 0$.

ANS. $3(y - x + c) = 4 \ln (3x + 6y - 7)$.

20. $y(x \tan x + \ln y)dx + \tan x\, dy = 0$.

ANS. $\sin x \ln y = x \cos x - \sin x + c$.

21. $xy' - y = x^k y^n$, where $n \neq 1$ and $k + n \neq 1$.

ANS. $(k + n - 1)y^{1-n} = (1 - n)x^k + cx^{1-n}$.

22. The equation of Ex. 21 for the values of k and n not included there.

ANS.   If $n = 1$ and $k \neq 0$, $x^k = k \ln (cy/x)$.

If $n = 1$ and $k = 0$, $y = cx^2$.

If $n \neq 1$ but $k + n = 1$, $y^{1-n} = (1 - n)x^{1-n} \ln (cx)$.

In Exs. 23–28 find the particular solution required.

23. $4(3x + y - 2)dx - (3x + y)dy = 0$; when $x = 1$, $y = 0$.

ANS. $7(4x - y - 4) = 8 \ln \dfrac{21x + 7y - 8}{13}$.

24. $y' = 2(3x + y)^2 - 1$; when $x = 0$, $y = 1$.

ANS. 4 Arctan $(3x + y) = 8x + \pi$.

25. $2xyy' = y^2 - 2x^3$. Find the solution which passes through the point $(1, 2)$.

ANS. $y^2 = x(5 - x^2)$.

26. $(y^4 - 2xy)dx + 3x^2\, dy = 0$; when $x = 2$, $y = 1$.

ANS. $x^2 = y^3(x + 2)$.

27. $(2y^3 - x^3)dx + 3xy^2\, dy = 0$; when $x = 1$, $y = 1$. Solve by two methods.

ANS. $5x^2y^3 = x^5 + 4$.

28. $(x^2 + 6y^2)dx - 4xy\, dy = 0$; when $x = 1$, $y = 1$. Solve by three methods.

ANS. $2y^2 = x^2(3x - 1)$.

18. Coefficients linear in the two variables. Consider the equation

$$(1) \qquad (a_1x + b_1y + c_1)dx + (a_2x + b_2y + c_2)dy = 0,$$

in which the a's, b's, and c's are constants. We know already how to solve the special case in which $c_1 = 0$ and $c_2 = 0$; for then the coefficients in (1) are each homogeneous and of degree one in x and y. It is reasonable to attempt to reduce equation (1) to that situation.

In connection with (1) consider the lines

$$(2) \qquad \begin{aligned} a_1x + b_1y + c_1 &= 0 \\ a_2x + b_2y + c_2 &= 0. \end{aligned}$$

They may be parallel or they may intersect. There will not be two lines if a_1 and b_1 are zero, or if a_2 and b_2 are zero, but equation (1) will then be linear in one of its variables.

If the lines (2) intersect, let the point of intersection be (h, k). Then the translation

$$(3) \qquad \begin{aligned} x &= u + h \\ y &= v + k \end{aligned}$$

will change the equations (2) into equations of lines through the origin of the uv coordinate system, namely,

$$(4) \qquad \begin{aligned} a_1u + b_1v &= 0 \\ a_2u + b_2v &= 0. \end{aligned}$$

Therefore, since $dx = du$ and $dy = dv$, the change of variables $x = u + h, y = v + k$, where (h, k) is the point of intersection of the lines (2), will transform the differential equation (1) into

$$(5) \qquad (a_1u + b_1v)du + (a_2u + b_2v)dv = 0,$$

an equation which we know how to solve.

If the lines (2) do not intersect, there exists a constant k such that

$$a_2x + b_2y = k(a_1x + b_1y),$$

so that equation (1) appears in the form

$$(6) \qquad (a_1x + b_1y + c_1)dx + [k(a_1x + b_1y) + c_2]dy = 0.$$

The recurrence of the expression $(a_1x + b_1y)$ in (6) suggests the introduction of a new variable $w = a_1x + b_1y$. Then the new equation, in w and x or in w and y, is one with variables separable, since its coefficients contain only w and constants.

EXAMPLE (a): Solve the equation

(7) $$(x + 2y - 4)dx - (2x + y - 5)dy = 0.$$

The lines

$$x + 2y - 4 = 0$$
$$2x + y - 5 = 0$$

intersect at the point $(2, 1)$. Hence put

$$x = u + 2$$
$$y = v + 1.$$

Then equation (7) becomes

(8) $$(u + 2v)du - (2u + v)dv = 0,$$

which has coefficients homogeneous and of degree one in u and v. Therefore let $u = vz$, which transforms (8) into

$$(z + 2)(z\,dv + v\,dz) - (2z + 1)dv = 0,$$

or

$$(z^2 - 1)dv + v(z + 2)dz = 0.$$

Separation of the variables v and z leads us to the equation

$$\frac{dv}{v} + \frac{(z + 2)dz}{z^2 - 1} = 0.$$

With the aid of partial fractions we can write the above equation in the form

$$\frac{2dv}{v} + \frac{3dz}{z - 1} - \frac{dz}{z + 1} = 0.$$

Hence we get

$$2 \ln v + 3 \ln (z - 1) - \ln (z + 1) = \ln c$$

from which it follows that

$$v^2(z - 1)^3 = c(z + 1),$$

or

$$(vz - v)^3 = c(vz + v).$$

Now $vz = u$, so our solution appears as

$$(u - v)^3 = c(u + v).$$

But $u = x - 2$ and $v = y - 1$. Therefore the desired result is

$$(x - y - 1)^3 = c(x + y - 3).$$

For other methods of solution of equation (7) see Exs. 23 and 30 below.

EXAMPLE (b): Solve the equation

(9) $$(2x + 3y - 1)dx + (2x + 3y + 2)dy = 0,$$

together with the condition that $y = 3$ when $x = 1$.
    The lines

$$2x + 3y - 1 = 0$$

and

$$2x + 3y + 2 = 0$$

are parallel. Therefore we proceed, as we should have done upon first glancing at the equation, to put

$$2x + 3y = v.$$

Then $2dx = dv - 3dy$ and equation (9) is transformed into

$$(v - 1)(dv - 3dy) + 2(v + 2)dy = 0,$$

or

(10) $$(v - 1)dv - (v - 7)dy = 0.$$

Equation (10) is easily solved, thus leading us to the relation

$$v - y + c + 6 \ln (v - 7) = 0.$$

Therefore the general solution of (9) is

$$2x + 2y + c = -6 \ln (2x + 3y - 7).$$

But $y = 3$ when $x = 1$, so $c = -8 - 6 \ln 4$. Hence the particular solution required is

$$x + y - 4 = -3 \ln [(2x + 3y - 7)/4].$$

EXERCISES

In Exs. 1–18 find the general solution.

1. $(y - 2)dx - (x - y - 1)dy = 0.$

ANS. $x - 3 = (2 - y) \ln [c(y - 2)].$

2. $(x - 4y - 9)dx + (4x + y - 2)dy = 0.$

ANS. $\ln [(x - 1)^2 + (y + 2)^2] - 8 \operatorname{Arctan} \dfrac{x - 1}{y + 2} = c.$

3. $(2x - y)dx + (4x + y - 6)dy = 0.$

ANS. $(x + y - 3)^3 = c(2x + y - 4)^2.$

4. $(x - 4y - 3)dx - (x - 6y - 5)dy = 0.$

ANS. $(x - 2y - 1)^2 = c(x - 3y - 2).$

5. $(2x + 3y - 5)dx + (3x - y - 2)dy = 0.$ Solve by two methods.

6. $2dx + (2x - y + 3)dy = 0.$ Use a change of variable.

ANS. $y + c = - \ln (2x - y + 4).$

7. Solve the equation of Ex. 6 by using the fact that the equation is linear in x.

8. $(x - y + 2)dx + 3dy = 0.$ ANS. $x + c = 3 \ln (x - y + 5).$

9. Solve Ex. 8 by another method.

10. $(x + y - 1)dx + (2x + 2y + 1)dy = 0.$

ANS. $x + 2y + c = 3 \ln (x + y + 2).$

11. $(3x + 2y + 7)dx + (2x - y)dy = 0.$ Solve by two methods.

12. $(x - 2)dx + 4(x + y - 1)dy = 0.$

ANS. $2(y + 1) = -(x + 2y) \ln [c(x + 2y)].$

13. $(x - 3y + 2)dx + 3(x + 3y - 4)dy = 0.$

ANS. $\ln [(x - 1)^2 + 9(y - 1)^2] - 2 \operatorname{Arctan} \dfrac{x - 1}{3(y - 1)} = c.$

14. $(6x - 3y + 2)dx - (2x - y - 1)dy = 0.$

ANS. $3x - y + c = 5 \ln (2x - y + 4).$

15. $(9x - 4y + 4)dx - (2x - y + 1)dy = 0.$

ANS. $y - 1 = 3(y - 3x - 1) \ln [c(3x - y + 1)].$

16. $(x + 3y - 4)dx + (x + 4y - 5)dy = 0.$

ANS. $y - 1 = (x + 2y - 3) \ln [c(x + 2y - 3)].$

17. $(x + 2y - 1)dx - (2x + y - 5)dy = 0.$

ANS. $(x - y - 4)^3 = c(x + y - 2)$

18. $(x - 1)dx - (3x - 2y - 5)dy = 0.$

ANS. $(2y - x + 3)^2 = c(y - x + 2).$

In Exs. 19–22 obtain the particular solution indicated.

19. $(2x - 3y + 4)dx + 3(x - 1)dy = 0;$ when $x = 3, y = 2.$

ANS. $3(y - 2) = -2(x - 1) \ln \dfrac{x - 1}{2}$

20. The equation of Ex. 19 but with the condition: when $x = -1$, $y = 2$.

ANS. $3(y - 2) = -2(x - 1) \ln \dfrac{1 - x}{2}$.

21. $(x + y - 4)dx - (3x - y - 4)dy = 0$; when $x = 4$, $y = 1$.

ANS. $2(x + 2y - 6) = 3(x - y) \ln \dfrac{x - y}{3}$.

22. The equation of Ex. 21 but with the condition: when $x = 3$, $y = 7$.

ANS. $y - 5x + 8 = 2(y - x) \ln \dfrac{y - x}{4}$.

23. Prove that the change of variables

$$x = \alpha_1 u + \alpha_2 v, \qquad y = u + v$$

will transform the equation

(A) $\qquad (a_1 x + b_1 y + c_1)dx + (a_2 x + b_2 y + c_2)dy = 0$

into an equation in which the variables u and v are separable, if α_1 and α_2 are roots of the equation

(B) $\qquad a_1 \alpha^2 + (a_2 + b_1)\alpha + b_2 = 0$,

and if $\alpha_2 \neq \alpha_1$.

Note that this method of solution of (A) is not practical for us unless the roots of equation (B) are real and distinct.

Solve Exs. 24–29 by the method indicated in Ex. 23.

24. Ex. 4 above. As a check, the equation (B) for this case is

$$\alpha^2 - 5\alpha + 6 = 0,$$

so we may choose $\alpha_1 = 2$ and $\alpha_2 = 3$.

The equation in u and v turns out to be

$$(v - 1)du - 2(u + 2)dv = 0.$$

25. Ex. 3 above.
26. Ex. 10 above.
27. Ex. 17 above.
28. Ex. 18 above.
29. Example (a) in the text of this section.
30. Prove that the change of variables

$$x = \alpha_1 u + \beta v, \qquad y = u + v$$

will transform the equation

(A) $\qquad (a_1 x + b_1 y + c_1)dx + (a_2 x + b_2 y + c_2)dy = 0$

into an equation which is linear in the variable u, if α_1 is a root of the equation

(B) $$a_1\alpha^2 + (a_2 + b_1)\alpha + b_2 = 0,$$

and if β is any number such that $\beta \neq \alpha_1$.

Note that this method is not practical for us unless the roots of equation (B) are real.   But they need not be distinct as they had to be in the theorem of Ex. 23.   The method of this exercise is particularly useful when the roots of (B) are equal.

Solve Exs. 31–35 by the method indicated in Ex. 30.

31. Ex. 16 above.   The only possible α_1 is (-2).   Then β may be chosen tó be anything else.
32. Ex. 12 above.
33. Ex. 15 above.
34. Ex. 18 above.
35. Ex. 4 above.   As seen in Ex. 24, the roots of the "α-equation" are 2 and 3.   If you choose $\alpha_1 = 2$, for example, then you may make β anything except 2.   Of course, if you choose $\alpha_1 = 2$ and $\beta = 3$, then you are reverting to the method of Ex. 23.

19. The determination of integrating factors.   Let us see what progress can be made on the problem of the determination of an integrating factor for the equation

(1) $$M\,dx + N\,dy = 0.$$

Suppose u, possibly a function of both x and y, is to be an integrating factor of (1).   Then the equation

(2) $$uM\,dx + uN\,dy = 0$$

must be exact.   Therefore, by the result of Section 10,

$$\frac{\partial}{\partial y}(uM) = \frac{\partial}{\partial x}(uN).$$

Hence u must satisfy the partial differential equation

$$u\,\frac{\partial M}{\partial y} + M\,\frac{\partial u}{\partial y} = u\,\frac{\partial N}{\partial x} + N\,\frac{\partial u}{\partial x},$$

or

(3) $$u\left(\frac{\partial M}{\partial y} - \frac{\partial N}{\partial x}\right) = N\,\frac{\partial u}{\partial x} - M\,\frac{\partial u}{\partial y}.$$

Furthermore, by reversing the argument above it can be seen that if u satisfies equation (3), then u is an integrating factor for equation (1). We have "reduced" the problem of solving the ordinary differential equation (1) to the problem of obtaining a particular solution of the partial differential equation (3).

Not much has been gained, since we have developed no methods for attacking an equation such as (3). Therefore, we turn the problem back into the realm of ordinary differential equations by restricting u to be a function of only one variable.

First let u be a function of x alone. Then $\dfrac{\partial u}{\partial y} = 0$ and $\dfrac{\partial u}{\partial x}$ becomes $\dfrac{du}{dx}$. Then (3) reduces to

$$u\left(\frac{\partial M}{\partial y} - \frac{\partial N}{\partial x}\right) = N\frac{du}{dx},$$

or

$$(4) \qquad \frac{1}{N}\left(\frac{\partial M}{\partial y} - \frac{\partial N}{\partial x}\right)dx = \frac{du}{u}.$$

If the left member of the above equation is a function of x alone, then we can determine u at once. Indeed, if

$$(5) \qquad \frac{1}{N}\left(\frac{\partial M}{\partial y} - \frac{\partial N}{\partial x}\right) = f(x),$$

then the desired integrating factor is $u = e^{\int f(x)dx}$.

By a similar argument, assuming that u is a function of y alone, we are led to the conclusion that if

$$(6) \qquad \frac{1}{M}\left(\frac{\partial M}{\partial y} - \frac{\partial N}{\partial x}\right) = g(y),$$

then an integrating factor for equation (1) is $u = e^{-\int g(y)dy}$.

Our two results are expressed in the following rules:

If $\dfrac{1}{N}\left(\dfrac{\partial M}{\partial y} - \dfrac{\partial N}{\partial x}\right) = f(x)$, a function of x alone, then $e^{\int f(x)dx}$ is an integrating factor for the equation

$$(1) \qquad M\,dx + N\,dy = 0.$$

If $\dfrac{1}{M}\left(\dfrac{\partial M}{\partial y} - \dfrac{\partial N}{\partial x}\right) = g(y)$, a function of y alone, then $e^{-\int g(y)\,dy}$

is an integrating factor for equation (1).

EXAMPLE (a): Solve the equation

$$(7) \qquad (4xy + 3y^2 - x)dx + x(x + 2y)dy = 0.$$

Here $M = 4xy + 3y^2 - x$, $N = x^2 + 2xy$, so that

$$\frac{\partial M}{\partial y} - \frac{\partial N}{\partial x} = 4x + 6y - (2x + 2y) = 2x + 4y.$$

Hence

$$\frac{1}{N}\left(\frac{\partial M}{\partial y} - \frac{\partial N}{\partial x}\right) = \frac{2x + 4y}{x(x + 2y)} = \frac{2}{x}.$$

Therefore an integrating factor for equation (7) is

$$e^{2\int \frac{dx}{x}} = e^{2\ln x} = x^2.$$

Returning to the original equation (7) we insert the integrating factor and obtain

$$(8) \qquad (4x^3y + 3x^2y^2 - x^3)dx + (x^4 + 2x^3y)dy = 0,$$

which we know must be an exact equation. The methods of Section 10 apply. We are then led to put equation (8) in the form

$$(4x^3y\,dx + x^4\,dy) + (3x^2y^2\,dx + 2x^3y\,dy) - x^3\,dx = 0,$$

from which the solution

$$x^4y + x^3y^2 - \tfrac{1}{4}x^4 = \tfrac{1}{4}c,$$

or

$$x^3(4xy + 4y^2 - x) = c$$

follows at once.

EXAMPLE (b): Solve the equation

$$(9) \qquad y(x + y + 1)dx + x(x + 3y + 2)dy = 0.$$

First we form

$$\frac{\partial M}{\partial y} = x + 2y + 1, \qquad \frac{\partial N}{\partial x} = 2x + 3y + 2.$$

Then we see that

$$\frac{\partial M}{\partial y} - \frac{\partial N}{\partial x} = -x - y - 1,$$

so that

$$\frac{1}{N}\left(\frac{\partial M}{\partial y} - \frac{\partial N}{\partial x}\right) = -\frac{x + y + 1}{x(x + 3y + 2)}$$

is not a function of x alone.   But

$$\frac{1}{M}\left(\frac{\partial M}{\partial y} - \frac{\partial N}{\partial x}\right) = -\frac{x + y + 1}{y(x + y + 1)} = -\frac{1}{y}.$$

Therefore $e^{\ln y} = y$ is the desired integrating factor for (9).
Using the integrating factor, we write

$$(xy^2 + y^3 + y^2)dx + (x^2y + 3xy^2 + 2xy)dy = 0,$$

or

$$(xy^2\,dx + x^2y\,dy) + (y^3\,dx + 3xy^2\,dy) + (y^2\,dx + 2xy\,dy) = 0.$$

Then the solution of (9) is found to be

$$\tfrac{1}{2}x^2y^2 + xy^3 + xy^2 = \tfrac{1}{2}c,$$

or

$$xy^2(x + 2y + 2) = c.$$

EXAMPLE (c): Solve the equation

(10) $$y(x + y)dx + (x + 2y - 1)dy = 0.$$

From $\dfrac{\partial M}{\partial y} = x + 2y$, $\dfrac{\partial N}{\partial x} = 1$, we conclude at once that

$$\frac{1}{N}\left(\frac{\partial M}{\partial y} - \frac{\partial N}{\partial x}\right) = \frac{x + 2y - 1}{x + 2y - 1} = 1.$$

Hence e^x is an integrating factor for (10).   Then

$$(xye^x + y^2e^x)dx + (xe^x + 2ye^x - e^x)dy = 0$$

is an exact equation. Grouping the terms in the following manner,

$$[xye^x\, dx + (xe^x - e^x)dy] + (y^2e^x\, dx + 2ye^x\, dy) = 0,$$

leads us at once to the solution

$$e^x(x - 1)y + y^2e^x = c,$$

or

$$y(x + y - 1) = ce^{-x}.$$

EXERCISES

Solve each of the following equations.

1. $(x^2 + y^2 + 1)dx + x(x - 2y)dy = 0.$ ANS. $x^2 - y^2 + xy - 1 = cx.$
2. $2y(x^2 - y + x)dx + (x^2 - 2y)dy = 0.$ ANS. $y(x^2 - y) = ce^{-2x}.$
3. $y(2x - y + 1)dx + x(3x - 4y + 3)dy = 0.$
                                   ANS. $xy^3(x - y + 1) = c.$
4. $y(4x + y)dx - 2(x^2 - y)dy = 0.$ ANS. $2x^2 + xy + 2y \ln y = cy.$
5. $(xy + 1)dx + x(x + 4y - 2)dy = 0.$
                                   ANS. $xy + \ln x + 2y^2 - 2y = c.$
6. $(2y^2 + 3xy - 2y + 6x)dx + x(x + 2y - 1)dy = 0.$
                                   ANS. $x^2(y^2 + xy - y + 2x) = c.$
7. $y(y + 2x - 2)dx - 2(x + y)dy = 0.$ ANS. $y(2x + y) = ce^x.$
8. $y^2\, dx + (3xy + y^2 - 1)dy = 0.$ ANS. $y^2(y^2 + 4xy - 2) = c.$
9. $2y(x + y + 2)dx + (y^2 - x^2 - 4x - 1)dy = 0.$
                                   ANS. $x^2 + 2xy + y^2 + 4x + 1 = cy.$
10. $2(2y^2 + 5xy - 2y + 4)dx + x(2x + 2y - 1)dy = 0.$
                                   ANS. $x^4(y^2 + 2xy - y + 2) = c.$
11. $3(x^2 + y^2)dx + x(x^2 + 3y^2 + 6y)dy = 0.$ ANS. $x(x^2 + 3y^2) = ce^{-y}.$
12. $y(8x - 9y)dx + 2x(x - 3y)dy = 0.$ ANS. $x^3y(2x - 3y) = c.$
13. Do Ex. 12 by another method.
14. $y(2x^2 - xy + 1)dx + (x - y)dy = 0.$ ANS. $y(2x - y) = ce^{-x^2}.$
15. Euler's theorem on homogeneous functions states that if F is a homogeneous function of degree k in x and y, then

$$x\frac{\partial F}{\partial x} + y\frac{\partial F}{\partial y} = kF.$$

Use Euler's theorem to prove the following result: If M and N are homogeneous functions of the same degree, and if $Mx + Ny \neq 0$, then

$$\frac{1}{Mx + Ny}$$

is an integrating factor for the equation

(1) $M\,dx + N\,dy = 0.$

16. In the result to be proved in Ex. 15 above there is an exceptional case, namely, when $Mx + Ny = 0$. Solve equation (1) when $Mx + Ny = 0$.

ANS. $y = cx.$

Use the integrating factor in the result of Ex. 15 above to solve each of the equations in Exs. 17–20. The student should realize, from its position in the exercises instead of in the text, that the method of Ex. 15 is not being strongly recommended.

17. $xy\,dx - (x^2 + 2y^2)dy = 0.$ (Ex. 2, page 27.)
18. $v^2\,dx + x(x + v)dv = 0.$ (Ex. 13, page 28.)
19. $v(u^2 + v^2)du - u(u^2 + 2v^2)dv = 0.$ ANS. $u^2 = 2v^2 \ln{(cv^2/u)}.$
20. $(x^2 + y^2)dx - xy\,dy = 0.$ (Ex. 9, page 28.)

20. Solutions involving nonelementary integrals. In solving differential equations we frequently are confronted with the need for integrating an expression which is not the differential of any elementary* function.   There follows a short list of nonelementary integrals:

$$\int e^{-x^2}\,dx \qquad \int \frac{e^{-x}}{x}\,dx \qquad \int x \tan x\,dx$$

$$\int \sin x^2\,dx \qquad \int \frac{\sin x}{x}\,dx \qquad \int \frac{dx}{\ln x}$$

$$\int \cos x^2\,dx \qquad \int \frac{\cos x}{x}\,dx \qquad \int \frac{dx}{\sqrt{1 - x^3}}.$$

Integrals involving the square root of a polynomial of degree greater than two are, in general, nonelementary.   In special instances they may degenerate into elementary integrals.

The following example presents two ways of dealing with problems in which nonelementary integrals arise.

---

* By an elementary function we mean a function studied in the ordinary beginning calculus course.   For example, polynomials, exponentials, logarithms, trigonometric and inverse trigonometric functions are elementary.   All functions obtained from them by a finite number of applications of the elementary operations of addition, subtraction, multiplication, division, extraction of roots and raising to powers are elementary.   Finally, we include such functions as sin (sin x) in which the argument in a function previously classed as elementary is replaced by an elementary function.

EXAMPLE: Solve the equation

$$y' - 2xy = 1,$$

with the boundary condition: when $x = 0$, $y = 1$.

The equation being linear in y, we write

$$dy - 2xy\, dx = dx,$$

obtain the integrating factor e^{-x^2}, and prepare to solve

(1) $$e^{-x^2}\, dy - 2xye^{-x^2}\, dx = e^{-x^2}\, dx.$$

The left member is, of course, the differential of ye^{-x^2}. But, the right member is not the differential of any elementary function; that is, $\int e^{-x^2}\, dx$ is a nonelementary integral.

There are various ways to proceed. We could write a "solution" as

$$ye^{-x^2} = \int e^{-x^2}\, dx,$$

but that is evidently incomplete. We cannot satisfy the boundary condition with the above form of solution because putting $x = 0$ in the indefinite integral is meaningless.

Let us turn to power series for help. From the series

$$e^{-x^2} = 1 - \frac{x^2}{1!} + \frac{x^4}{2!} - \frac{x^6}{3!} + \cdots + (-1)^n \frac{x^{2n}}{n!} + \cdots$$

$$= \sum_{n=0}^{\infty} (-1)^n \frac{x^{2n}}{n!},$$

obtained in calculus, it follows that our indefinite integral may be written as follows:

$$\int e^{-x^2}\, dx = c + \frac{x}{1} - \frac{x^3}{3 \cdot 1!} + \frac{x^5}{5 \cdot 2!} - \frac{x^7}{7 \cdot 3!} + \cdots$$

$$+ (-1)^n \frac{x^{2n+1}}{(2n+1) \cdot n!} + \cdots = c + \sum_{n=0}^{\infty} (-1)^n \frac{x^{2n+1}}{(2n+1) \cdot n!}.$$

Thus the differential equation (1) has the solution

$$ye^{-x^2} = c + \sum_{n=0}^{\infty} (-1)^n \frac{x^{2n+1}}{(2n+1) \cdot n!}.$$

Since $y = 1$ when $x = 0$, c may be found from

$$1 = c + 0.$$

Therefore the particular solution desired is

$$ye^{-x^2} = 1 + \sum_{n=0}^{\infty} (-1)^n \frac{x^{2n+1}}{(2n+1) \cdot n!},$$

or

$$y = e^{x^2} + e^{x^2} \sum_{n=0}^{\infty} (-1)^n \frac{x^{2n+1}}{(2n+1) \cdot n!}.$$

An alternative procedure is the introduction of the definite integral. Let $G(x)$ be a (nonelementary) function whose differential is $e^{-x^2} dx$. Then

$$\int e^{-x^2} dx = G(x) + c.$$

We wish to show that the definite integral

$$\int_a^x e^{-w^2} dw$$

also has the differential $e^{-x^2} dx$, no matter what constant a is used as a lower limit. Now

$$\int_a^x e^{-w^2} dw = G(x) - G(a)$$

from the indefinite integral above, and $G(a)$ is a constant. Hence the differential of the definite integral is seen to be the same as that of $G(x)$, as desired.

Now the equation

$$e^{-x^2} dy - 2xye^{-x^2} dx = e^{-x^2} dx$$

may be solved by writing

$$ye^{-x^2} = \int_0^x e^{-w^2} dw + c,$$

where the choice of zero as the lower limit was made for ease in applying the boundary condition, $y = 1$ when $x = 0$. Putting $x = 0$ in the general solution yields

$$1 = \int_0^0 e^{-w^2} dw + c = 0 + c.$$

Hence

$$ye^{-x^2} = \int_0^x e^{-w^2} dw + 1.$$

In writing a solution in the form directly above it is implied that the definite integral is to be evaluated by power series, approximate integration such as Simpson's rule, mechanical quadrature, or any other available tool. If it happens, as in this case,* that the definite integral is itself a tabulated function, that is a great convenience, but it is not vital. The essential thing is to reduce the solution to a computable form.

EXERCISES

In each exercise express the solution with the aid of power series or definite integrals.

1. $y' = y(1 - e^{-x^2})$.   ANS. $\ln (cy) = x - \int_0^x e^{-\beta^2} d\beta,$

$$\text{or } \ln (cy) = \sum_{n=1}^{\infty} (-1)^{n+1} \frac{x^{2n+1}}{(2n+1)n!}.$$

---

* See B. O. Peirce, *A Short Table of Integrals*, Boston, Ginn and Co., 1929.

2. $(xy - \sin x)dx + x^2\, dy = 0.$ ANS. $xy = c + \displaystyle\int_0^x \frac{\sin w}{w}\, dw,$

or $y = cx^{-1} + \displaystyle\sum_{n=0}^{\infty} (-1)^n \frac{x^{2n}}{(2n+1)(2n+1)!}.$

3. $y' = 1 - 4x^3 y.$ ANS. $y = e^{-x^4} \displaystyle\int_0^x e^{\beta^4}\, d\beta + ce^{-x^4}.$

4. $(y \cos^2 x - x \sin x)dx + \sin x \cos x\, dy = 0.$

ANS. $y \sin x = c + \displaystyle\int_0^x \beta \tan \beta\, d\beta.$

5. $(1 + xy)dx - x\, dy = 0;$ when $x = 1,\ y = 0.$

ANS. $y = e^x \displaystyle\int_1^x \frac{e^{-\beta}}{\beta}\, d\beta.$

6. $(xe^{y^2/x^2} - y)dx + x\, dy = 0;$ when $x = 1,\ y = 2.$

ANS. $\ln x = \displaystyle\int_{y/x}^2 e^{-w^2}\, dw.$

7. $x(2y + x)dx - dy = 0;$ when $x = 0,\ y = 1.$

ANS. $2y = 2e^{x^2} - x + e^{x^2} \displaystyle\int_0^x e^{-z^2}\, dz.$

MISCELLANEOUS EXERCISES

In each exercise find the general solution unless the statement of the exercise stipulates otherwise.

1. $(y^2 - 3y - x)dx + (2y - 3)dy = 0.$ ANS. $y^2 - 3y - x + 1 = ce^{-x}.$
2. $(y^3 + y + 1)dx + x(x - 3y^2 - 1)dy = 0.$
ANS. $y^3 - xy + y + 1 = cx.$
3. $(x + 3y - 5)dx - (x - y - 1)dy = 0.$
ANS. $2(y - 1) = (x + y - 3)\ln[c(x + y - 3)].$
4. $(x - 2y + 3)dx + 2(x + 2y - 1)dy = 0.$
ANS. $\ln[(x+1)^2 + 4(y-1)^2] = c + 2\,\text{Arctan}\,\dfrac{x+1}{2(y-1)}.$

5. $(2x + y - 4)dx + (x - 3y + 12)dy = 0.$

ANS. $2x^2 + 2xy - 3y^2 - 8x + 24y = c.$

6. Solve in two ways the equation $y' = ax + by + c$ with $b \neq 0.$

ANS. $b^2y = c_1e^{bx} - abx - a - cb.$

7. $y^3 \sec^2 x \, dx - (1 - 2y^2 \tan x)dy = 0.$ ANS. $y^2 \tan x = \ln (cy).$

8. $x^3y \, dx + (3x^4 - y^3)dy = 0.$ ANS. $15x^4y^{12} = 4y^{15} + c.$

9. $(a_1x + ky + c_1)dx + (kx + b_2y + c_2)dy = 0.$

ANS. $a_1x^2 + 2kxy + b_2y^2 + 2c_1x + 2c_2y = c.$

10. $(x - 4y + 7)dx + (x + 2y + 1)dy = 0.$

ANS. $(x - y + 4)^3 = c(x - 2y + 5)^2.$

11. $xy' = x^3y^3 - 2y.$ ANS. $x^3y^2(2 + cx) = 1.$

12. $y(2x - 1)dx + 2(x^2 + y^2 - x)dy = 0.$ Solve by two methods.

ANS. $y^2(2x^2 - 2x + y^2) = c.$

13. $(5x + 3e^y)dx + 2xe^y \, dy = 0.$ ANS. $x^3(x + e^y)^2 = c.$

14. $(3x + y - 2)dx + (3x + y + 4)dy = 0.$

ANS. $x + y + c = 3 \ln (3x + y + 7).$

15. $(6xy - 3y^2 + 2y)dx + 2(x - y)dy = 0.$ ANS. $y(2x - y) = ce^{-3x}.$

16. $y' = x - y + 2.$ Solve by two methods.

ANS. $\ln (x - y + 1) = c - x.$

17. $(x + y - 2)dx - (x - 4y - 2)dy = 0.$

ANS. $\ln [(x - 2)^2 + 4y^2] + \text{Arctan} \dfrac{x - 2}{2y} = c.$

18. $4dx + (x - y + 2)^2 \, dy = 0.$ ANS. $y + 2 \, \text{Arctan} \dfrac{x - y + 2}{2} = c.$

19. $(2x + 4y - 1)dx - (x + 2y - 3)dy = 0.$

ANS. $\ln (x + 2y - 1) = y - 2x + c.$

20. $4y \, dx + 3(2x - 1)(dy + y^4 \, dx) = 0$; when $x = 1, y = 1.$

ANS. $y^3(2x - 1)(5x - 4) = 1.$

21. $y(x - 1)dx - (x^2 - 2x - 2y)dy = 0.$ ANS. $x^2 - 2x - 4y = cy^2.$

22. $\dfrac{dy}{dx} = \tan y \cot x - \sec y \cos x.$ ANS. $\sin y + \sin x \ln (c \sin x) = 0.$

23. $[1 + (x + y)^2]dx + [1 + x(x + y)]dy = 0.$

ANS. $y^2 = (x + y)^2 + 2 \ln (x + y) + c.$

24. $(x - 2y - 1)dx - (x - 3)dy = 0.$ Solve by two methods.

ANS. $(x - 3)^2(x - 3y) = c.$

25. $(2x - 3y + 1)dx - (3x + 2y - 4)dy = 0.$ Solve by two methods.

ANS. $x^2 + x - 3xy - y^2 + 4y = c.$

26. $(4x + 3y - 7)dx + (4x + 3y + 1)dy = 0.$

ANS. $x + y + c = 8 \ln (4x + 3y + 25).$

27. Find a change of variables which will reduce any equation of the form

$$xy' = yf(xy)$$

to an equation in which the variables are separable.

28. $(x + 4y + 3)dx - (2x - y - 3)dy = 0.$

ANS. $3(y + 1) = (x + y) \ln [c(x + y)].$

29. $(3x - 3y - 2)dx - (x - y + 1)dy = 0.$

ANS. $2(y - 3x + c) = 5 \ln (2x - 2y - 3).$

30. $(x - 6y + 2)dx + 2(x + 2y + 2)dy = 0.$

ANS. $4y = -(x - 2y + 2) \ln [c(x - 2y + 2)].$

31. $(x^4 - 4x^2y^2 - y^4)dx + 4x^3y \, dy = 0;$ when $x = 1, y = 2.$

ANS. $y^2(5 - 3x) = x^2(5 + 3x).$

32. $(x - y - 1)dx - 2(y - 2)dy = 0.$

ANS. $(x + y - 5)^2(x - 2y + 1) = c.$

33. $(x - 3y + 3)dx + (3x + y + 9)dy = 0.$

ANS. $\ln [(x + 3)^2 + y^2] = c + 6 \text{ Arctan } [(x + 3)/y].$

Chapter 5

Orthogonal Trajectories

21. Orthogonal trajectories; rectangular coordinates. Suppose that we have given a family of curves

$$(1) \qquad\qquad f(x, y, c) = 0,$$

one curve corresponding to each c in some range of values of the parameter c. In certain applications, as illustrated in Section 23 below, it is found desirable to know what curves have the property that wherever any one of them intersects a curve of the family (1) it does so at right angles.

That is, we wish to determine a family of curves

$$(2) \qquad\qquad g(x, y, k) = 0$$

such that at any intersection of a curve of the family (2) with a curve of the family (1) the tangents to the two curves are perpendicular. The families (1) and (2) are then said to be *orthogonal trajectories** of each other.

If two curves are to be orthogonal, then at each point of intersection the slopes of the curves must be negative reciprocals of each other. That fact leads us to a method for finding orthogonal trajectories to a given family of curves. First we find the differential equation of the given family. Then replacing $\dfrac{dy}{dx}$ by $-\dfrac{dx}{dy}$ in that equation yields the differential equation of the orthogonal trajectories to the given curves. It remains only to solve the latter differential equation.

---

* The word orthogonal comes from the Greek $o\rho\theta\eta$ (right) and $\gamma\omega\nu\alpha$ (angle); the word trajectory comes from the Latin *trajectus* (cut across). Hence a curve which cuts across certain others at right angles is called an orthogonal trajectory of those others.

So far we have solved differential equations of only one form,

$$M\ dx + N\ dy = 0.$$

For such an equation

$$\frac{dy}{dx} = -\frac{M}{N}$$

so that the differential equation of the orthogonal trajectories is

$$\frac{dy}{dx} = \frac{N}{M}$$

or

$$N\ dx - M\ dy = 0.$$

EXAMPLE: Find the orthogonal trajectories of all parabolas with vertex at the origin and focus on the x-axis.

The algebraic equation of such parabolas is

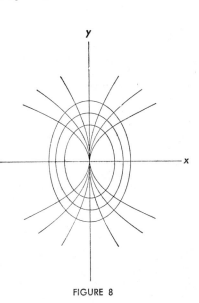

(3) $y^2 = 4ax.$

Hence, from

$$\frac{y^2}{x} = 4a$$

we find the differential equation of the family (3) to be

(4) $2x\ dy - y\ dx = 0.$

Therefore the orthogonal trajectories of the family (3) must satisfy the equation

FIGURE 8

(5) $2x\ dx + y\ dy = 0.$

From (5) it follows that

(6) $2x^2 + y^2 = b^2,$

where b is the arbitrary constant. Thus the orthogonal trajectories of (3) are certain ellipses (6) with centers at the origin. See Figure 8.

EXERCISES

In each exercise find the orthogonal trajectories of the given family of curves. Draw a few representative curves of each family whenever a figure is requested.

1. $x - 4y = c$. Draw the figure. ANS. $4x + y = k$.
2. $x^2 + y^2 = c^2$. Draw the figure. ANS. $y = kx$.
3. $x^2 - y^2 = c_1$. Draw the figure. ANS. $xy = c_2$.
4. Circles through the origin with centers on the x-axis. Draw the figure.
   ANS. Circles through the origin with centers on the y-axis.
5. Straight lines with slope and y-intercept equal. Draw the figure.
   ANS. $(x + 1)^2 + y^2 = a^2$.
6. $y^2 = cx^3$. Draw the figure. ANS. $2x^2 + 3y^2 = k^2$.
7. $e^x + e^{-y} = c_1$. ANS. $e^y - e^{-x} = c_2$.
8. $y = c_1(\sec x + \tan x)$. ANS. $y^2 = 2(c_2 - \sin x)$.
9. $y^3 = 3(x - c)$. Draw the figure. ANS. $y = 1/(x - k)$.
10. $y = ce^{-mx}$, with m held fixed. Draw the figure.
    ANS. $my^2 = 2(x - c_1)$.
11. Ellipses with centers at $(0, 0)$ and two vertices at $(1, 0)$ and $(-1, 0)$.
    ANS. $x^2 + y^2 = 2 \ln (cx)$.
12. $y = ce^{-x^2}$ ANS. $x = c_1 e^{y^2}$.
13. $x^2 - y^2 = cx$. ANS. $y(y^2 + 3x^2) = c_1$.
14. The cissoids, $y^2 = x^3/(a - x)$. See also Ex. 14 of Section 22 below.
    ANS. $(x^2 + y^2)^2 = b(2x^2 + y^2)$.
15. The trisectrices of Maclaurin, $(a + x)y^2 = x^2(3a - x)$. See also Ex. 15 of Section 22 below. ANS. $(x^2 + y^2)^5 = cy^3(5x^2 + y^2)$.
16. $ax^2 + by^2 = c$, with a and b held fixed. ANS. $y^a = kx^b$.
17. $ax^2 + y^2 = 2acx$, with a held fixed.
    ANS. If $a \neq 2$, $(2 - a)x^2 + y^2 = c_1 y^a$.
    If $a = 2$, $x^2 = -y^2 \ln (c_2 y)$.
18. $y(x^2 + c) + 2 = 0$. ANS. $y^3 = -3 \ln (kx)$.
19. $x^n + y^n = a^n$, with n held fixed and $n \neq 2$. ANS. $x^{2-n} - y^{2-n} = c$.
20. $y^2 = x^2(1 - cx)$. ANS. $x^2 + 3y^2 = c_1 y$.
21. $y^2 = 4x^2(1 - cx)$. ANS. $2x^2 = 3y^2(1 - c_1 y^2)$.
22. $y^2 = ax^2(1 - cx)$, with a held fixed.
    ANS. If $a \neq 2$, $(a - 2)x^2 = 3y^2(1 - c_1 y^{a-2})$.
    If $a = 2$, $x^2 = -3y^2 \ln (c_2 y)$.
23. $y(x^2 + 1) = cx$. ANS. $y^2 = x^2 + 2 \ln [k(x^2 - 1)]$.
24. $y = 3x - 1 + ce^{-3x}$. ANS. $27x = 9y - 1 + ke^{-9y}$.
25. $y^2(2x^2 + y^2) = c^2$. ANS. $y^2 = 2x^2 \ln (kx)$.
26. $y^4 = c^2(x^2 + 4y^2)$. ANS. $x^8(2x^2 + 5y^2) = k^2$.
27. $x^4(4x^2 + 3y^2) = c^2$. ANS. $y^8 = k^2(3x^2 + 2y^2)$.
28. For the family $x^2 + 3y^2 = cy$, find that member of the orthogonal trajectories which passes through $(1, 2)$. ANS. $y^2 = x^2(3x + 1)$.

22. Orthogonal trajectories; polar coordinates.

Consider a curve whose equation is expressed in polar coordinates. In calculus it is shown that the angle ψ (Figure 9), measured positive in the counterclockwise direction from the radius vector to the tangent line at a point, is given by

$$\tan \psi = r \frac{d\theta}{dr}.$$

FIGURE 9

FIGURE 10

If two curves are orthogonal, as they are shown in Figure 10, then $\psi_2 = \psi_1 + \pi/2$ and thus $\tan \psi_2 = - \cot \psi_1 = -1/\tan \psi_1$. Therefore, if two curves are to cut one another at right angles, then at the point of intersection the value of the product

$$r \frac{d\theta}{dr}$$

for one curve must be the negative reciprocal of the value of that product for the other curve.

When polar coordinates are used, suppose a family of curves has the differential equation

(1) $P \, dr + Q \, d\theta = 0.$

Then

$$\frac{d\theta}{dr} = - \frac{P}{Q}$$

so that

(2) $r \frac{d\theta}{dr} = - \frac{Pr}{Q}.$

Hence the family of orthogonal trajectories of the solutions of (1) must be solutions of the equation

$$r\frac{d\theta}{dr} = +\frac{Q}{Pr},$$

or

(3) $$Q\,dr - r^2P\,d\theta = 0.$$

EXAMPLE: Find the orthogonal trajectories of the family of cardioids $r = a(1 + \cos\theta)$. A few curves of each family are shown in Figure 11.

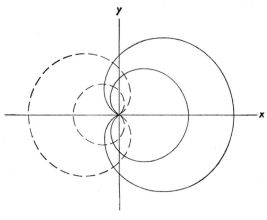

FIGURE 11

From

$$\frac{r}{1 + \cos\theta} = a$$

the differential equation

$$(1 + \cos\theta)dr + r\sin\theta\,d\theta = 0$$

follows at once. Then the differential equation of the orthogonal trajectories is

$$r\sin\theta\,dr - r^2(1 + \cos\theta)d\theta = 0$$

or

$$\sin\theta\,dr - r(1 + \cos\theta)d\theta = 0.$$

Separating the variables, we use the form

$$\frac{dr}{r} - \frac{(1 + \cos \theta)d\theta}{\sin \theta} = 0,$$

or

$$\frac{dr}{r} - \csc \theta \, d\theta - \frac{\cos \theta}{\sin \theta} \, d\theta = 0.$$

Hence

$$\ln r - \ln (\csc \theta - \cot \theta) - \ln \sin \theta = \ln b$$

so that the orthogonal trajectories of the original family of cardioids are seen to be

$$r = b \sin \theta(\csc \theta - \cot \theta),$$

or

$$r = b(1 - \cos \theta).$$

The student should show that this is the same family as the one we started with; that is, the family of cardioids is self-orthogonal.

EXERCISES

In each exercise find the orthogonal trajectories of the given family of curves. Draw the figures in Exs. 1–8.

1. $r = a \cos^2 \theta$.   ANS. $r^2 = b \sin \theta$.

2. $r = a \cos 2\theta$.   ANS. $r^4 = b \sin 2\theta$.

3. $r = 2a \sin \theta$.   ANS. $r = 2b \cos \theta$.

4. $r = 2a(\sin \theta + \cos \theta)$.   ANS. $r = 2b(\sin \theta - \cos \theta)$.

5. $r = a(1 + \sin \theta)$.   ANS. $r = b(1 - \sin \theta)$.

6. $r^2 = a \sin 2\theta$.   ANS. $r^2 = b \cos 2\theta$.

7. $r = 4a \sec \theta \tan \theta$.   ANS. $r^2(1 + \sin^2 \theta) = b^2$.

8. $r^2 \cos 2\theta = c_1$.   ANS. $r^2 \sin 2\theta = c_2$.

9. $r = k/(1 + 2 \cos \theta)$.   ANS. $r^2 \sin^3 \theta = b(1 + \cos \theta)$.

10. $r = k/(2 + \cos \theta)$.   ANS. $r \sin^3 \theta = b(1 + \cos \theta)^2$.

11. $r = k/(1 + \epsilon \cos \theta)$ with ϵ fixed. What are k and ϵ geometrically?
     ANS. $r^\epsilon \sin^{\epsilon+1} \theta = b(1 + \cos \theta)$.

12. $r = a(1 - 2 \sin \theta)$.   ANS. $r^2 = b \cos \theta(1 + \sin \theta)$.

13. The strophoids, $r = a(\sec \theta + \tan \theta)$.   ANS. $r = be^{-\sin \theta}$.

14. The cissoids, $r = a \sin \theta \tan \theta$.   ANS. $r^2 = b(1 + \cos^2 \theta)$.

15. The trisectrices of Maclaurin, $r = a(4 \cos \theta - \sec \theta)$.
     ANS. $r^5 = b \sin^3 \theta(4 \cos^2 \theta + 1)$.

16. $r = a(1 + \sin^2 \theta)$.   ANS. $r^2 = b \cos \theta \cot \theta$.

23. Electric potential. The electric force between two particles charged with electricity is proportional to the magnitude of the two charges and inversely proportional to the square of the distance between them.   An electric field is a portion of space the electrical properties of which we wish to consider.   Those properties are determined by the distribution of electric* charges in the field. Very often interest is centered not upon the whole field but upon some portion which may itself not contain any electric charges.

The resultant electric force at a point P in an electric field is the force which would be exerted on a unit positive charge of electricity placed at P without disturbing the previous distribution of electric charges in the field.   That resultant force has direction as well as magnitude at each point; it is a vector.

A curve whose tangent at each point on the curve is in the direction of the resultant electric force at that point is called a line of force or a flux line.

The difference in electric potential between two points in an electric field is the amount of work which it is necessary for the electric force to perform in order to move a unit positive charge from one point to the other.   Thus electric potential is defined except for algebraic sign and an additive constant.   If some fixed position in the electric field is used as a place of zero potential and if a convention of signs is introduced, then the electric potential is completely defined.   Since our interest will be concentrated upon the family of curves on which the potential is constant, the concept of difference in potential† suffices.

Laplace showed that in any region in space not occupied by an electric charge the potential function V satisfies the partial differential equation

$$(1) \qquad \frac{\partial^2 V}{\partial x^2} + \frac{\partial^2 V}{\partial y^2} + \frac{\partial^2 V}{\partial z^2} = 0$$

---

* Electrostatic charges are the only ones being considered in this discussion.
† For the student who has had advanced calculus it may help to know that electric potential is a function of the coordinates such that at each point the directional derivative of the potential is the negative of the component of electric force in that direction.

where x, y, z are the rectangular space coordinates in the electric field. If the distribution of charges in the field is such that the potential function is independent of the z coordinate, then the problem is two-dimensional and the potential function must satisfy the equation

$$(2) \qquad \frac{\partial^2 V}{\partial x^2} + \frac{\partial^2 V}{\partial y^2} = 0.$$

We shall restrict our study to two-dimensional situations but we are not yet prepared to attack the relatively difficult problem of determining appropriate solutions of (2).

Curves along which the potential is constant,

$$(3) \qquad V = c,$$

are called equipotential curves. An important theorem in electricity states that:

The flux lines are the orthogonal trajectories of the equipotential curves.

Given the potential function, or the family of equipotential curves, for an electric field we shall determine the corresponding flux lines. This is simply a problem of finding the orthogonal trajectories of a given family of curves. The material of this and the next two sections is in the nature of physical interpretations of problems in orthogonal trajectories rather than actual applications. In practice it is not necessary to resort to our present methods to determine, for example, the flux lines when the equipotential curves are known.

EXAMPLE: Suppose two wires perpendicular to the xy-plane and piercing it at the points $(1, 0)$ and $(-1, 0)$ carry static electric charges of equal intensity but opposite sign. Then it can be shown that the equipotential lines are the circles

$$(4) \qquad x^2 + y^2 - 2cx + 1 = 0.$$

Obtain the flux lines and draw the figure.

From (4) it follows by elimination of c that the family of equipotential curves has the differential equation

$$(5) \qquad (x^2 - y^2 - 1)dx + 2xy \, dy = 0.$$

Since the flux lines must be orthogonal to the solutions of (5), the differential equation of the family of flux lines is

(6) $$2xy \, dx - (x^2 - y^2 - 1)dy = 0.$$

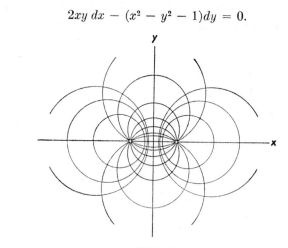

FIGURE 12

Equation (6) is linear in x^2. It can also be solved by finding the integrating factor y^{-2} by inspection. By one or the other of these methods the general solution of equation (6) is found to be

(7) $$x^2 + y^2 - 1 = 2ky.$$

Equation (7) is the desired equation of the family of flux lines. From (7) we get

(8) $$x^2 + (y - k)^2 = 1 + k^2$$

so the flux lines are seen to be circles with centers on the y-axis and passing through both the points $(1, 0)$ and $(-1, 0)$. See Figure 12.

24. Steady-state temperatures. Consider the situation in which some physical object has been subjected to unvarying temperature conditions for a time sufficiently long that the temperatures within the object have stopped changing. In such an instance the temperatures in the object are said to have reached the steady-state condition.

If x, y, z are rectangular space coordinates and T denotes steady-state temperature, then it can be shown that in the interior of the object the function T must satisfy Laplace's equation

(1) $$\frac{\partial^2 T}{\partial x^2} + \frac{\partial^2 T}{\partial y^2} + \frac{\partial^2 T}{\partial z^2} = 0.$$

If the temperature conditions are such that there is no variation of temperature (no flow of heat) in some one direction, taken as the direction of the z-axis, then the problem is two-dimensional and equation (1) may be replaced by

(2) $$\frac{\partial^2 T}{\partial x^2} + \frac{\partial^2 T}{\partial y^2} = 0.$$

Again we make no attempt to solve the partial differential equation (2) with its associated boundary conditions.

The curves along which the temperature is constant,

$$T = c$$

are called isotherms. The orthogonal trajectories of the isotherms are the curves whose tangents give the direction of heat flow at any point. They are called the lines of flow. Being given the isotherms we shall determine the corresponding lines of flow.

EXAMPLE: A very long concrete wedge whose right section is a circular sector of angle α and radius R has one of its plane faces kept at temperature T_1 and the other at temperature T_2, while the curved surface is insulated against heat transfer. Except near the ends of the wedge the steady-state temperature variation is essentially two-dimensional and T is known to be given by

$$T = T_1 + \frac{T_2 - T_1}{\alpha} \text{Arctan } (y/x)$$

where the coordinates x and y are defined in Figure 13. Draw the isotherms and the lines of flow.

In this problem when T is constant, then y/x is also constant, so the isotherms have the form

$$y = cx.$$

Hence the differential equation of the isotherms is

$$y \, dx - x \, dy = 0$$

and that of the lines of flow is

$$x \, dx + y \, dy = 0.$$

Therefore the lines of flow are

$$x^2 + y^2 = k^2.$$

Both families of curves are shown in Figure 13.

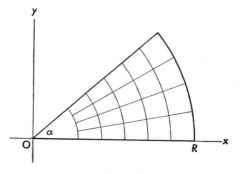

FIGURE 13

25. Two-dimensional steady-state fluid flow. If certain problems in the flow of a fluid are sufficiently idealized, they become two-dimensional steady-state problems in which orthogonal trajectories play an important part. In such problems the members of one family of curves

(1) $\psi(x, y) = c$

are called streamlines and the members of the family orthogonal to the family (1),

(2) $\varphi(x, y) = k$

are called equipotential curves. Also the function ψ is known as the stream function and φ is the velocity potential. The functions ψ and φ are each solutions of the same partial differential equation as is satisfied by steady-state temperature and by electrostatic potential. The directional derivative of the velocity potential represents the component of the fluid velocity in that direction.

We are considering a two-dimensional fluid flow such that conditions are identical in all planes parallel to the xy-plane, and there is no flow in the direction perpendicular to the xy-plane. As an example we may visualize such a problem as that in which a large body of the fluid is flowing with uniform velocity parallel to the x-axis. An object is immersed in the fluid and allowed to remain for a long time. We are interested in the streamline pattern near the immersed object after the temporary disturbances due to the immersion of the object have disappeared so far as measurable effects are concerned.

Since streamlines are perhaps easier for us to visualize and therefore make interesting answers, we shall assume given either the equipotential curves or, what amounts to the same thing, the velocity potential function. Then we are to determine and draw the streamlines. Natural boundaries of the flow are streamlines.

EXAMPLE: Consider the effect of a long cylindrical object immersed in a fluid which is flowing with uniform velocity in a direction perpendicular to the axis of the cylinder. Away from the ends of the cylinder the pattern of streamlines will be identical in planes perpendicular to the axis of the cylinder. Let us choose as our unit of length the radius of the cylinder.

Given the equipotential curves

(3) $$(r^2 + 1) \cos \theta = cr$$

in polar coordinates with the origin $r = 0$ at the center of the circular cross section, determine and sketch the streamlines.

We are to find the orthogonal trajectories of the family (3). First we obtain the differential equation of the equipotentials (3) in the usual manner, by isolating c and differentiating both members of the equation to get

$$\left(1 - \frac{1}{r^2}\right) \cos \theta \, dr - \left(r + \frac{1}{r}\right) \sin \theta \, d\theta = 0,$$

or

(4) $$(r^2 - 1) \cos \theta \, dr - r(r^2 + 1) \sin \theta \, d\theta = 0.$$

Then the differential equation of the streamlines is

(5) $$(r^2 + 1) \sin \theta \, dr + r(r^2 - 1) \cos \theta \, d\theta = 0.$$

FIGURE 14

From (5) it follows that

$$\frac{r^2 + 1}{r(r^2 - 1)} \, dr + \frac{\cos \theta}{\sin \theta} \, d\theta = 0,$$

or

$$\frac{2r^2 - (r^2 - 1)}{r(r^2 - 1)} \, dr + \frac{\cos \theta}{\sin \theta} \, d\theta = 0,$$

so that we need merely to solve the equation

(6) $$\frac{2r \, dr}{r^2 - 1} - \frac{dr}{r} + \frac{\cos \theta}{\sin \theta} \, d\theta = 0.$$

The solution of (6) is

$$\ln (r^2 - 1) - \ln r + \ln \sin \theta = \ln k,$$

which may be written as

(7) $$(r^2 - 1) \sin \theta = kr.$$

Equation (7) is the desired family of streamlines, of which several are shown in Figure 14.

Chapter 6

Hyperbolic Functions

26. Definition of the hyperbolic functions. Two particular combinations of exponential functions appear with such frequency in both pure and applied mathematics that it has been worth while to use special symbols for those combinations. The hyperbolic sine of x, written sinh x, is defined by

$$(1) \qquad \sinh x = \frac{e^x - e^{-x}}{2};$$

the hyperbolic cosine of x, written* cosh x, is defined by

$$(2) \qquad \cosh x = \frac{e^x + e^{-x}}{2}.$$

The use of symbols and names so similar to those of trigonometry may seem unwise. Some justification will appear in the next section where the basic formulas for these new functions are shown to bear a striking resemblance to those of ordinary trigonometry. It will be shown also that the hyperbolic sine and cosine are related to the equilateral hyperbola in much the same way that the ordinary (circular) sine and cosine are related to the circle.

Four more hyperbolic functions are defined in a manner to be expected, namely,

$$\tanh x = \frac{\sinh x}{\cosh x},$$

$$\operatorname{csch} x = \frac{1}{\sinh x},$$

_____
* Another common notation is Ch x to replace our cosh x, and with it Sh x to replace our sinh x.

$$\operatorname{sech} x = \frac{1}{\cosh x},$$

$$\coth x = \frac{1}{\tanh x}.$$

In solving differential equations the functions $\sinh x$ and $\cosh x$ are used more often than the other four functions.

27. Basic formulas of hyperbolic trigonometry. From the definitions of $\sinh x$ and $\cosh x$ it follows that

$$\sinh^2 x = \tfrac{1}{4}(e^{2x} - 2 + e^{-2x})$$

and

$$\cosh^2 x = \tfrac{1}{4}(e^{2x} + 2 + e^{-2x})$$

so that

(1) $$\cosh^2 x - \sinh^2 x = 1,$$

an identity similar to the well-known identity $\cos^2 x + \sin^2 x = 1$ in circular trigonometry. See also Exs. 2 and 3 below.

Directly from the definition we find that

$$y = \sinh u$$

is equivalent to

$$y = \tfrac{1}{2}(e^u - e^{-u}).$$

Hence, if u is a function of x, then

$$\frac{dy}{dx} = \tfrac{1}{2}(e^u + e^{-u})\frac{du}{dx};$$

that is,

(2) $$\frac{d}{dx}\sinh u = \cosh u\,\frac{du}{dx}.$$

The same method yields the result

(3) $$\frac{d}{dx}\cosh u = \sinh u\,\frac{du}{dx}.$$

The derivations of the corresponding formulas for the derivatives of the other hypberolic functions are left as exercises.

The curves $y = \cosh x$ and $y = \sinh x$ are exhibited in Figure 15.

Note the important properties:

(a) cosh $x \geqq 1$ for all real x;

(b) the only real value of x for which sinh $x = 0$ is $x = 0$;

(c) cosh $(-x) =$ cosh x; that is, cosh x is an even function of x;

(d) sinh $(-x) = -$ sinh x; sinh x is an odd function of x.

The hyperbolic functions have no real period. Corresponding to the period 2π possessed by the circular functions there is a period $2\pi i$ for the six hyperbolic functions.

The hyperbolic cosine curve is that in which a transmission line, cable, piece of string, watch chain, etc., hangs between two points at which it is suspended. This result is obtained in Chapter 17.

With regard to the word hyperbolic in the names of the functions being treated here, consider the equations

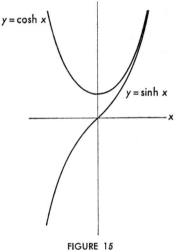

(4) $x = a$ cosh $t, \quad y = a$ sinh t.

In the equations (4) let t be a parameter and a a fixed constant. Then those equations are parametric equations of an equilateral hyperbola because from

$$\cosh^2 t - \sinh^2 t = 1$$

it follows that

$$\frac{x^2}{a^2} - \frac{y^2}{a^2} = 1$$

or

$$x^2 - y^2 = a^2.$$

FIGURE 15

This is analogous to the result that the two equations $x = a \cos t$, $y = a \sin t$, are parametric equations of the circle $x^2 + y^2 = a^2$.

In elementary trigonometry texts there is usually given a line representation of the six trigonometric functions in a figure based upon a circle of radius unity. A similar line representation* of the six hyperbolic functions can be obtained.

---

* See C. A. Hutchinson, "Line Representation of the Hyperbolic Functions," *Amer. Math. Monthly*, **40**, 413–414 (1933).

The formulas used to define the hyperbolic sine and cosine also have analogs in the study of the trigonometric functions. The definition given on page 123 for the exponential function with pure imaginary exponent may be used to derive the pertinent formulas. The results are exhibited in Ex. 24, page 97.

EXERCISES

In Exs. 1–16 prove the stated property of the hyperbolic functions. Use the definitions, the results in the text, or the properties obtained in any previous exercise.

1. $\sinh(-x) = -\sinh x$; $\cosh(-x) = \cosh x$; $\tanh(-x) = -\tanh x$.
2. $\operatorname{sech}^2 x = 1 - \tanh^2 x$.
3. $\operatorname{csch}^2 x = \coth^2 x - 1$.
4. $e^x = \cosh x + \sinh x$; $e^{-x} = \cosh x - \sinh x$.
5. $\sinh^2 y = \frac{1}{2}(\cosh 2y - 1)$.
6. $\cosh^2 y = \frac{1}{2}(\cosh 2y + 1)$.
7. $\cosh 2y = \cosh^2 y + \sinh^2 y$
$\qquad = 2\cosh^2 y - 1$
$\qquad = 2\sinh^2 y + 1$.
8. $\sinh 2y = 2\sinh y \cosh y$.
9. $\sinh(x + y) = \sinh x \cosh y + \cosh x \sinh y$;
$\sinh(x - y) = \sinh x \cosh y - \cosh x \sinh y$.
10. $\cosh(x + y) = \cosh x \cosh y + \sinh x \sinh y$;
$\cosh(x - y) = \cosh x \cosh y - \sinh x \sinh y$.
11. $\tanh(x + y) = \dfrac{\tanh x + \tanh y}{1 + \tanh x \tanh y}$;

$\tanh(x - y) = \dfrac{\tanh x - \tanh y}{1 - \tanh x \tanh y}$.
12. $\dfrac{d}{dx} \cosh u = \sinh u \dfrac{du}{dx}$.
13. $\dfrac{d}{dx} \tanh u = \operatorname{sech}^2 u \dfrac{du}{dx}$.
14. $\dfrac{d}{dx} \operatorname{csch} u = -\operatorname{csch} u \coth u \dfrac{du}{dx}$.
15. $\dfrac{d}{dx} \operatorname{sech} u = -\operatorname{sech} u \tanh u \dfrac{du}{dx}$.
16. $\dfrac{d}{dx} \coth u = -\operatorname{csch}^2 u \dfrac{du}{dx}$.

17. Obtain the differential equation formed by eliminating the constants c_1 and c_2 from

$$y = c_1 \sinh(kx) + c_2 \cosh(kx).$$

ANS. $\dfrac{d^2y}{dx^2} - k^2 y = 0.$

18. Solve the equation

$$(y \sinh x - y + 2x)dx + (\cosh x - x)dy = 0.$$

ANS. $y \cosh x - xy + x^2 = c.$

19. Solve the equation $xy\,dx + (x^2 + 1)(1 - y \tanh y)dy = 0.$

ANS. $y^2(x^2 + 1) = c \cosh^2 y.$

20. Solve the equation $y' \sinh x = 1 - 2y \cosh x.$

ANS. $y \sinh^2 x = c + \cosh x.$

21. Find the orthogonal trajectories of the curves $\sin x \cosh y = c.$

ANS. $\cos x \sinh y = k.$

22. Define the inverse hyperbolic sine of x, written $y = \sinh^{-1} x$, by the equation

$$x = \sinh y$$

or

(A) $\qquad\qquad x = \tfrac{1}{2}(e^y - e^{-y}).$

Put (A) in the form

$$e^{2y} - 2xe^y - 1 = 0$$

and thus conclude that

$$y = \sinh^{-1} x = \ln(x + \sqrt{x^2 + 1}),$$

pointing out why $y = \ln(x - \sqrt{x^2 + 1})$ is thrown out.

23. With the notation of Ex. 22 show that

$$d \sinh^{-1} x = \frac{dx}{\sqrt{1 + x^2}}.$$

24. For real x define e^{ix} by

$$e^{ix} = \cos x + i \sin x.$$

Then prove that

$$\sin x = \frac{e^{ix} - e^{-ix}}{2i}, \quad \cos x = \frac{e^{ix} + e^{-ix}}{2}.$$

Chapter 7

Linear Differential Equations

28. The general linear equation. The general linear differential equation of order n may be written

$$(1) \quad b_0(x) \frac{d^n y}{dx^n} + b_1(x) \frac{d^{n-1}y}{dx^{n-1}} + \cdots + b_{n-1}(x) \frac{dy}{dx} + b_n(x)y = R(x).$$

The functions $R(x)$ and $b_i(x)$; $i = 0, 1, \cdots, n$, are to be independent of the variable y. If $R(x)$ is identically zero, equation (1) is said to be *homogeneous;* if $R(x)$ is not identically zero, equation (1) is called *nonhomogeneous.* Here the word homogeneous is being used with reference to the quantities $y, y', y'', \cdots, y^{(n)}$; it has nothing to do with the way in which x enters the equation. In this chapter we shall obtain some fundamental and important properties of linear equations.

In order to simplify the wording of statements relating to solutions of linear differential equations, we shall adopt a common convention. When a relation $y = f(x)$ is a solution of a linear differential equation, we shall also call $f(x)$ itself a solution of the differential equation.

First we prove that: if y_1 and y_2 are solutions of the homogeneous equation

$$(2) \quad b_0(x)y^{(n)} + b_1(x)y^{(n-1)} + \cdots + b_{n-1}(x)y' + b_n(x)y = 0,$$

and if c_1 and c_2 are constants, then

$$y = c_1 y_1 + c_2 y_2$$

is a solution of equation (2).

The statement that y_1 and y_2 are solutions of (2) means that

(3) $b_0 y_1^{(n)} + b_1 y_1^{(n-1)} + \cdots + b_{n-1} y_1' + b_n y_1 = 0$

and

(4) $b_0 y_2^{(n)} + b_1 y_2^{(n-1)} + \cdots + b_{n-1} y_2' + b_n y_2 = 0.$

Now let us multiply each member of (3) by c_1, each member of (4) by c_2, and add the results.   We get

(5) $b_0[c_1 y_1^{(n)} + c_2 y_2^{(n)}] + b_1[c_1 y_1^{(n-1)} + c_2 y_2^{(n-1)}] + \cdots$
$+ b_{n-1}[c_1 y_1' + c_2 y_2'] + b_n[c_1 y_1 + c_2 y_2] = 0.$

Since $c_1 y_1' + c_2 y_2' = (c_1 y_1 + c_2 y_2)'$, etc., equation (5) is neither more nor less than the statement that $c_1 y_1 + c_2 y_2$ is a solution of equation (2).   The proof is completed.   The special case $c_2 = 0$ is worth noting; that is, for a homogeneous linear equation any constant times a solution is also a solution.

In a similar manner, or by iteration of the above result, it can be seen that if y_i; $i = 1, 2, \cdots, k$, are solutions of equation (2) and if c_i; $i = 1, 2, \cdots, k$, are constants, then

$$ y = c_1 y_1 + c_2 y_2 + \cdots + c_k y_k $$

is a solution of equation (2).

29. Linear independence.   Given the functions $f_1(x), \cdots,$ $f_n(x)$, then if constants $c_1, c_2, \cdots, c_n$, not all zero, exist such that

(1) $c_1 f_1(x) + c_2 f_2(x) + \cdots + c_n f_n(x) = 0$

identically in some interval $a \leqq x \leqq b$, then the functions $f_1(x)$, $f_2(x), \cdots, f_n(x)$ are said to be *linearly dependent*. If no such relation exists, the functions are said to be *linearly independent*. That is, the functions $f_1, f_2, \cdots, f_n$ are linearly independent when equation (1) implies that $c_1 = c_2 = \cdots = c_n = 0$.

If the functions of a set are linearly dependent, then at least one of them is a linear combination of the others; if they are linearly independent, then none of them is a linear combination of the others.

30. The Wronskian.   With the definitions of Section 29 in mind, we shall now obtain a sufficient condition that n functions be linearly independent over an interval $a \leqq x \leqq b$.

Let us assume that each of the functions $f_1(x)$, $f_2(x)$, $\cdots$, $f_n(x)$ is differentiable at least $(n - 1)$ times in the interval $a \leqq x \leqq b$. Then from the equation

$$(1) \qquad c_1 f_1 + c_2 f_2 + \cdots + c_n f_n = 0,$$

it follows by successive differentiation that

$$c_1 f_1' + c_2 f_2' + \cdots + c_n f_n' = 0,$$
$$c_1 f_1'' + c_2 f_2'' + \cdots + c_n f_n'' = 0,$$
$$\cdots$$
$$c_1 f_1^{(n-1)} + c_2 f_2^{(n-1)} + \cdots + c_n f_n^{(n-1)} = 0.$$

Considered as a system of equations in c_1, c_2, $\cdots$, c_n, the n linear equations directly above will have no solution except that with each of the c's equal to zero, if the determinant of the system does not vanish. That is, if

$$(2) \qquad \begin{vmatrix} f_1 & f_2 & \cdots & f_n \\ f_1' & f_2' & \cdots & f_n' \\ f_1'' & f_2'' & \cdots & f_n'' \\ \cdots & & & \\ f_1^{(n-1)} & f_2^{(n-1)} & \cdots & f_n^{(n-1)} \end{vmatrix} \neq 0,$$

then the functions f_1, f_2, $\cdots$, f_n are linearly independent. The determinant in (2) is called the *Wronskian* of the n functions involved. We have shown that the nonvanishing of the Wronskian is a sufficient condition that the functions be linearly independent.

The nonvanishing of the Wronskian on an interval is not a necessary condition for linear independence. The Wronskian may vanish even when the functions are linearly independent, as exhibited in Ex. 10 below.

If the n functions involved are solutions of a homogeneous linear differential equation, the situation is simplified as is shown by the theorem below. Proof is omitted.

THEOREM: *If, on the interval $a \leqq x \leqq b$, $b_0(x) \neq 0$, b_0, b_1, $\cdots$, b_n are continuous, and y_1, y_2, $\cdots$, y_n are solutions of the equation*

$$(3) \qquad b_0 y^{(n)} + b_1 y^{(n-1)} + \cdots + b_{n-1} y' + b_n y = 0,$$

then a necessary and sufficient condition that $y_1, \cdots, y_n$ be linearly independent is the nonvanishing of the Wronskian of $y_1, \cdots, y_n$ on the interval $a \leqq x \leqq b$.

The functions $\cos \omega t$, $\sin \omega t$, $\sin (\omega t + \alpha)$, in which t is the variable and ω and α are constants, are linearly dependent because there exist constants c_1, c_2, c_3 such that

$$c_1 \cos \omega t + c_2 \sin \omega t + c_3 \sin (\omega t + \alpha) = 0$$

for all t. Indeed, one set of such constants is $c_1 = \sin \alpha$, $c_2 = \cos \alpha$, $c_3 = -1$.

One of the best-known sets of n linearly independent functions of x is the set $1, x, x^2, \cdots, x^{n-1}$. The linear independence of the powers of x follows at once from the fact that if $c_1, c_2, \cdots, c_n$ are not all zero, the equation

$$c_1 + c_2 x + \cdots + c_n x^{n-1} = 0$$

can have at most $(n - 1)$ distinct roots and so cannot vanish identically in any interval. See also Ex. 1 below.

EXERCISES

1. Obtain the Wronskian of the functions

$$1, x, x^2, \cdots, x^{n-1} \text{ for } n > 1.$$

ANS. $W = 0!1!2! \cdots (n-1)!$.

2. Show that the functions e^x, e^{2x}, e^{3x} are linearly independent.

ANS. $W = 2e^{6x} \neq 0$.

3. Show that the functions e^x, $\cos x$, $\sin x$ are linearly independent.

ANS. $W = 2e^x \neq 0$.

4. By determining constants c_1, c_2, c_3, c_4, not all zero and which are such that $c_1 f_1 + c_2 f_2 + c_3 f_3 + c_4 f_4 = 0$ identically, show that the functions

$$f_1 = x, f_2 = e^x, f_3 = xe^x, f_4 = (2 - 3x)e^x,$$

are linearly dependent.

ANS. One such set of c's is: $c_1 = 0$, $c_2 = -2$, $c_3 = 3$, $c_4 = 1$.

5. Show that the functions x, e^x, xe^x are linearly independent.
6. Show that $\cos (\omega t - \beta)$, $\cos \omega t$, $\sin \omega t$ are linearly dependent functions of t.
7. Show that 1, $\sin x$. $\cos x$ are linearly independent.

8. Show that 1, $\sin^2 x$, $\cos^2 x$ are linearly dependent.

9. Show that two nonvanishing differentiable functions of x are linearly dependent if, and only if, their Wronskian vanishes identically. This statement is not true for more than two functions.

10. Let $f_1(x) = 1 + x^3$ for $x \leqq 0$, $f_1(x) = 1$ for $x \geqq 0$;

$f_2(x) = 1$ for $x \leqq 0$, $f_2(x) = 1 + x^3$ for $x \geqq 0$;

$f_3(x) = 3 + x^3$ for all x.

Show that: (a) f, f', f'' are continuous for all x for each of f_1, f_2, f_3,

(b) The Wronskian of f_1, f_2, f_3 is zero for all x,

(c) f_1, f_2, f_3 are linearly independent over the interval $-1 \leqq x \leqq 1$.

In part (c) you must show that, if $c_1 f_1(x) + c_2 f_2(x) + c_3 f_3(x) = 0$ for all x in $-1 \leqq x \leqq 1$, $c_1 = c_2 = c_3 = 0$. Use $x = -1$, 0, 1 successively to obtain three equations to solve for c_1, c_2, and c_3.

31. General solution of a homogeneous equation.

Let y_1, $y_2, \cdots, y_n$ be linearly independent solutions of the homogeneous equation

$$(1) \quad b_0(x) y^{(n)} + b_1(x) y^{(n-1)} + \cdots + b_{n-1}(x) y' + b_n(x) y = 0.$$

Then the general solution of equation (1) is

$$(2) \qquad y = c_1 y_1 + c_2 y_2 + \cdots + c_n y_n$$

where $c_1, c_2, \cdots, c_n$ are arbitrary constants.

In a sense each particular solution of the linear differential equation (1) is a special case (some choice of the c's) of the general solution (2). The basic ideas needed for a proof of this important result are exhibited here for the equation of order two. No additional complications enter for equations of higher order.

Consider the equation

$$(3) \qquad b_0(x) y'' + b_1(x) y' + b_2(x) y = 0.$$

Let the relation

$$(4) \qquad y = f(x)$$

be any particular solution of equation (3), the solution being valid in some interval $a < x < b$ in which $b_0(x)$ does not vanish and in which the functions b_1/b_0 and b_2/b_0 possess derivatives of all orders.

We assume (it can be proved) that, at $x = \alpha$, $f(x)$ is sufficiently well behaved to insure that the Taylor series for $f(x)$,

$$(5) \qquad f(x) = \sum_{k=0}^{\infty} \frac{f^{(k)}(\alpha)(x-\alpha)^k}{k!},$$

converges to $f(x)$ in some interval about $x = \alpha$.

Then the solution $f(x)$ is completely determined by knowledge of $f(\alpha)$ and $f'(\alpha)$, the values of f and f' taken at some point α within the interval. For, since we can divide by $b_0(x)$, equation (3) yields y'' in terms of y, y', and the known coefficients in the equation. Then $y''(\alpha) = f''(\alpha)$ can be determined. Successive differentiation of the equation for y'' will yield the higher derivatives. Thus $f^{(k)}(\alpha)$ can be computed for $k = 2, 3, \cdots$, from the values of $f(\alpha)$ and $f'(\alpha)$. Then, using Taylor's series (5) we see that $f(x)$ is determined by the differential equation and the two values $f(\alpha)$ and $f'(\alpha)$.

Now let $y_1(x)$, $y_2(x)$ be any two linearly independent solutions of equation (3). Further, let α be chosen as some point in the interval, $a < \alpha < b$, where the Wronskian of y_1 and y_2 does not vanish,

$$(6) \qquad \begin{vmatrix} y_1(\alpha) & y_2(\alpha) \\ y_1'(\alpha) & y_2'(\alpha) \end{vmatrix} \neq 0.$$

Consider the solution

$$(7) \qquad y = c_1 y_1(x) + c_2 y_2(x),$$

from which

$$y' = c_1 y_1'(x) + c_2 y_2'(x).$$

We wish to choose c_1 and c_2 so that the y of equation (7) will become the solution $f(x)$. But we can surely force that y to be such that $y(\alpha) = f(\alpha)$ and $y'(\alpha) = f'(\alpha)$. That is, the equations

$$(8) \qquad \begin{aligned} c_1 y_1(\alpha) + c_2 y_2(\alpha) &= f(\alpha), \\ c_1 y_1'(\alpha) + c_2 y_2'(\alpha) &= f'(\alpha), \end{aligned}$$

can be solved for c_1 and c_2 because of the inequality (6), the non-vanishing of the Wronskian. Then $f(x)$ and $y(x)$ have the same Taylor series (5), so they are identical.

It is necessary to keep in mind that the above proof used the fact that $b_0(x) \neq 0$ in the interval $a < x < b$. It is easy to see that the linear equation

$$xy' - 2y = 0,$$

has the general solution $y = cx^2$ and also such particular solutions as

$$y_1 = x^2, \qquad 0 \leq x,$$
$$= -4x^2, \qquad x < 0.$$

The solution y_1 is not a special case of the general solution. But in any interval throughout which $b_0(x) = x \neq 0$, this particular solution is a special case of the general solution. It was, of course, made up by piecing together at $x = 0$ two parts, each drawn from the general solution.

32. General solution of a nonhomogeneous equation.

Let y_p be any particular solution (not necessarily involving any arbitrary constants) of the equation

$$(1) \qquad b_0 y^{(n)} + b_1 y^{(n-1)} + \cdots + b_{n-1} y' + b_n y = R(x)$$

and let y_c be a solution of the corresponding homogeneous equation

$$(2) \qquad b_0 y^{(n)} + b_1 y^{(n-1)} + \cdots + b_{n-1} y' + b_n y = 0.$$

Then

$$(3) \qquad y = y_c + y_p$$

is a solution of equation (1). For, using the y of equation (3) we see that

$$b_0 y^{(n)} + \cdots + b_n y = (b_0 y_c^{(n)} + \cdots + b_n y_c)$$
$$+ (b_0 y_p^{(n)} + \cdots + b_n y_p)$$
$$= 0 + R(x) = R(x).$$

If $y_1, y_2, \cdots, y_n$ are linearly independent solutions of equation (2), then

$$(4) \qquad y_c = c_1 y_1 + c_2 y_2 + \cdots + c_n y_n,$$

in which the c's are arbitrary constants, is the general solution of equation (2). The right member of equation (4) is called the *complementary function* for equation (1).

The general solution of the nonhomogeneous equation (1) is the sum of the complementary function and any particular solution.

For instance, consider the equation

(5) $$y'' - y = 4.$$

It is easily seen that $y = -4$ is a solution of equation (5). Therefore the y_p in equation (3) may be taken to be (-4). As we shall see later, the homogeneous equation

$$y'' - y = 0$$

has as its general solution

$$y_c = c_1 e^x + c_2 e^{-x}.$$

Thus the complementary function for equation (5) is $(c_1 e^x + c_2 e^{-x})$ and a particular solution of (5) is $y_p = -4$. Hence the general solution of equation (5) is

$$y = c_1 e^x + c_2 e^{-x} - 4$$

in which c_1 and c_2 are arbitrary constants.

33. Differential operators. Let D denote differentiation with respect to x, D^2 differentiation twice with respect to x and so on; that is, for integral k,

$$D^k y = \frac{d^k y}{dx^k}.$$

The expression

(1) $$A = a_0 D^n + a_1 D^{n-1} + \cdots + a_{n-1} D + a_n$$

is called a differential operator of order n. It may be defined as that operator which, when applied to any function* y, yields the result

(2) $$Ay = a_0 \frac{d^n y}{dx^n} + a_1 \frac{d^{n-1} y}{dx^{n-1}} + \cdots + a_{n-1} \frac{dy}{dx} + a_n y.$$

The coefficients $a_0, a_1, \cdots, a_n$ in the operator A may be functions

---

* The function y is assumed to possess as many derivatives as may be encountered in whatever operations take place.

of x, but in this book the only operators used will be those with constant coefficients.

Two operators A and B are said to be equal if, and only if, the same result is produced when each acts upon the function y. That is, $A = B$ if, and only if, $Ay = By$ for all functions y possessing the derivatives necessary for the operations involved.

The product AB of two operators A and B is defined as that operator which produces the same result as is obtained by using the operator B followed by the operator A. Thus $ABy = A(By)$. The product of two differential operators always exists and is a differential operator. For operators with *constant coefficients*, but not usually for those with variable coefficients, it is true that $AB = BA$.

EXAMPLE (a): Let $A = D + 2$ and $B = 3D - 1$.
Then

$$By = (3D - 1)y = 3\frac{dy}{dx} - y$$

and

$$\begin{aligned}
A(By) &= (D + 2)\left(3\frac{dy}{dx} - y\right) \\
&= 3\frac{d^2y}{dx^2} - \frac{dy}{dx} + 6\frac{dy}{dx} - 2y \\
&= 3\frac{d^2y}{dx^2} + 5\frac{dy}{dx} - 2y \\
&= (3D^2 + 5D - 2)y.
\end{aligned}$$

Hence $AB = (D + 2)(3D - 1) = 3D^2 + 5D - 2$.

Now consider BA. Acting upon y, the operator BA yields

$$\begin{aligned}
B(Ay) &= (3D - 1)\left(\frac{dy}{dx} + 2y\right) \\
&= 3\frac{d^2y}{dx^2} + 6\frac{dy}{dx} - \frac{dy}{dx} - 2y \\
&= 3\frac{d^2y}{dx^2} + 5\frac{dy}{dx} - 2y.
\end{aligned}$$

Hence

$$BA = 3D^2 + 5D - 2 = AB.$$

EXAMPLE (b): Let $G = xD + 2$, and $H = D - 1$.   Then

$$G(Hy) = (xD + 2)\left(\frac{dy}{dx} - y\right)$$

$$= x\frac{d^2y}{dx^2} - x\frac{dy}{dx} + 2\frac{dy}{dx} - 2y$$

$$= x\frac{d^2y}{dx^2} + (2 - x)\frac{dy}{dx} - 2y,$$

so that

$$GH = xD^2 + (2 - x)D - 2.$$

On the other hand

$$H(Gy) = (D - 1)\left(x\frac{dy}{dx} + 2y\right)$$

$$= \frac{d}{dx}\left(x\frac{dy}{dx} + 2y\right) - \left(x\frac{dy}{dx} + 2y\right)$$

$$= x\frac{d^2y}{dx^2} + \frac{dy}{dx} + 2\frac{dy}{dx} - x\frac{dy}{dx} - 2y$$

$$= x\frac{d^2y}{dx^2} + (3 - x)\frac{dy}{dx} - 2y;$$

that is,

$$HG = xD^2 + (3 - x)D - 2.$$

It is worthy of notice that here we have two operators G and H (one of them with variable coefficients), the product of which is dependent on the order of the factors.   On this topic see also Exs. 17–22 in the next section.

The sum of two differential operators is obtained by expressing each in the form

$$a_0D^n + a_1D^{n-1} + \cdots + a_{n-1}D + a_n$$

and adding corresponding coefficients.   For instance, if

$$A = 3D^2 - D + x - 2$$

and

$$B = x^2D^2 + 4D + 7,$$

then

$$A + B = (3 + x^2)D^2 + 3D + x + 5.$$

Differential operators are linear operators; that is, if A is any differential operator, if c_1 and c_2 are constants, and if f_1 and f_2 are any functions of x possessing the required number of derivatives, then

$$A(c_1f_1 + c_2f_2) = c_1Af_1 + c_2Af_2.$$

34. The fundamental laws of operation. Let A, B, and C be any differential operators as defined in Section 33. With the above definitions of addition and multiplication, it follows that differential operators satisfy the following:

(1) The commutative law of addition:

$$A + B = B + A.$$

(2) The associative law of addition:

$$(A + B) + C = A + (B + C).$$

(3) The associative law of multiplication:

$$(AB)C = A(BC).$$

(4) The distributive law of multiplication with respect to addition:

$$A(B + C) = AB + AC.$$

If A, B, and C are operators with *constant coefficients*, then they also satisfy

(5) The commutative law of multiplication:

$$AB = BA.$$

Therefore differential operators with constant coefficients satisfy all the laws of ordinary algebra* with regard to addition and multiplication. In Chapter 10 we shall touch upon the question of division of operators.

If m and n are any two positive integers, then

$$D^mD^n = D^{m+n},$$

a useful result which follows immediately from the definitions.

---

* See any college algebra, for example, J. R. Britton and L. C. Snively. *Algebra for College Students*, New York, Rinehart and Co., 1954, pp. 31–32.

Since for purposes of addition and multiplication the operators with constant coefficients behave just as algebraic polynomials behave, it is legitimate to use the tools of elementary algebra. In particular, synthetic division may be used to factor operators with constant coefficients.

EXERCISES

Perform the indicated multiplications in Exs. 1–4.

1. $(2D + 1)(D - 4)$.   ANS. $2D^2 - 7D - 4$.
2. $(3D - 2)(3D + 2)$.   ANS. $9D^2 - 4$.
3. $(D - 2)(D^2 + 2D + 5)$.   ANS. $D^3 + D - 10$.
4. $(D + 1)(D - 2)^2$.   ANS. $D^3 - 3D^2 + 4$.

In Exs. 5–16 factor each of the operators.

5. $2D^2 - 5D - 3$.   ANS. $(D - 3)(2D + 1)$.
6. $3D^2 + 7D + 2$.
7. $D^3 - 4D^2 + D + 6$.   ANS. $(D + 1)(D - 2)(D - 3)$.
8. $2D^3 - 7D^2 + 2D + 3$.
9. $D^4 - 9D^2$.   ANS. $D^2(D - 3)(D + 3)$.
10. $D^3 - 3D + 2$.
11. $D^3 - 19D - 30$.   ANS. $(D + 2)(D + 3)(D - 5)$.
12. $4D^3 - 8D^2 - 11D - 3$.
13. $2D^4 - 11D^3 + 18D^2 - 4D - 8$.   ANS. $(D - 2)^3(2D + 1)$.
14. $2D^4 + 9D^3 + 6D^2 - 20D - 24$.
15. $D^4 + D^3 + 7D^2 + 9D - 18$.   ANS. $(D - 1)(D + 2)(D^2 + 9)$.
16. $D^3 + D - 10$.   ANS. $(D - 2)(D^2 + 2D + 5)$.

Perform the indicated multiplications in Exs. 17–22.

17. $(D - x)(D + x)$.   ANS. $D^2 + 1 - x^2$.
18. $(D + x)(D - x)$.   ANS. $D^2 - 1 - x^2$.
19. $D(xD - 1)$.   ANS. xD^2.
20. $(xD - 1)D$.   ANS. $xD^2 - D$.
21. $(xD + 2)(xD - 1)$.   ANS. $x^2D^2 + 2xD - 2$.
22. $(xD - 1)(xD + 2)$.   ANS. $x^2D^2 + 2xD - 2$.

35. Some properties of differential operators. Since for constant m and integral k,

(1) $$D^k e^{mx} = m^k e^{mx},$$

it is easy to find the effect an operator has upon e^{mx}. Let $f(D)$ be a polynomial in D,

$$(2) \qquad f(D) = a_0 D^n + a_1 D^{n-1} + \cdots + a_{n-1} D + a_n.$$

Then

$$f(D)e^{mx} = a_0 m^n e^{mx} + a_1 m^{n-1} e^{mx} + \cdots + a_{n-1} m e^{mx} + a_n e^{mx},$$

so that

$$(3) \qquad\qquad f(D)e^{mx} = e^{mx} f(m).$$

If m is a root of the equation $f(m) = 0$, then in view of equation (3), $f(D)e^{mx} = 0$.

EXAMPLE: Let $f(D) = 2D^2 + 5D - 12$. Then the equation $f(m) = 0$ is

$$2m^2 + 5m - 12 = 0,$$

or

$$(m + 4)(2m - 3) = 0,$$

of which the roots are $m_1 = -4$ and $m_2 = 3/2$.

With the aid of equation (3) above it can be seen that

$$(2D^2 + 5D - 12)e^{-4x} = 0$$

and that

$$(2D^2 + 5D - 12)e^{(3/2)x} = 0.$$

In other words, $y_1 = e^{-4x}$ and $y_2 = e^{(3/2)x}$ are solutions of the differential equation

$$(2D^2 + 5D - 12)y = 0.$$

Next consider the effect of the operator $(D - m)$ on the product of e^{mx} and a power of x. Since

$$(D - m)(x^k e^{mx}) = k x^{k-1} e^{mx} + m x^k e^{mx} - m x^k e^{mx},$$

we get

$$(D - m)(x^k e^{mx}) = k x^{k-1} e^{mx}.$$

Then

$$\begin{aligned}(D - m)^2(x^k e^{mx}) &= k(D - m)(x^{k-1} e^{mx}) \\ &= k(k - 1)x^{k-2} e^{mx}.\end{aligned}$$

Repeating the operation, we are led to

$$(D - m)^k(x^k e^{mx}) = k(k - 1) \cdots 2 \cdot 1 x^0 e^{mx}$$
$$= k! e^{mx}.$$

But $(D - m)e^{mx} = 0$. Therefore, for all $n > k$,

(4) $$(D - m)^n(x^k e^{mx}) = 0.$$

It will be convenient to think of the exponent of x in (4) as varying rather than the exponent of the operator $(D - m)$. Hence we rewrite (4) as

(5) $$(D - m)^n(x^k e^{mx}) = 0 \text{ for } k = 0, 1, 2 \cdots , (n - 1).$$

Equation (5) forms the basis for all the solutions obtained in the next chapter.

36. The nth derivative of a product. It is often convenient to be able to write down for a product of functions a derivative of fairly high order without first obtaining the derivatives of lower order. For instance, we may wish to form the fourth derivative of the function

$$y = x^2 e^{3x},$$

but may have no need for the first, second, or third derivatives.

A formula for the nth derivative of the product of two functions was discovered by Leibnitz. Since that formula is not always included in a first course in calculus, it will be stated here.

Consider the product

(1) $$y = uv$$

in which u and v are functions of the independent variable x. Let us use the notation

$$u^{(n)} = \frac{d^n u}{dx^n},$$

including $u^{(0)} = u$ and $u^{(1)} = u'$, together with similar notations for derivatives of v and y. From equation (1) we obtain, by the usual rule for the derivative of a product, the result

$$y' = u'v + uv',$$

or

(2) $$y^{(1)} = u^{(1)}v^{(0)} + u^{(0)}v^{(1)}.$$

Let us now differentiate both members of equation (2) with respect to x, keeping in mind that each term on the right side of equation (2) is itself a product of functions. We thus get

$$y^{(2)} = u^{(2)}v^{(0)} + u^{(1)}v^{(1)} + u^{(1)}v^{(1)} + u^{(0)}v^{(2)},$$

or

$$(3) \qquad y^{(2)} = u^{(2)}v^{(0)} + 2u^{(1)}v^{(1)} + u^{(0)}v^{(2)}.$$

Another such step brings us to the result

$$(4) \qquad y^{(3)} = u^{(3)}v^{(0)} + 3u^{(2)}v^{(1)} + 3u^{(1)}v^{(2)} + u^{(0)}v^{(3)},$$

for the third derivative of a product. The resemblance of equations (3) and (4) to the binomial expansions

$$(a + b)^2 = a^2 + 2ab + b^2$$

and

$$(a + b)^3 = a^3 + 3a^2b + 3ab^2 + b^3$$

is striking. It encourages one to go on to the general formula.

Leibnitz' rule for the nth derivative of a product is: If $y = uv$, then

$$(5) \qquad y^{(n)} = \sum_{k=0}^{n} C_{n,k} u^{(n-k)} v^{(k)},$$

in which $C_{n,k}$ is the binomial coefficient,

$$C_{n,k} = \frac{n!}{k!(n-k)!} = \frac{n(n-1) \cdots (n-k+1)}{k!}.$$

Equation (5) may be proved quite easily by induction with the aid of the relation

$$(6) \qquad C_{n,k} + C_{n,k+1} = C_{n+1,k+1},$$

the latter being a fundamental property of the Pascal triangle.*

Leibnitz' rule is particularly simple to use when the factors involved are simple exponentials, powers of x, or sines or cosines.

---

* See J. R. Britton and L. C. Snively, *Algebra for College Students*, New York, Rinehart and Co., 1954, pp. 277–279.

EXAMPLE (a): Find the fourth derivative of the product

$$y = x^2 e^{3x}.$$

First we have in mind the coefficients in the binomial expansion $(a + b)^4$—or we build the Pascal triangle far enough to obtain them. The required coefficients are 1, 4, 6, 4, 1. As we write down the product we form the successive derivatives from each end, first writing

$$y^{(4)} = 1 \cdot (x^2)(\ ) + 4(\ )(\ ) + 6(\ )(\ ) + 4(\ )(\ ) + 1(\ )(e^{3x})$$

and then filling in the empty spaces with the proper derivatives in succession. Thus we arrive, in one step after a bit of practice, at the result

$$y^{(4)} = (x^2)(81e^{3x}) + 4(2x)(27e^{3x}) + 6(2)(9e^{3x}) + 4(0)(3e^{3x}) + (0)(e^{3x}),$$

or

$$y^{(4)} = 9e^{3x}(9x^2 + 24x + 12).$$

EXAMPLE (b): Find the third derivative of $w = e^{2x} \cos 3x$.
We form

$$w^{(3)} = (e^{2x})(\ ) + 3(\ )(\ )$$
$$+ 3(\ )(\ ) + (\ )(\cos 3x),$$

and fill in the spaces to obtain

$$w^{(3)} = (e^{2x})(27 \sin 3x) + 3(2e^{2x})(-9 \cos 3x)$$
$$+ 3(4e^{2x})(-3 \sin 3x) + (8e^{2x})(\cos 3x),$$

or

$$w^{(3)} = e^{2x}[(27 - 36) \sin 3x + (8 - 54) \cos 3x].$$

Finally, we have

$$w^{(3)} = -e^{2x}(9 \sin 3x + 46 \cos 3x).$$

The method is particularly pleasant, of course, when some of the terms drop out as happened in Example (a).

EXAMPLE (c): Find the fourth derivative of $v = x \sin 3x$.
At once, since $3^4 = 81$ and $3^3 \cdot 4 = 108$, we write

$$v^{(4)} = 81x \sin 3x - 108 \cos 3x.$$

EXERCISES

Answers to these exercises can be verified, and the efficacy of the method investigated, by also obtaining the desired derivative by successive differentiation.

1. Find $y^{(2)}$ from $y = x^3 e^x$.   ANS. $y^{(2)} = e^x(x^3 + 6x^2 + 6x)$.

2. Find $y^{(2)}$ from $y = x^4 e^{-x}$.

3. Find $y^{(2)}$ from $y = x \sin 2x$.   ANS. $y^{(2)} = -4x \sin 2x + 4 \cos 2x$.

4. Find $y^{(2)}$ from $y = x \cos 2x$.

5. Find $y^{(3)}$ from $y = x^2 \cos 4x$.
        ANS. $y^{(3)} = 64x^2 \sin 4x - 96x \cos 4x - 24 \sin 4x$.

6. Find $y^{(3)}$ from $y = x^2 \sin 3x$.

7. Find $v^{(3)}$ from $v = xe^{3x}$.   ANS. $v^{(3)} = 27e^{3x}(x + 1)$.

8. Find $v^{(3)}$ from $v = x \sin 4x$.   ANS. $v^{(3)} = -64x \cos 4x - 48 \sin 4x$.

9. Find $y^{(4)}$ from $y = xe^{-2x}$.   ANS. $y^{(4)} = 16e^{-2x}(x - 2)$.

10. Find $y^{(4)}$ from $y = xe^{-3x}$.

11. Find $y^{(4)}$ from $y = x \sin 2x$.   ANS. $y^{(4)} = 16x \sin 2x - 32 \cos 2x$.

12. Find $y^{(4)}$ from $y = x \cos 2x$.

13. Find $y^{(4)}$ from $y = x^2 e^x$.

14. Find $y^{(4)}$ from $y = x^2 e^{-x}$.

15. Find $y^{(4)}$ from $y = x^2 \sin x$.
        ANS. $y^{(4)} = x^2 \sin x - 8x \cos x - 12 \sin x$.

16. Find $y^{(4)}$ from $y = x^2 \cos x$.

Chapter 8

Linear Equations with Constant Coefficients

37. The auxiliary equation; distinct roots. Any linear homogeneous differential equation with constant coefficients,

$$(1) \qquad a_0 \frac{d^n y}{dx^n} + a_1 \frac{d^{n-1}y}{dx^{n-1}} + \cdots + a_{n-1}\frac{dy}{dx} + a_n y = 0,$$

may be written in the form

$$(2) \qquad\qquad f(D)y = 0,$$

where $f(D)$ is a linear differential operator. As we saw in the preceding chapter, if m is any root of the algebraic equation $f(m) = 0$, then

$$f(D)e^{mx} = 0,$$

which means simply that $y = e^{mx}$ is a solution of equation (2). The equation

$$(3) \qquad\qquad f(m) = 0$$

is called the *auxiliary equation* associated with (1) or (2).

The auxiliary equation for (1) is of degree n. Let its roots be m_1, $m_2, \cdots, m_n$. If those roots are all real and distinct, then the n solutions $y = e^{m_1 x}$, $y = e^{m_2 x}, \cdots, y = e^{m_n x}$ are linearly independent and the general solution of (1) can be written down at once. It is

$$y = c_1 e^{m_1 x} + c_2 e^{m_2 x} + \cdots + c_n e^{m_n x},$$

where $c_1, c_2, \cdots, c_n$ are arbitrary constants.

Repeated roots of the auxiliary equation will be treated in the next section.

Imaginary roots will be avoided until Section 40 where the corresponding solutions will be put into a desirable form. At present the solution associated with such a root as $m_1 = 3 + 2i$ would necessarily appear in the form $y = e^{(3+2i)x}$ which is correct (with the definition given in Section 39 below) but awkward in applications.

EXAMPLE (a): Solve the equation

$$\frac{d^3y}{dx^3} - 4\frac{d^2y}{dx^2} + \frac{dy}{dx} + 6y = 0.$$

First write the auxiliary equation

$$m^3 - 4m^2 + m + 6 = 0,$$

whose roots $m = -1, 2, 3$ may be obtained by synthetic division. Then the general solution is seen to be

$$y = c_1 e^{-x} + c_2 e^{2x} + c_3 e^{3x}.$$

EXAMPLE (b): Solve the equation

$$(3D^3 + 5D^2 - 2D)y = 0.$$

The auxiliary equation is

$$3m^3 + 5m^2 - 2m = 0$$

and its roots are $m = 0, -2, \frac{1}{3}$. Using the fact that $e^{0x} = 1$, the desired solution may be written

$$y = c_1 + c_2 e^{-2x} + c_3 e^{x/3}.$$

EXAMPLE (c): Solve the equation

$$\frac{d^2x}{dt^2} - 4x = 0$$

together with the conditions: when $t = 0$, $x = 0$ and $\frac{dx}{dt} = 3$.

The auxiliary equation is

$$m^2 - 4 = 0,$$

with roots $m = 2, -2$. Hence the general solution of the differential equation is

$$x = c_1 e^{2t} + c_2 e^{-2t}.$$

It remains to enforce the conditions at $t = 0$. Now

$$\frac{dx}{dt} = 2c_1 e^{2t} - 2c_2 e^{-2t}.$$

Thus the condition that $x = 0$ when $t = 0$ requires that

$$0 = c_1 + c_2$$

while the condition that $\frac{dx}{dt} = 3$ when $t = 0$ requires that

$$3 = 2c_1 - 2c_2.$$

From the simultaneous equations for c_1 and c_2 we conclude that $c_1 = \frac{3}{4}$ and $c_2 = -\frac{3}{4}$. Therefore

$$x = \tfrac{3}{4}(e^{2t} - e^{-2t}),$$

which can also be put in the form

$$x = \tfrac{3}{2} \sinh (2t).$$

EXERCISES

In Exs. 1–22 find the general solution. When the operator D is used it is implied that the independent variable is x.

1. $(D^2 - D - 2)y = 0.$ ANS. $y = c_1 e^{-x} + c_2 e^{2x}.$
2. $(D^2 + 3D)y = 0.$
3. $(D^2 - D - 6)y = 0.$ ANS. $y = c_1 e^{-2x} + c_2 e^{3x}.$
4. $(D^2 + 5D + 6)y = 0.$
5. $(D^3 + 2D^2 - 15D)y = 0.$ ANS. $y = c_1 + c_2 e^{3x} + c_3 e^{-5x}.$
6. $(D^3 + 2D^2 - 8D)y = 0.$
7. $(D^3 - D^2 - 4D + 4)y = 0.$ ANS. $y = c_1 e^{-2x} + c_2 e^{x} + c_3 e^{2x}$
8. $(D^3 - 3D^2 - D + 3)y = 0.$

9. $(4D^3 - 13D + 6)y = 0.$ ANS. $y = c_1 e^{x/2} + c_2 e^{3x/2} + c_3 e^{-2x}.$

10. $(4D^3 - 49D - 60)y = 0.$

11. $\dfrac{d^3x}{dt^3} - 2\dfrac{d^2x}{dt^2} - 3\dfrac{dx}{dt} = 0.$ ANS. $x = c_1 + c_2 e^{-t} + c_3 e^{3t}.$

12. $\dfrac{d^3x}{dt^3} - 7\dfrac{dx}{dt} + 6x = 0.$

13. $(10D^3 + D^2 - 7D + 2)y = 0.$ ANS. $y = c_1 e^{-x} + c_2 e^{x/2} + c_3 e^{2x/5}.$

14. $(4D^3 - 13D - 6)y = 0.$

15. $(D^3 - 5D - 2)y = 0.$ ANS. $y = c_1 e^{-2x} + c_2 e^{(1+\sqrt{2})x} + c_3 e^{(1-\sqrt{2})x}.$

16. $(D^3 - 3D^2 - 3D + 1)y = 0.$

17. $(4D^4 - 15D^2 + 5D + 6)y = 0.$

ANS. $y = c_1 e^{-2x} + c_2 e^{-x/2} + c_3 e^{3x/2} + c_4 e^x.$

18. $(D^4 - 2D^3 - 13D^2 + 38D - 24)y = 0.$

19. $(6D^4 + 23D^3 + 28D^2 + 13D + 2)y = 0.$

20. $(4D^4 - 45D^2 - 70D - 24)y = 0.$

21. $(D^2 - 4aD + 3a^2)y = 0,$ a real $\neq 0.$

22. $[D^2 - (a + b)D + ab]y = 0,$ a and b real and unequal.

In Exs. 23–24 find the particular solution indicated.

23. $(D^2 - 2D - 3)y = 0;$ when $x = 0,$ $y = 0$ and $y' = -4.$

ANS. $y = e^{-x} - e^{3x}.$

24. $(D^2 - D - 6)y = 0;$ when $x = 0,$ $y = 0$ and when $x = 1,$ $y = e^3.$

ANS. $y = (e^{3x} - e^{-2x})/(1 - e^{-5}).$

In Exs. 25–29, find for $x = 1$ the y value for the particular solution required.

25. $(D^2 - 2D - 3)y = 0;$ when $x = 0,$ $y = 4$ and $y' = 0.$

ANS.   When $x = 1,$ $y = e^3 + 3e^{-1} = 21.2.$

26. $(D^3 - 4D)y = 0;$ when $x = 0,$ $y = 0,$ $y' = 0,$ and $y'' = 2.$

ANS.   When $x = 1,$ $y = \sinh^2 1.$

27. $(D^2 - D - 6)y = 0;$ when $x = 0,$ $y = 3$ and $y' = -1.$

ANS.   When $x = 1,$ $y = 20.4.$

28. $(D^2 + 3D - 10)y = 0;$ when $x = 0,$ $y = 0$ and when $x = 2,$ $y = 1.$

ANS.   When $x = 1,$ $y = 0.135.$

29. $(D^3 - 2D^2 - 5D + 6)y = 0;$ when $x = 0,$ $y = 1,$ $y' = -7,$ and $y'' = -1.$ ANS.   When $x = 1,$ $y = -19.8.$

38. The auxiliary equation; repeated roots. Suppose that in the equation

(1) $$f(D)y = 0$$

the operator $f(D)$ has repeated factors; that is, the auxiliary equation $f(m) = 0$ has repeated roots. Then the method of the previous

section does not yield the general solution. Let the auxiliary
equation have three equal roots $m_1 = b$, $m_2 = b$, $m_3 = b$. The
corresponding part of the solution yielded by the method of Section 37 is

$$y = c_1 e^{bx} + c_2 e^{bx} + c_3 e^{bx},$$

or

$$(2) \qquad y = (c_1 + c_2 + c_3)e^{bx}.$$

Now (2) can be replaced by

$$(3) \qquad y = c_4 e^{bx}$$

with $c_4 = c_1 + c_2 + c_3$. Thus corresponding to the three roots
under consideration this method has yielded only the solution (3).
The difficulty is present, of course, because the three solutions
corresponding to the roots $m_1 = m_2 = m_3 = b$ are not linearly
independent.

What is needed is a method for obtaining n linearly independent
solutions corresponding to n equal roots of the auxiliary equation.
Suppose the auxiliary equation $f(m) = 0$ has the n equal roots
$m_1 = m_2 = \cdots = m_n = b$. Then the operator $f(D)$ must have a
factor $(D - b)^n$. We wish to find n linearly independent y's for
which

$$(4) \qquad (D - b)^n y = 0.$$

Turning to the result (5) near the end of Section 35 and writing
$m = b$, we find that

$$(5) \qquad (D - b)^n(x^k e^{bx}) = 0 \text{ for } k = 0, 1, 2, \cdots, (n - 1).$$

The functions $y_k = x^k e^{bx}$; $k = 0, 1, 2, \cdots, (n - 1)$ are linearly
independent because aside from the common factor e^{bx} they contain
only the respective powers $x^0, x^1, x^2, \cdots, x^{n-1}$.

The general solution of equation (4) is

$$(6) \qquad y = c_1 e^{bx} + c_2 x e^{bx} + \cdots + c_n x^{n-1} e^{bx}.$$

Furthermore, if $f(D)$ contains the factor $(D - b)^n$, then the equation

$$(1) \qquad f(D)y = 0$$

can be written

$$(7) \qquad\qquad g(D)(D - b)^n y = 0$$

where $g(D)$ contains all the factors of $f(D)$ except for $(D - b)^n$. Then any solution of

$$(4) \qquad\qquad (D - b)^n y = 0$$

is also a solution of (7) and therefore of (1).

Now we are in a position to write down the solution of equation (1) whenever the auxiliary equation has only real roots.   Each root of the auxiliary equation is either distinct from all the other roots or it is one of a set of equal roots.   Corresponding to a root m_i distinct from all others there is the solution

$$(8) \qquad\qquad y_i = c_i e^{m_i x}$$

and corresponding to n equal roots $m_1, m_2, \cdots, m_n$ each equal to b, there is the solution

$$(9) \qquad\qquad y = c_1 e^{bx} + c_2 x e^{bx} + \cdots + c_n x^{n-1} e^{bx}.$$

The sum of such solutions (8) and (9) yields the proper number of solutions, a number equal to the order of the differential equation, because there is one solution corresponding to each root of the auxiliary equation.   The solutions thus obtained can be proved to be linearly independent.

EXAMPLE (a): Solve the equation

$$(10) \qquad\qquad (D^4 - 7D^3 + 18D^2 - 20D + 8)y = 0.$$

With the aid of synthetic division it is easily seen that the auxiliary equation

$$m^4 - 7m^3 + 18m^2 - 20m + 8 = 0$$

has the roots $m = 1, 2, 2, 2$.   Then the general solution of equation (10) is

$$y = c_1 e^x + c_2 e^{2x} + c_3 x e^{2x} + c_4 x^2 e^{2x},$$

or

$$y = c_1 e^x + (c_2 + c_3 x + c_4 x^2) e^{2x}.$$

EXAMPLE (b): Solve the equation

$$\frac{d^4y}{dx^4} + 2\frac{d^3y}{dx^3} + \frac{d^2y}{dx^2} = 0.$$

The auxiliary equation is

$$m^4 + 2m^3 + m^2 = 0$$

with roots $m = 0, 0, -1, -1$. Hence the desired solution is

$$y = c_1 + c_2x + c_3e^{-x} + c_4xe^{-x}.$$

EXERCISES

In Exs. 1–20 find the general solution.

1. $(4D^2 - 4D + 1)y = 0.$ ANS. $y = (c_1 + c_2x)e^{x/2}.$
2. $(D^2 + 6D + 9)y = 0.$
3. $(D^3 - 4D^2 + 4D)y = 0.$ ANS. $y = c_1 + (c_2 + c_3x)e^{2x}.$
4. $(9D^3 + 6D^2 + D)y = 0.$
5. $(2D^4 - 3D^3 - 2D^2)y = 0.$ ANS. $y = c_1 + c_2x + c_3e^{2x} + c_4e^{-x/2}.$
6. $(2D^4 - 5D^3 - 3D^2)y = 0.$
7. $(D^3 + 3D^2 - 4)y = 0.$ ANS. $y = c_1e^x + (c_2 + c_3x)e^{-2x}.$
8. $(4D^3 - 27D + 27)y = 0.$
9. $(D^3 + 3D^2 + 3D + 1)y = 0.$ ANS. $y = (c_1 + c_2x + c_3x^2)e^{-x}.$
10. $(D^3 + 6D^2 + 12D + 8)y = 0.$
11. $(D^5 - D^3)y = 0.$ ANS. $y = c_1 + c_2x + c_3x^2 + c_4e^x + c_5e^{-x};$
      or $y = c_1 + c_2x + c_3x^2 + c_6 \cosh x + c_7 \sinh x.$
12. $(D^5 - 16D^3)y = 0.$
13. $(4D^4 + 4D^3 - 3D^2 - 2D + 1)y = 0.$
                        ANS. $y = (c_1 + c_2x)e^{x/2} + (c_3 + c_4x)e^{-x}.$
14. $(4D^4 - 4D^3 - 23D^2 + 12D + 36)y = 0.$
                        ANS. $y = (c_1 + c_2x)e^{-3x/2} + (c_3 + c_4x)e^{2x}.$
15. $(D^4 + 3D^3 - 6D^2 - 28D - 24)y = 0.$
                        ANS. $y = c_1e^{3x} + (c_2 + c_3x + c_4x^2)e^{-2x}.$
16. $(27D^4 - 18D^2 + 8D - 1)y = 0.$
17. $(4D^5 - 23D^3 - 33D^2 - 17D - 3)y = 0.$
            ANS. $y = c_1e^{3x} + (c_2 + c_3x)e^{-x} + (c_4 + c_5x)e^{-x/2}.$
18. $(4D^5 - 15D^3 - 5D^2 + 15D + 9)y = 0.$
19. $(D^4 - 5D^2 - 6D - 2)y = 0.$
            ANS. $y = (c_1 + c_2x)e^{-x} + c_3e^{(1+\sqrt{3})x} + c_4e^{(1-\sqrt{3})x}.$
20. $(D^5 - 5D^4 + 7D^3 + D^2 - 8D + 4)y = 0.$

In Exs. 21–26, find the particular solution indicated.

21. $(D^2 + 4D + 4)y = 0$; when $x = 0$, $y = 1$ and $y' = -1$.

ANS. $y = (1 + x)e^{-2x}$.

22. The equation of Ex. 21 with the conditions that the graph of the solution pass through the points $(0, 2)$ and $(2, 0)$.

ANS. $y = (2 - x)e^{-2x}$.

23. $(D^3 - 3D - 2)y = 0$; when $x = 0$, $y = 0$, $y' = 9$, $y'' = 0$.

ANS. $y = 2e^{2x} + (3x - 2)e^{-x}$.

24. $(D^4 + 3D^3 + 2D^2)y = 0$;   when $x = 0$, $y = 0$, $y' = 4$, $y'' = -6$, $y''' = 14$.

ANS. $y = 2(x + e^{-x} - e^{-2x})$.

25. The equation of Ex. 24 with the conditions: when $x = 0$, $y = 0$, $y' = 3$, $y'' = -5$, $y''' = 9$.

ANS. $y = 2 - e^{-x} - e^{-2x}$.

26. $(D^3 + D^2 - D - 1)y = 0$; when $x = 0$, $y = 1$, when $x = 2$, $y = 0$, and also as $x \rightarrow \infty$, $y \rightarrow 0$.

ANS. $y = \frac{1}{2}(2 - x)e^{-x}$.

In Exs. 27–29 find for $x = 2$ the y value for the particular solution required.

27. $(4D^2 - 4D + 1)y = 0$; when $x = 0$, $y = -2$, $y' = 2$.

ANS.   When $x = 2$, $y = 4e$.

28. $(D^3 + 2D^2)y = 0$; when $x = 0$, $y = -3$, $y' = 0$, $y'' = 12$.

ANS.   When $x = 2$, $y = 3e^{-4} + 6$.

29. $(D^3 + 5D^2 + 3D - 9)y = 0$;   when $x = 0$, $y = -1$,   when $x = 1$, $y = 0$, and also as $x \rightarrow \infty$, $y \rightarrow 0$.

ANS.   When $x = 2$, $y = e^{-6}$.

39. A definition of e^z for imaginary z.

It is evident that such a symbol as $e^{(2+3i)}$, where $i = \sqrt{-1}$, has no meaning from the standpoint of elementary algebra; that is, it would be meaningless to speak of "e used as a factor $(2 + 3i)$ times." Furthermore, no such simple extension of the meaning of an exponent as saves the day for the symbols $e^{1/2}$, e^{-2}, $e^{2/3}$, etc., is available for $e^{(2+3i)}$. Let us search for a reasonable definition for e^z, where z is imaginary.

Let $z = \alpha + i\beta$ with α and β real. Since it is desirable to have the ordinary laws of exponents remain valid, it is wise to require that

$$(1) \qquad e^{\alpha + i\beta} = e^\alpha \cdot e^{i\beta}.$$

To e^α with α real we attach its usual meaning.

Now consider $e^{i\beta}$, β real. In calculus it is shown that for all real x

$$(2) \qquad e^x = 1 + \frac{x}{1!} + \frac{x^2}{2!} + \frac{x^3}{3!} + \cdots + \frac{x^n}{n!} + \cdots,$$

or

$$(2) \qquad e^x = \sum_{n=0}^{\infty} \frac{x^n}{n!}.$$

If we now tentatively put $x = i\beta$ in (2) as a definition of $e^{i\beta}$, we get

$$(3) \quad e^{i\beta} = 1 + \frac{i\beta}{1!} + \frac{i^2\beta^2}{2!} + \frac{i^3\beta^3}{3!} + \frac{i^4\beta^4}{4!} + \cdots + \frac{i^n\beta^n}{n!} + \cdots .$$

Separating the even powers of β from the odd powers of β in (3) yields

$$(4) \qquad e^{i\beta} = 1 + \frac{i^2\beta^2}{2!} + \frac{i^4\beta^4}{4!} + \cdots + \frac{i^{2k}\beta^{2k}}{(2k)!} + \cdots$$

$$+ \frac{i\beta}{1!} + \frac{i^3\beta^3}{3!} + \cdots + \frac{i^{2k+1}\beta^{2k+1}}{(2k+1)!} + \cdots ,$$

or

$$(4) \qquad e^{i\beta} = \sum_{k=0}^{\infty} \frac{i^{2k}\beta^{2k}}{(2k)!} + \sum_{k=0}^{\infty} \frac{i^{2k+1}\beta^{2k+1}}{(2k+1)!}.$$

Now $i^{2k} = (-1)^k$, so that we may write

$$(5) \qquad e^{i\beta} = 1 - \frac{\beta^2}{2!} + \frac{\beta^4}{4!} + \cdots + \frac{(-1)^k\beta^{2k}}{(2k)!} + \cdots$$

$$+ i\left[\frac{\beta}{1!} - \frac{\beta^3}{3!} + \cdots + \frac{(-1)^k\beta^{2k+1}}{(2k+1)!} + \cdots \right],$$

or

$$(5) \qquad e^{i\beta} = \sum_{k=0}^{\infty} \frac{(-1)^k\beta^{2k}}{(2k)!} + i\sum_{k=0}^{\infty} \frac{(-1)^k\beta^{2k+1}}{(2k+1)!}.$$

But the series on the right in (5) are precisely those for $\cos\beta$ and $\sin\beta$ as developed in calculus. Hence we are led to the tentative result

$$(6) \qquad e^{i\beta} = \cos\beta + i\sin\beta.$$

The student should realize that the manipulations above have no meaning in themselves at this stage (assuming that infinite series with complex terms are not a part of the content of elementary mathematics). What has been accomplished is this: the formal manipulations above have suggested the meaningful definition (6). Combining (6) with (1) we now put forward a reasonable *definition* of $e^{\alpha+i\beta}$, namely,

$$(7) \qquad e^{\alpha+i\beta} = e^{\alpha}(\cos \beta + i \sin \beta), \; \alpha \text{ and } \beta \text{ real.}$$

Replacing β by $-\beta$ in (7) yields a result which is of value to us in the next section,

$$e^{\alpha-i\beta} = e^{\alpha}(\cos \beta - i \sin \beta).$$

It is interesting and important that with the definition (7) the function e^z for complex z retains many of the properties possessed by the function e^x for real x. Such matters are often studied in detail in books on complex variables.* Here we need in particular to know that if

$$y = e^{(a+ib)x},$$

a, b, and x real, then

$$(D - a - ib)y = 0.$$

The result desired follows at once by differentiation, with respect to x, of the function

$$y = e^{ax}(\cos bx + i \sin bx).$$

40. The auxiliary equation; imaginary roots. Consider a differential equation $f(D)y = 0$ for which the auxiliary equation $f(m) = 0$ has real coefficients. From elementary algebra we know that if the auxiliary equation has any imaginary roots, those roots must occur in conjugate pairs. Thus if

$$m_1 = a + ib$$

is a root of the equation $f(m) = 0$, with a and b real and $b \neq 0$, then

---

* For example, R. V. Churchill, *Complex Variables and Applications*, New York, McGraw-Hill Book Co., 1948, pp. 37–40.

$$m_2 = a - ib$$

is also a root of $f(m) = 0$. It must be kept in mind that this result is a consequence of the reality of the coefficients in the equation $f(m) = 0$. Imaginary roots do not necessarily appear in pairs in an algebraic equation whose coefficients involve imaginaries.

We can now construct in usable form solutions of

$$(1) \qquad\qquad f(D)y = 0$$

corresponding to imaginary roots of $f(m) = 0$. For, since $f(m)$ is assumed to have real coefficients, any imaginary roots appear in conjugate pairs $m_1 = a + ib$ and $m_2 = a - ib$. Then according to the preceding section equation (1) is satisfied by

$$(2) \qquad\qquad y = c_1 e^{(a+ib)x} + c_2 e^{(a-ib)x}.$$

Taking x to be real along with a and b, we get from (2) the result

$$(3) \qquad y = c_1 e^{ax}(\cos bx + i \sin bx) + c_2 e^{ax}(\cos bx - i \sin bx).$$

Now (3) may be written

$$y = (c_1 + c_2)e^{ax} \cos bx + i(c_1 - c_2)e^{ax} \sin bx.$$

Finally, let $c_1 + c_2 = c_3$, and $i(c_1 - c_2) = c_4$ where c_3 and c_4 are new arbitrary constants. Then equation (1) is seen to have the solutions

$$(4) \qquad\qquad y = c_3 e^{ax} \cos bx + c_4 e^{ax} \sin bx,$$

corresponding to the two roots $m_1 = a + ib$ and $m_2 = a - ib(b \neq 0)$ of the auxiliary equation.

Taking a, b, x, and y to be real, it follows readily from equation (4) that c_3 and c_4 are real. But $c_1 + c_2 = c_3$, and $i(c_1 - c_2) = c_4$, so that $c_1 = \frac{1}{2}(c_3 - ic_4)$ and $c_2 = \frac{1}{2}(c_3 + ic_4)$. Hence, if $c_4 \neq 0$, the c_1 and c_2 are conjugate complex numbers.

The reduction of the solution (2) above to the desirable form (4) has been done once and that is enough. Whenever a pair of conjugate imaginary roots of the auxiliary equation appears, we write down at once in the form given on the right in equation (4) the particular solution corresponding to those two roots.

EXAMPLE (a): Solve the equation

$$(D^3 - 3D^2 + 9D + 13)y = 0.$$

For the auxiliary equation

$$m^3 - 3m^2 + 9m + 13 = 0$$

one root, $m_1 = -1$, is easily found. When the factor $(m + 1)$ is removed by synthetic division, it is seen that the other two roots are solutions of the quadratic

$$m^2 - 4m + 13 = 0.$$

Those roots are found to be $m_2 = 2 + 3i$ and $m_3 = 2 - 3i$. The auxiliary equation has the roots $m = -1, 2 \pm 3i$. Hence the general solution of the differential equation is

$$y = c_1 e^{-x} + c_2 e^{2x} \cos 3x + c_3 e^{2x} \sin 3x.$$

Repeated imaginary roots lead to solutions analogous to those brought in by repeated real roots. For instance, if the roots $m = a \pm ib$ occur three times, then the corresponding six linearly independent solutions of the differential equation are those appearing in the expression

$$(c_1 + c_2 x + c_3 x^2)e^{ax} \cos bx + (c_4 + c_5 x + c_6 x^2)e^{ax} \sin bx.$$

EXAMPLE (b): Solve the equation

$$(D^4 + 8D^2 + 16)y = 0.$$

The auxiliary equation $m^4 + 8m^2 + 16 = 0$ may be written $(m^2 + 4)^2 = 0$ so that its roots are seen to be $m = \pm 2i, \pm 2i$. The roots $m_1 = 2i$ and $m_2 = -2i$ each occur twice. Thinking of $2i$ as $0 + 2i$ and recalling that $e^{0x} = 1$, we write the solution of the differential equation as

$$y = (c_1 + c_2 x) \cos 2x + (c_3 + c_4 x) \sin 2x.$$

In such exercises as those below a fine check can be obtained by direct substitution of the result and its appropriate derivatives into the differential equation. The verification is particularly effective because the operations performed in the check are so different from those performed in obtaining the solution.

EXERCISES

Find the general solution except where the exercise stipulates otherwise.

1. Verify directly that the relation

   (4) $y = c_3 e^{ax} \cos bx + c_4 e^{ax} \sin bx$

   satisfies the equation

   $$[(D - a)^2 + b^2]y = 0.$$

2. $(D^2 - 2D + 5)y = 0$. Verify your answer.
   ANS. $y = c_1 e^x \cos 2x + c_2 e^x \sin 2x$.

3. $(D^2 - 2D + 2)y = 0$.

4. $(D^2 + 9)y = 0$. Verify your answer. ANS. $y = c_1 \cos 3x + c_2 \sin 3x$.

5. $(D^2 - 9)y = 0$.   ANS. $y = c_1 \cosh 3x + c_2 \sinh 3x$.

6. $(D^2 + 6D + 13)y = 0$. Verify your answer.

7. $(D^2 - 4D + 7)y = 0$.   ANS. $y = c_1 e^{2x} \cos \sqrt{3}\, x + c_2 e^{2x} \sin \sqrt{3}\, x$.

8. $(D^3 + 2D^2 + D + 2)y = 0$. Verify your answer.

9. $(D^2 - 1)y = 0$; when $x = 0$, $y = y_0$ and $y' = 0$.
   ANS. $y = y_0 \cosh x$.

10. $(D^2 + 1)y = 0$; when $x = 0$, $y = y_0$ and $y' = 0$. ANS. $y = y_0 \cos x$.

11. $(D^4 + 2D^3 + 10D^2)y = 0$.
    ANS. $y = c_1 + c_2 x + c_3 e^{-x} \cos 3x + c_4 e^{-x} \sin 3x$.

12. $(D^3 + 7D^2 + 19D + 13)y = 0$; when $x = 0$, $y = 0$, $y' = 2$, and $y'' = -12$.
    ANS. $y = e^{-3x} \sin 2x$.

13. $(D^5 + D^4 - 7D^3 - 11D^2 - 8D - 12)y = 0$.
    ANS. $y = c_1 \cos x + c_2 \sin x + c_3 e^{-2x} + c_4 x e^{-2x} + c_5 e^{3x}$.

14. $(D^4 - 2D^3 + 2D^2 - 2D + 1)y = 0$. Verify your answer.

15. $(D^4 + 18D^2 + 81)y = 0$.
    ANS. $y = (c_1 + c_2 x) \cos 3x + (c_3 + c_4 x) \sin 3x$.

16. $(2D^4 + 11D^3 - 4D^2 - 69D + 34)y = 0$. Verify your answer.

17. $(D^6 + 9D^4 + 24D^2 + 16)y = 0$.
    ANS. $y = c_1 \cos x + c_2 \sin x + (c_3 + c_4 x) \cos 2x + (c_5 + c_6 x) \sin 2x$.

18. $(2D^3 - D^2 + 36D - 18)y = 0$.
    ANS. $y = c_1 e^{x/2} + c_2 \cos (3 \sqrt{2}\, x) + c_3 \sin (3 \sqrt{2}\, x)$.

19. $\dfrac{d^2 x}{dt^2} + k^2 x = 0$, k real; when $t = 0$, $x = 0$ and $\dfrac{dx}{dt} = v_0$. Verify your result completely.   ANS. $x = (v_0/k) \sin kt$.

20. $(D^3 + D^2 + 4D + 4)y = 0$; when $x = 0$, $y = 0$, $y' = -1$, and $y'' = 5$.
    ANS. $y = e^{-x} - \cos 2x$.

21. $\dfrac{d^2 x}{dt^2} + 2b \dfrac{dx}{dt} + k^2 x = 0$, $k > b > 0$; when $t = 0$, $x = 0$ and $\dfrac{dx}{dt} = v_0$.
    ANS. $x = (v_0/a)e^{-bt} \sin at$, where $a = \sqrt{k^2 - b^2}$.

MISCELLANEOUS EXERCISES

Obtain the general solution unless otherwise instructed.   Your answer can be checked by direct substitution.

1. $(D^3 - D^2 + D - 1)y = 0.$
2. $(D^3 + 4D^2 + 5D)y = 0.$
3. $(D^4 - 13D^2 + 36)y = 0.$
4. $(D^4 - 5D^3 + 5D^2 + 5D - 6)y = 0.$
5. $(4D^3 + 8D^2 - 11D + 3)y = 0.$
6. $(D^3 + D^2 - 16D - 16)y = 0.$
7. $(D^4 - D^3 - 3D^2 + D + 2)y = 0.$
8. $(D^3 - 2D^2 - 3D + 10)y = 0.$
9. $(D^5 + D^4 - 6D^3)y = 0.$
10. $(4D^3 + 28D^2 + 61D + 37)y = 0.$
11. $(4D^3 + 12D^2 + 13D + 10)y = 0.$
12. $(18D^3 - 33D^2 + 20D - 4)y = 0.$
13. $(D^2 - D - 6)y = 0$; when $x = 0$, $y = 2$ and $y' = 1$.
14. $(D^4 + 6D^3 + 9D^2)y = 0$; when $x = 0$, $y = 0$, $y' = 0$, and $y'' = 6$ and as $x \to \infty$, $y' \to 1$.   For this particular solution find the value of y when $x = 1$.   ANS. $y = 1 - e^{-3}$.
15. $(D^3 + 6D^2 + 12D + 8)y = 0$;   when $x = 0$, $y = 1$, $y' = -2$,   and $y'' = 2$.
16. $(8D^3 - 4D^2 - 2D + 1)y = 0.$
17. $(D^4 + D^3 - 4D^2 - 4D)y = 0.$
18. $(D^4 - 2D^3 + 5D^2 - 8D + 4)y = 0.$
19. $(D^4 + 2D^2 + 1)y = 0.$
20. $(D^4 + 5D^2 + 4)y = 0.$
21. $(D^4 + 3D^3 - 4D)y = 0.$
22. $(D^5 + D^4 - 9D^3 - 13D^2 + 8D + 12)y = 0.$
23. $(D^4 - 11D^3 + 36D^2 - 16D - 64)y = 0.$
24. $(D^2 + 2D + 5)y = 0.$
25. $(D^4 + 4D^3 + 2D^2 - 8D - 8)y = 0.$
26. $(4D^4 - 24D^3 + 35D^2 + 6D - 9)y = 0.$
27. $(4D^4 + 20D^3 + 35D^2 + 25D + 6)y = 0.$
28. $(D^4 - 7D^3 + 11D^2 + 5D - 14)y = 0.$
29. $(D^3 + 5D^2 + 7D + 3)y = 0.$
30. $(D^3 - 2D^2 + D - 2)y = 0.$

Chapter 9

Nonhomogeneous Equations:
Undetermined Coefficients

41. Solution by inspection. In Section 32 we saw that the general solution of the equation

$$(1) \qquad (b_0 D^n + b_1 D^{n-1} + \cdots + b_{n-1} D + b_n)y = R(x)$$

is

$$y = y_c + y_p$$

where y_c, the complementary function, is the general solution of the homogeneous equation

$$(2) \qquad (b_0 D^n + b_1 D^{n-1} + \cdots + b_{n-1} D + b_n)y = 0$$

and y_p is any particular solution of the original equation (1).

Various methods for getting a particular solution of (1) when the $b_0, b_1, \cdots, b_n$ are constants will be presented in this chapter and in Chapters 10 and 11. Except in Chapter 11 the methods used will be dependent upon the character of the function $R(x)$.

If $R(x)$ is a constant R_0 and if $b_n \neq 0$, then a particular solution can be found by inspection. Indeed,

$$(3) \qquad y_p = \frac{R_0}{b_n}$$

is a solution of

$$(4) \quad (b_0 D^n + b_1 D^{n-1} + \cdots + b_n)y = R_0; \; b_n \neq 0, \; R_0 \text{ constant,}$$

because all derivatives of y_p are zero, so that

$$(b_0 D^n + b_1 D^{n-1} + \cdots + b_n)y_p = b_n R_0 / b_n = R_0.$$

Suppose that $b_n = 0$ in equation (4). Let $D^k y$ be the lowest-ordered derivative which actually appears in the differential equation. Then the equation may be written

(5) $(b_0 D^n + \cdots + b_{n-k} D^k)y = R_0; \; b_{n-k} \neq 0, \; R_0$ constant.

Now $D^k x^k = k!$, a constant, so that all higher derivatives of x^k are zero. Thus it becomes evident that (5) has a solution

(6) $$y_p = \frac{R_0 x^k}{k! \, b_{n-k}}$$

for then $(b_0 D^n + \cdots + b_{n-k} D^k)y_p = b_{n-k} R_0 k! / (k! \, b_{n-k}) = R_0$.

EXAMPLE (a): Solve the equation

(7) $$(D^2 - 3D + 2)y = 16.$$

By the methods of Chapter 8 we obtain the complementary function,

$$y_c = c_1 e^x + c_2 e^{2x}.$$

By inspection a particular solution of the original equation is $y_p = \frac{16}{2} = 8$. Hence the general solution of (7) is

$$y = c_1 e^x + c_2 e^{2x} + 8.$$

EXAMPLE (b): Solve the equation

(8) $$\frac{d^5 y}{dx^5} + 4 \frac{d^3 y}{dx^3} = 7.$$

From the auxiliary equation $m^5 + 4m^3 = 0$ we get $m = 0, 0, 0, \pm 2i$. Hence

$$y_c = c_1 + c_2 x + c_3 x^2 + c_4 \cos 2x + c_5 \sin 2x.$$

A particular solution of (8) is

$$y_p = \frac{7x^3}{3! \cdot 4} = \frac{7x^3}{24}.$$

As a check note that

$$(D^5 + 4D^3) \frac{7x^3}{24} = 0 + 4 \cdot \frac{7 \cdot 6}{24} = 7.$$

The general solution of equation (8) is

$$y = c_1 + c_2 x + c_3 x^2 + \frac{7}{24} x^3 + c_4 \cos 2x + c_5 \sin 2x,$$

in which the $c_1, \cdots, c_5$ are arbitrary constants.

ORAL EXERCISES

Find a particular solution for each equation.

1. $(D^2 + 1)y = 4$.
2. $(D^2 + 4)y = 8$.
3. $(D^3 + D + 2)y = 5$.
4. $(D^2 + 4D - 5)y = 20$.
5. $(D^4 + 2D^2 + 1)y = 3$.
6. $(D^3 - 5D^2 + 4)y = 14$.
7. $(D^3 + 4D)y = 12$.
8. $(D^3 + 4D^2)y = 12$.
9. $(D^3 - 7D^2 + 14D - 8)y = 2$.
10. $(D^3 + 9D)y = 11$.
11. $(D^3 + 9D^2)y = 11$.
12. $(D^4 + 9D^3)y = 11$.
13. $(D^4 - 2D^3)y = 12$.
14. $(D^4 - 5D)y = 12$.
15. $(D^4 - 5D^2)y = 12$.
16. $(D^4 - 5D^3)y = 12$.

42. Construction of a homogeneous equation from a specified solution. In preparation for the method of undetermined coefficients it is wise to obtain proficiency in writing down a homogeneous differential equation of which a given relation of proper form is a solution.

Recall that in solutions of homogeneous equations with constant coefficients a term such as $c_1 e^{ax}$ occurred only when the auxiliary equation $f(m) = 0$ had a root $m = a$ and then the operator $f(D)$ had a factor $(D - a)$. In like manner $c_2 x e^{ax}$ appeared only when $f(D)$ contained the factor $(D - a)^2$, $c_3 x^2 e^{ax}$ only when $f(D)$ contained $(D - a)^3$, etc. Such terms as $ce^{ax} \cos bx$ or $ce^{ax} \sin bx$ correspond to roots $m = a \pm ib$, or to a factor $[(D - a)^2 + b^2]$.

EXAMPLE (a): Find a homogeneous linear equation, with constant coefficients, which has as a particular solution

(1) $$y = 7e^{3x} + 2x.$$

First note that the coefficients (7 and 2) are quite irrelevant for the present problem, so long as they are not zero. We shall obtain an equation satisfied by $y = c_1 e^{3x} + c_2 x$, no matter what the constants c_1 and c_2 may be.

A term c_1e^{3x} occurs along with a root $m = 3$ of the auxiliary equation. The term c_2x will appear if the auxiliary equation has $m = 0$, 0; that is, a double root $m = 0$. We have recognized that the equation

$$(2) \qquad D^2(D - 3)y = 0,$$

or

$$(2) \qquad (D^3 - 3D^2)y = 0$$

has $y = c_1e^{3x} + c_2x + c_3$ as its general solution, and therefore that (2) has $y = 7e^{3x} + 2x$ as a particular solution.

EXAMPLE (b): Find a homogeneous linear equation with real, constant coefficients which is satisfied by

$$(3) \qquad y = 6 + 3xe^x - \cos x.$$

The term 6 is associated with $m = 0$, the term $3xe^x$ with a double root $m = 1, 1$ and the term $(- \cos x)$ with the pair of imaginary roots $m = 0 \pm i$. Hence the auxiliary equation is

$$m(m - 1)^2(m^2 + 1) = 0,$$

or

$$m^5 - 2m^4 + 2m^3 - 2m^2 + m = 0.$$

Therefore the relation (3) is a solution of the differential equation

$$(4) \qquad (D^5 - 2D^4 + 2D^3 - 2D^2 + D)y = 0.$$

That is, from the general solution

$$y = c_1 + (c_2 + c_3x)e^x + c_4 \cos x + c_5 \sin x$$

of equation (4), the relation (3) follows by an appropriate choice of the constants: $c_1 = 6$, $c_2 = 0$, $c_3 = 3$, $c_4 = -1$, $c_5 = 0$.

EXAMPLE (c): Find a homogeneous linear equation with real, constant coefficients which is satisfied by

$$y = 4xe^x \sin 2x.$$

The desired equation must have its auxiliary equation with roots $m = 1 \pm 2i, 1 \pm 2i$. The roots $m = 1 \pm 2i$ correspond to factors

$(m - 1)^2 + 4$, so that the auxiliary equation must be

$$[(m - 1)^2 + 4]^2 = 0,$$

or

$$m^4 - 4m^3 + 14m^2 - 20m + 25 = 0.$$

Hence the desired equation is

$$(D^4 - 4D^3 + 14D^2 - 20D + 25)y = 0.$$

Note that in all such problems a correct (but undesirable) solution may be obtained by inserting additional roots of the auxiliary equation.

ORAL EXERCISES

In Exs. 1–14 obtain in factored form a linear differential equation, with real, constant coefficients which is satisfied by the given relation.

1. $y = 4e^{2x} + 3e^{-x}$.   ANS. $(D - 2)(D + 1)y = 0$.
2. $y = 7 - 2x + \frac{1}{2}e^{4x}$.   ANS. $D^2(D - 4)y = 0$.
3. $y = -2x + \frac{1}{2}e^{4x}$.   ANS. $D^2(D - 4)y = 0$.
4. $y = x^2 - 5 \sin 3x$.   ANS. $D^3(D^2 + 9)y = 0$.
5. $y = 2e^x \cos 3x$.
ANS. $(D - 1 - 3i)(D - 1 + 3i)y = 0$; or $[(D - 1)^2 + 9]y = 0$; or $(D^2 - 2D + 10)y = 0$.

6. $y = 8xe^x + 4e^{-2x}$.
7. $y = 3e^{2x} - e^x$.
8. $y = 2 - e^{-3x}$.
9. $y = x^2 - 4$.
10. $y = \cos x$.
11. $y = \cos x - 4 \sin x$.
12. $y = \sin kx$.
13. $y = 2x \cos x$.
14. $y = 5 \cosh 2x$.

In Exs. 15–30 state the roots of the auxiliary equation for a homogeneous linear equation with real, constant coefficients and containing the given relation as a particular solution.

15. $y = 3xe^{2x}$.   ANS. $m = 2, 2$.
16. $y = x^2e^{-x} + 4e^x$.   ANS. $m = -1, -1, -1, 1$.
17 $y = e^{-x} \cos 4x$.   ANS. $m = -1 \pm 4i$.
18 $y = 3e^{-x} \cos 4x + 15e^{-x} \sin 4x$.   ANS. $m = -1 \pm 4i$.

19. $y = x(e^x - 1)$.   ANS. $m = 1, 1, 0, 0$.
20. $y = 7 + e^{-3x}$.
21. $y = 6x^2 - e^{-4x}$.
22. $y = 3 + 6x^2 - e^{-4x}$.
23. $y = 5 \cos 3x$.
24. $y = 5 \cos 3x - 2 \sin 3x$.
25. $y = x \cos 3x - 2 \sin 3x$.
26. $y = e^{-x}(\sin 2x + \cos 2x)$.
27. $y = e^{-x} \sin 2x$.
28. $y = x^2 - 3x + e^{-3x} + 4e^x \cos 7x$.
29. $y = \sin^3 x$. Use the fact that $\sin^3 x = \frac{1}{4}(3 \sin x - \sin 3x)$.
30. $y = \cos^2 x$.

43. Solution of a nonhomogeneous equation.   Before proceeding to the theoretical basis and the actual working technique
of the useful method of undetermined coefficients, let us examine
the underlying ideas as applied to a simple numerical example.

Consider the equation

$$(1)\qquad\qquad D^2(D - 1)y = 3e^x + \sin x.$$

The complementary function may be determined at once from the
roots

$$(2)\qquad\qquad m = 0, 0, 1$$

of the auxiliary equation.   The complementary function is

$$(3)\qquad\qquad y_c = c_1 + c_2 x + c_3 e^x.$$

Since the general solution of (1) is

$$y = y_c + y_p$$

where y_c is as given in (3) and y_p is any particular solution of (1), all
that remains is for us to find a particular solution of (1).

The right-hand member of (1),

$$(4)\qquad\qquad R(x) = 3e^x + \sin x$$

is a particular solution of a homogeneous linear differential equation
whose auxiliary equation has the roots

$$(5)\qquad\qquad m' = 1, \pm i.$$

Therefore the relation (4) is a particular solution of the equation

(6) $$(D - 1)(D^2 + 1)R = 0.$$

We wish to convert (1) into a homogeneous linear differential equation with constant coefficients, because we know how to solve any such equation. But, by (6) the operator $(D - 1)(D^2 + 1)$ will annihilate the right member of (1). Therefore we apply that operator to both sides of equation (1) and get

(7) $$(D - 1)(D^2 + 1)D^2(D - 1)y = 0.$$

Any solution of (1) must be a particular solution of (7). The general solution of (7) can be written down at once from the roots of its auxiliary equation, those roots being the values $m = 0, 0, 1$ from (2) together with the values $m' = 1, \pm i$ from (5). Thus the general solution of (7) is

(8) $$y = c_1 + c_2x + c_3e^x + c_4xe^x + c_5 \cos x + c_6 \sin x.$$

But the desired general solution of (1) is

(9) $$y = y_c + y_p,$$

where

$$y_c = c_1 + c_2x + c_3e^x,$$

the c_1, c_2, c_3 being arbitrary constants as in (8). Thus there must exist a particular solution of (1) containing at most the remaining terms in (8). Using different letters as coefficients to emphasize that they are not arbitrary, we conclude that (1) has a particular solution

(10) $$y_p = Axe^x + B \cos x + C \sin x.$$

It remains only to determine the numerical coefficients A, B, C by direct use of the original equation

(1) $$D^2(D - 1)y = 3e^x + \sin x.$$

From (10) it follows that

$$Dy_p = A(xe^x + e^x) - B \sin x + C \cos x,$$
$$D^2y_p = A(xe^x + 2e^x) - B \cos x - C \sin x,$$
$$D^3y_p = A(xe^x + 3e^x) + B \sin x - C \cos x.$$

Substitution of y_p into (1) then yields

(11) $Ae^x + (B + C) \sin x + (B - C) \cos x = 3e^x + \sin x.$

Since (11) is to be an identity and since e^x, $\sin x$, and $\cos x$ are linearly independent, the corresponding coefficients in the two members of (11) must be equal; that is,

$$A = 3$$
$$B + C = 1$$
$$B - C = 0.$$

Therefore $A = 3$, $B = \frac{1}{2}$, $C = \frac{1}{2}$. Returning to (10) we find that a particular solution of equation (1) is

$$y_p = 3xe^x + \tfrac{1}{2} \cos x + \tfrac{1}{2} \sin x.$$

The general solution of the original equation

(1) $D^2(D - 1)y = 3e^x + \sin x$

is therefore obtained by adding to the complementary function the y_p found above:

(12) $y = c_1 + c_2 x + c_3 e^x + 3xe^x + \tfrac{1}{2} \cos x + \tfrac{1}{2} \sin x.$

A careful analysis of the ideas behind the process used above shows that in order to arrive at the solution (12) we need perform only the following steps:

(a) From (1) find the values of m and m' as exhibited in (2) and (5);
(b) From the values of m and m' write y_c and y_p as in (3) and (10);
(c) Substitute y_p into (1), equate corresponding coefficients, and obtain the numerical values of the coefficients in y_p;
(d) Write the general solution of (1).

44. The method of undetermined coefficients. Let us examine the general problem of the type treated in the preceding section. Let $f(D)$ be a polynomial in the operator D. Consider the equation

(1) $f(D)y = R(x).$

Let the roots of the auxiliary equation $f(m) = 0$ be

(2) $m = m_1, m_2, \cdots, m_n.$

The general solution of (1) is

(3) $y = y_c + y_p$

where y_c can be obtained at once from the values of m in (2) and where $y = y_p$ is any particular solution (yet to be obtained) of (1).

Now suppose that the right member $R(x)$ of (1) is itself a particular solution of some homogeneous linear differential equation with constant coefficients,

(4) $g(D)R = 0,$

whose auxiliary equation has the roots

(5) $m' = m_1', m_2', \cdots, m_k'.$

Recall that the values of m' in (5) can be obtained by inspection from $R(x)$.

The differential equation

(6) $g(D)f(D)y = 0$

has as the roots of its auxiliary equation the values of m from (2) and m' from (5). Hence the general solution of (6) contains the y_c of (3) and so is of the form

$$y = y_c + y_q.$$

But also any particular solution of (1) must satisfy (6). Now, if $f(D)(y_c + y_q) = R(x)$, then $f(D)y_q = R(x)$ because $f(D)y_c = 0$. Then deleting the y_c from the general solution of (6) leaves a function y_q which for some numerical values of its coefficients must satisfy (1); that is, the coefficients in y_q can be determined so that $y_q = y_p$. The determination of those numerical coefficients may be accomplished as in the examples below.

It must be kept in mind that the method of this section is applicable when, and only when, the right member of the equation is itself a particular solution of some homogeneous linear differential equation with constant coefficients. Methods which apply to equations with less restricted right-hand members will be studied in Chapter 11.

EXAMPLE (a): Solve the equation

(7) $$(D^2 + D - 2)y = 2x - 40 \cos 2x.$$

Here we have

$$m = 1, -2$$

and

$$m' = 0, 0, \pm 2i.$$

Therefore we may write

$$y_c = c_1 e^x + c_2 e^{-2x},$$
$$y_p = A + Bx + C \cos 2x + E \sin 2x,$$

in which c_1 and c_2 are arbitrary constants, while A, B, C, and E are to be determined numerically so that y_p will satisfy the equation (7). Since

$$Dy_p = B - 2C \sin 2x + 2E \cos 2x$$

and

$$D^2 y_p = -4C \cos 2x - 4E \sin 2x,$$

direct substitution of y_p into (7) yields

(8) $-4C \cos 2x - 4E \sin 2x + B - 2C \sin 2x + 2E \cos 2x - 2A$
$-2Bx - 2C \cos 2x - 2E \sin 2x = 2x - 40 \cos 2x.$

But (8) is to be an identity in x, so we must equate coefficients of each of the set of linearly independent functions $\cos 2x$, $\sin 2x$, x, 1 appearing in the identity. Thus it follows that

$$-6C + 2E = -40$$
$$-6E - 2C = 0$$
$$-2B = 2$$
$$B - 2A = 0.$$

The above equations determine A, B, C, and E. Indeed, they lead to $A = -\frac{1}{2}$, $B = -1$, $C = 6$, $E = -2$.

Since the general solution of (7) is $y = y_c + y_p$ we can now write the desired result,

$$y = c_1 e^x + c_2 e^{-2x} - \tfrac{1}{2} - x + 6 \cos 2x - 2 \sin 2x.$$

EXAMPLE (b): Solve the equation

(9) $$(D^2 + 1)y = \sin x.$$

At once $m = \pm i$ and $m' = \pm i$.   Therefore

$$y_c = c_1 \cos x + c_2 \sin x,$$
$$y_p = Ax \cos x + Bx \sin x.$$

Now

$$y_p'' = A(-x \cos x - 2 \sin x) + B(-x \sin x + 2 \cos x)$$

so that the requirement that y_p satisfy equation (9) yields

$$-2A \sin x + 2B \cos x = \sin x$$

from which $A = -\frac{1}{2}$ and $B = 0$.

The general solution of (9) is

$$y = c_1 \cos x + c_2 \sin x - \tfrac{1}{2}x \cos x.$$

EXAMPLE (c): Determine y so that it will satisfy the equation

(10) $$y''' - y' = 4e^{-x} + 3e^{2x}$$

together with the conditions that when $x = 0$, $y = 0$, $y' = -1$, and $y'' = 2$.

First we note that $m = 0, 1, -1$, and $m' = -1, 2$.   Thus

$$y_c = c_1 + c_2e^x + c_3e^{-x}$$
$$y_p = Axe^{-x} + Be^{2x}.$$

Now

$$y_p' = A(-xe^{-x} + e^{-x}) + 2Be^{2x},$$
$$y_p'' = A(xe^{-x} - 2e^{-x}) + 4Be^{2x},$$

and

$$y_p''' = A(-xe^{-x} + 3e^{-x}) + 8Be^{2x}.$$

Then

$$y_p''' - y_p' = 2Ae^{-x} + 6Be^{2x},$$

so that from (10) we may conclude that $A = 2$ and $B = \frac{1}{2}$.

The general solution of (10) is therefore

(11) $$y = c_1 + c_2e^x + c_3e^{-x} + 2xe^{-x} + \tfrac{1}{2}e^{2x}.$$

We must determine c_1, c_2, c_3 so that (11) will satisfy the conditions: when $x = 0$, $y = 0$, $y' = -1$, and $y'' = 2$.

From (11) it follows that

$$(12) \qquad y' = c_2 e^x - c_3 e^{-x} - 2xe^{-x} + 2e^{-x} + e^{2x}$$

and

$$(13) \qquad y'' = c_2 e^x + c_3 e^{-x} + 2xe^{-x} - 4e^{-x} + 2e^{2x}.$$

We put $x = 0$ in each of (11), (12), and (13) to get the equations for the determination of c_1, c_2, and c_3. These are

$$0 = c_1 + c_2 + c_3 + \tfrac{1}{2},$$
$$-1 = c_2 - c_3 + 3,$$
$$2 = c_2 + c_3 - 2,$$

from which $c_1 = -\tfrac{9}{2}$, $c_2 = 0$, $c_3 = 4$. Therefore the final result is

$$y = -\tfrac{9}{2} + 4e^{-x} + 2xe^{-x} + \tfrac{1}{2}e^{2x}.$$

An important point, sometimes overlooked by students, is that it is the general solution, the y of (11), which must be made to satisfy the boundary conditions.

EXERCISES

Obtain the general solution in Exs. 1–26.

1. $(D^2 + D)y = -\cos x$.   ANS. $y = c_1 + c_2 e^{-x} + \tfrac{1}{2}\cos x - \tfrac{1}{2}\sin x$.
2. $(D^2 - 6D + 9)y = e^x$.   ANS. $y = (c_1 + c_2 x)e^{3x} + \tfrac{1}{4}e^x$.
3. $(D^2 - 2D - 3)y = 27x^2$.   ANS. $y = c_1 e^{-x} + c_2 e^{3x} - 14 + 12x - 9x^2$.
4. $(D^2 - 2D - 3)y = 4 - 8x - 6x^2$.   ANS. $y = c_1 e^{-x} + c_2 e^{3x} + 2x^2$.
5. $(D^2 + 4)y = 15e^x - 8x$.   ANS. $y = c_1 \cos 2x + c_2 \sin 2x + 3e^x - 2x$.
6. $(D^2 + 4)y = 15e^x - 8x^2$.
        ANS. $y = c_1 \cos 2x + c_2 \sin 2x + 3e^x - 2x^2 + 1$.
7. $(D^2 + D - 2)y = 12e^{2x}$.   ANS. $y = c_1 e^x + c_2 e^{-2x} + 3e^{2x}$.
8. $(D^2 + D - 2)y = 12e^{-2x}$.   ANS. $y = c_1 e^x + (c_2 - 4x)e^{-2x}$.
9. $(D^2 - 4)y = e^{2x} + 2$.   ANS. $y = c_1 e^{-2x} + (c_2 + \tfrac{1}{4}x)e^{2x} - \tfrac{1}{2}$.
10. $(D^2 - D - 2)y = 6x + 6e^{-x}$.
     ANS. $y = c_1 e^{-x} + c_2 e^{2x} - 3x + 3/2 - 2xe^{-x}$.
11. $y'' - 4y' + 3y = 20\cos x$.   ANS. $y = c_1 e^x + c_2 e^{3x} + 2\cos x - 4\sin x$.
12. $y'' - 4y' + 3y = 2\cos x + 4\sin x$.   ANS. $y = c_1 e^x + c_2 e^{3x} + \cos x$.

13. $y'' + 2y' + y = 7 + 75 \sin 2x$.

ANS. $y = e^{-x}(c_1 + c_2 x) + 7 - 12 \cos 2x - 9 \sin 2x$.

14. $(D^2 + 4D + 5)y = 50x + 13e^{3x}$.

ANS. $y = e^{-2x}(c_1 \cos x + c_2 \sin x) + 10x - 8 + \frac{1}{2}e^{3x}$.

15. $(D^2 + 1)y = \cos x$. ANS. $y = c_1 \cos x + c_2 \sin x + \frac{1}{2}x \sin x$.

16. $(D^2 - 4D + 4)y = e^{2x}$. ANS. $y = e^{2x}(c_1 + c_2 x + \frac{1}{2}x^2)$.

17. $(D^2 - 1)y = e^{-x}(2 \sin x + 4 \cos x)$.

ANS. $y = c_1 e^x + (c_2 - 2 \sin x)e^{-x}$.

18. $(D^2 - 1)y = 8xe^x$. ANS. $y = c_1 e^{-x} + e^x(c_2 - 2x + 2x^2)$.

19. $(D^3 - D)y = x$. ANS. $y = c_1 + c_2 e^x + c_3 e^{-x} - \frac{1}{2}x^2$.

20. $(D^3 - D^2 + D - 1)y = 4 \sin x$.

ANS. $y = c_1 e^x + (c_2 + x) \cos x + (c_3 - x) \sin x$.

21. $(D^3 + D^2 - 4D - 4)y = 3e^{-x} - 4x - 6$.

ANS. $y = c_1 e^{2x} + c_2 e^{-2x} + (c_3 - x)e^{-x} + x + \frac{1}{2}$.

22. $(D^4 - 1)y = 7x^2$.

ANS. $y = c_1 e^x + c_2 e^{-x} + c_3 \cos x + c_4 \sin x - 7x^2$.

23. $(D^4 - 1)y = e^{-x}$.

ANS. $y = c_1 e^x + (c_2 - \frac{1}{4}x)e^{-x} + c_3 \cos x + c_4 \sin x$.

24. $(D^2 - 1)y = 10 \sin^2 x$. Use the identity $\sin^2 x = \frac{1}{2}(1 - \cos 2x)$.

ANS. $y = c_1 e^x + c_2 e^{-x} - 5 + \cos 2x$.

25. $(D^2 + 1)y = 12 \cos^2 x$.

ANS. $y = c_1 \cos x + c_2 \sin x + 6 - 2 \cos 2x$.

26. $(D^2 + 4)y = 4 \sin^2 x$.

ANS. $y = c_1 \cos 2x + c_2 \sin 2x + \frac{1}{2}(1 - x \sin 2x)$.

In Exs. 27–32 find the particular solution indicated.

27. $(D^2 + 1)y = 10e^{2x}$; when $x = 0$, $y = 0$ and $y' = 0$.

ANS. $y = 2(e^{2x} - \cos x - 2 \sin x)$.

28. $(D^2 - 4)y = 2 - 8x$; when $x = 0$, $y = 0$ and $y' = 5$.

ANS. $y = e^{2x} - \frac{1}{2}e^{-2x} + 2x - \frac{1}{2}$.

29. $(D^2 + 3D)y = -18x$; when $x = 0$, $y = 0$ and $y' = 5$.

ANS. $y = 1 + 2x - 3x^2 - e^{-3x}$.

30. $(D^2 + 4D + 5)y = 10e^{-3x}$; when $x = 0$, $y = 4$ and $y' = 0$.

ANS. $y = e^{-2x}(13 \sin x - \cos x) + 5e^{-3x}$.

31. $\dfrac{d^2x}{dt^2} + 4\dfrac{dx}{dt} + 5x = 10$; when $t = 0$, $x = 0$ and $\dfrac{dx}{dt} = 0$.

ANS. $x = 2(1 - e^{-2t} \cos t - 2e^{-2t} \sin t)$.

32. $\ddot{x} + 4\dot{x} + 5x = 8 \sin t$; when $t = 0$, $x = 0$ and $\dot{x} = 0$. Note that $\dot{x} = \dfrac{dx}{dt}$, $\ddot{x} = \dfrac{d^2x}{dt^2}$ is a common notation when the independent variable is time.*

ANS. $x = (1 + e^{-2t}) \sin t - (1 - e^{-2t}) \cos t$.

---

* The disadvantage of such a notation when derivatives of high order appear must be evident. Other objections can be raised; flies have been known to perform undesired differentiations.

In Exs. 33–36 obtain from the particular solution indicated the value of y and the value of y' at $x = 2$.

33. $y'' + 2y' + y = x$; at $x = 0$, $y = -3$ and at $x = 1$, $y = -1$.

ANS. At $x = 2$, $y = e^{-2}$ and $y' = 1$.

34. $y'' + 2y' + y = x$; at $x = 0$, $y = -2$ and $y' = 2$.

ANS. At $x = 2$, $y = 2e^{-2}$ and $y' = 1 - e^{-2}$.

35. $4y'' + y = 2$; at $x = \pi$, $y = 0$ and $y' = 1$.

ANS. At $x = 2$, $y = -0.7635$ and $y' = +0.3012$.

36. $2y'' - 5y' - 3y = -9x^2 - 1$; at $x = 0$, $y = 1$ and $y' = 0$.

ANS. At $x = 2$, $y = 5.64$ and $y' = 5.68$.

37. $(D^2 + D)y = x + 1$; when $x = 0$, $y = 1$ and when $x = 1$, $y = \frac{1}{2}$. Compute the value of y at $x = 4$.

ANS. At $x = 4$, $y = 8 - e^{-1} - e^{-2} - e^{-3}$.

38. $(D^2 + 1)y = x^3$; when $x = 0$, $y = 0$ and when $x = \pi$, $y = 0$. Show that this boundary value problem has no solution.

39. $(D^2 + 1)y = 2 \cos x$; when $x = 0$, $y = 0$ and when $x = \pi$. $y = 0$. Show that this boundary value problem has an unlimited number of solutions and obtain them. ANS. $y = (c + x) \sin x$.

40. For the equation $(D^2 + D^2)y = 4$ find the solution whose graph has at the origin a point of inflection with a horizontal tangent line.

ANS. $y = 4 - 4x + 2x^2 - 4e^{-x}$.

41. For the equation $(D^2 - D)y = 2 - 2x$ find a particular solution which has at some point (to be determined) on the x-axis an inflection point with a horizontal tangent line.

ANS. The point is $(1, 0)$; the solution is $y = x^2 + 1 - 2e^{x-1}$.

42. $(D^2 + 9)y = \sin 3x$; when $x = 0$, $y = 1$ and when $x = \pi/2$, $y = 1$. Compute the value of y at $x = \pi/4$. ANS. At $x = \pi/4$, $y = -1.3$.

45. Remarks on the methods of this chapter. There are equations other than those mentioned in Section 41 for which particular solutions can be obtained by inspection. For instance, an examination of

$$(1) \qquad (D^2 + 4)y = \sin 3x$$

leads us to search for a solution proportional to $\sin 3x$ because, if y is proportional to $\sin 3x$, so is D^2y. Indeed from

$$(2) \qquad y = A \sin 3x$$

we get

$$D^2y = -9A \sin 3x,$$

so that (2) is a solution of (1) if

$$(-9 + 4)A = 1; A = -\tfrac{1}{5}.$$

Thus (1) has the general solution

$$y = c_1 \cos 2x + c_2 \sin 2x - \tfrac{1}{5} \sin 3x,$$

a result easily obtained mentally.

For equation (1) the general method of undetermined coefficients leads us to write: $m = \pm 2i$, $m' = \pm 3i$, and so to write

(3) $$y_p = A \sin 3x + B \cos 3x.$$

When the y_p of (3) is substituted into (1) it is found, of course, that

$$A = -1/5,\ B = 0.$$

In contrast to the above, consider the equation

(4) $$(D^2 + 4D + 4)y = \sin 3x.$$

Here any attempt to find a solution proportional to $\sin 3x$ is doomed to failure because, although $D^2 y$ will also be proportional to $\sin 3x$, the term Dy will involve $\cos 3x$. There is no other term on either side of (4) to compensate for this cosine term, so no solution of the form $y = A \sin 3x$ is possible. For this equation $m = -2,\ -2$; $m' = \pm 3i$ and in the particular solution

$$y_p = A \sin 3x + B \cos 3x,$$

it must turn out that $B \neq 0$. No saving of labor has been accomplished by the inspection.

In more complicated situations such as

$$(D^2 + 4)y = x \sin 3x - 2 \cos 3x$$

the method of inspection will effect no saving of work.

For the equation

(5) $$(D^2 + 4)y = e^{5x}$$

we see, since $(D^2 + 4)e^{5x} = 29e^{5x}$, that

$$y_p = \tfrac{1}{29}e^{5x}$$

is a solution of (5).

Finally, note that if y_1 is a solution of

$$f(D)y = R_1(x)$$

and y_2 is a solution of

$$f(D)y = R_2(x),$$

then

$$y_p = y_1 + y_2$$

is a solution of

$$f(D)y = R_1(x) + R_2(x).$$

It follows readily that the task of obtaining a particular solution of

$$f(D)y = R(x)$$

may be split up into parts by treating separate terms of $R(x)$ independently, if convenient. See the examples below. This is the basis of the "method of superposition" which plays a useful role in applied mathematics.

EXAMPLE (a): Find a particular solution of

(6) $$(D^2 - 9)y = 3e^x + x - \sin 4x.$$

Since $(D^2 - 9)e^x = -8e^x$, we see by inspection that

$$y_1 = -\tfrac{3}{8}e^x$$

is a particular solution of

$$(D^2 - 9)y_1 = 3e^x.$$

In a similar manner we see that $y_2 = -x/9$ satisfies

$$(D^2 - 9)y_2 = x$$

and that

$$y_3 = (1/25)\sin 4x$$

satisfies

$$(D^2 - 9)y_3 = -\sin 4x.$$

Hence

$$y_p = -\tfrac{3}{8}e^x - x/9 + \tfrac{1}{25}\sin 4x$$

is a solution of equation (6).

EXAMPLE (b): Find a particular solution of

(7) $$(D^2 + 4)y = \sin x + \sin 2x.$$

At once we see that $y_1 = (1/3) \sin x$ is a solution of

$$(D^2 + 4)y_1 = \sin x.$$

Then we seek a solution of

(8) $$(D^2 + 4)y_2 = \sin 2x$$

by the method of undetermined coefficients. Since $m = \pm 2i$ and $m' = \pm 2i$, we put

$$y_2 = Ax \sin 2x + Bx \cos 2x$$

into (8) and easily determine that

$$4A \cos 2x - 4B \sin 2x = \sin 2x,$$

from which $A = 0$, $B = -\frac{1}{4}$.

Thus a particular solution of (7) is

$$y_p = \tfrac{1}{3} \sin x - \tfrac{1}{4}x \cos 2x.$$

EXERCISES

1. Show that if $b \neq a$, then

$$(D^2 + a^2)y = \sin bx$$

has the particular solution $y = (a^2 - b^2)^{-1} \sin bx$.

2. Show that the equation

$$(D^2 + a^2)y = \sin ax$$

has no solution of the form $y = A \sin ax$, with A constant. Find a particular solution of the equation. ANS. $y = -\dfrac{x}{2a} \cos ax$.

In Exs. 3–8 find a particular solution by inspection.

3. $(D^2 + 9)y = 4 \cos x$. ANS. $y = \frac{1}{2} \cos x$.

4. $(D^2 + 9)y = 15 \cos 2x$. ANS. $y = 3 \cos 2x$.

5. $(D^2 + 9)y = 18x - 3 + 20e^x$. ANS. $y = 2x - \frac{1}{3} + 2e^x$.

6. $(D^2 - D)y = 7 + 6e^{4x}$. ANS. $y = -7x + \frac{1}{2}e^{4x}$.

7. $(D^2 - 4D + 3)y = e^{2x}$. ANS. $y = -e^{2x}$.

8. $(D^2 + 6D + 14)y = 42e^x - 7$. ANS. $y = 2e^x - \frac{1}{2}$.

ORAL EXERCISES

For each equation determine a particular solution.

1. $(D^2 + 1)y = e^{3x}$.

2. $(D^2 + 1)y = 4x + 1$.

3. $(D^2 + 1)y = \sin 2x$.

4. $(D^2 + 1)y = \cos 2x$.

5. $(D^2 + 1)y = e^x - x + \sin 3x$.

6. $(D^2 - 1)y = 2x - 3$.

7. $(D^2 - 1)y = x + \sin x$.

8. $(D^2 - 1)y = e^{2x}$.

9. $(D^2 - 1)y = 16e^{3x}$.

10. $(D^2 - 1)y = \cos 4x$.

11. $(D^2 + D + 1)y = 6e^x$.

12. $(D^2 + D + 1)y = e^{-x}$.

13. $(D^2 + D + 1)y = 4 - e^{2x}$.

14. $(D^2 - 2D + 1)y = e^{-x}$.

15. $(D^2 - 2D + 1)y = e^{2x}$.

16. $(D^2 - 2D + 1)y = e^{3x}$.

17. $(4D^2 - 1)y = e^x$.

18. $(4D^2 - 1)y = x$.

19. $(4D^2 - 1)y = e^x + x$.

20. $(D^2 + 2D + 1)y = e^x$.

21. $(D^2 + 2D + 1)y = e^{2x}$.

22. $(D^2 + 2D + 1)y = 7 + e^x + e^{2x}$.

23. $(D^3 - 1)y = e^{2x}$.

24. $(D^3 - 1)y = x^2 + 8$.

25. $(D^3 - 1)y = e^{-x}$.

26. $(D^4 + 4)y = \cos x$.

27. $(D^4 + 4)y = \sin x$.

28. $(D^4 + 4)y = \sin 2x$.

Chapter 10

Nonhomogeneous Equations: Operational Methods

46. The exponential shift. Let $D \equiv d/dx$ as usual, and let $V(x)$ possess as many derivatives as may be encountered in the operations performed. Then

$$D[e^{-ax}V(x)] = e^{-ax}DV(x) - ae^{-ax}V(x)$$
$$= e^{-ax}(D - a)V(x).$$

Hence, operating with D again, we are led to

$$D^2[e^{-ax}V(x)] = D[e^{-ax}\{(D - a)V(x)\}]$$
$$= e^{-ax}(D - a)^2V(x).$$

Iteration of the process yields, for n any positive integer,

$$D^n[e^{-ax}V(x)] = e^{-ax}(D - a)^nV(x).$$

Using the linearity of differential operators, we conclude that when $f(D)$ is a polynomial in D with constant coefficients, then

$$(1) \qquad f(D)[e^{-ax}V(x)] = e^{-ax}f(D - a)V(x).$$

In equation (1) put $e^{-ax}V(x) = y$. Then (1) becomes

$$f(D)y = e^{-ax}f(D - a)[e^{ax}y],$$

or

$$(2) \qquad e^{ax}f(D)y = f(D - a)[e^{ax}y].$$

The relation (2) shows us how to shift an exponential factor from the left of a differential operator to the right of the operator. This relation has many uses, one of which is exhibited in the examples below.

147

EXAMPLE (a): Solve the equation

(3) $$(D^2 - 2D + 5)y = 16x^3e^{3x}.$$

Note that the complementary function is

(4) $$y_c = c_1e^x \cos 2x + c_2e^x \sin 2x.$$

By the method of Chapter 9 we can conclude also that there is a particular solution

(5) $$y_p = Ax^3e^{3x} + Bx^2e^{3x} + Cxe^{3x} + Ee^{3x}$$

which can be obtained by the method of Chapter 9. But the task of obtaining the derivatives of y_p and finding the numerical values of A, B, C, and E is a little tedious. It can be made easier by using the exponential shift (2).

Let us write (3) in the form

$$e^{-3x}(D^2 - 2D + 5)y = 16x^3,$$

and then apply the relation (2), with $a = -3$. In shifting the exponential e^{-3x} from the left to the right of the differential operator, we must replace D by $(D + 3)$ throughout, thus obtaining

$$[(D + 3)^2 - 2(D + 3) + 5](e^{-3x}y) = 16x^3,$$

or

(6) $$(D^2 + 4D + 8)(e^{-3x}y) = 16x^3.$$

In equation (6) the dependent variable is $(e^{-3x}y)$. We know at once that (6) has a particular solution of the form

(7) $$e^{-3x}y_p = Ax^3 + Bx^2 + Cx + E.$$

Successive differentiations of (7) are simple. Indeed,

$$D(e^{-3x}y_p) = 3Ax^2 + 2Bx + C$$
$$D^2(e^{-3x}y_p) = 6Ax + 2B,$$

so that from (6) we get

$$6Ax + 2B + 12Ax^2 + 8Bx + 4C + 8Ax^3 + 8Bx^2 + 8Cx + 8E$$
$$= 16x^3.$$

Hence

$$8A = 16,$$
$$12A + 8B = 0,$$
$$6A + 8B + 8C = 0,$$
$$2B + 4C + 8E = 0,$$

from which $A = 2$, $B = -3$, $C = \frac{3}{2}$, $E = 0$.

Therefore

$$e^{-3x}y_p = 2x^3 - 3x^2 + \tfrac{3}{2}x,$$

or

$$y_p = (2x^3 - 3x^2 + \tfrac{3}{2}x)e^{3x}$$

and the general solution of the original equation (3) is

$$y = c_1e^x \cos 2x + c_2e^x \sin 2x + (2x^3 - 3x^2 + \tfrac{3}{2}x)e^{3x}.$$

The complementary function could also have been obtained from equation (6).

EXAMPLE (b): Solve the equation

$$(8) \qquad (D^2 - 2D + 1)y = xe^x + 7x - 2.$$

Here the immediate use of the exponential shift would do no good because removing the e^x factor from the first term on the right would only insert a factor e^{-x} in the second and third terms on the right. The terms $7x - 2$ on the right give us no trouble as they stand. Therefore we break (8) into two problems, obtaining a particular solution for each of the equations

$$(9) \qquad (D^2 - 2D + 1)y_1 = xe^x$$

and

$$(10) \qquad (D^2 - 2D + 1)y_2 = 7x - 2.$$

On (9) we use the exponential shift, passing from

$$e^{-x}(D - 1)^2y_1 = x$$

to

$$(11) \qquad D^2(e^{-x}y_1) = x.$$

A particular solution of (11) is evident:

$$e^{-x}y_1 = \tfrac{1}{6}x^3,$$

so that

(12) $$y_1 = \tfrac{1}{6}x^3 e^x.$$

Equation (10) is treated as in Chapter 9. Put

$$y_2 = Ax + B.$$

Then $Dy_2 = A$ and from (10) it is easily found that $A = 7$, $B = 12$. Thus a particular solution of (10) is

(13) $$y_2 = 7x + 12.$$

Using (12), (13), and the roots of the auxiliary equation for (8), the general solution of (8) may now be written. It is

$$y = (c_1 + c_2 x)e^x + \tfrac{1}{6}x^3 e^x + 7x + 12.$$

EXAMPLE (c): Solve the equation

(14) $$D^2(D + 4)^2 y = 96e^{-4x}.$$

At once we have $m = 0, 0, -4, -4$ and $m' = -4$. We seek first a particular solution. Therefore we integrate each member of (14) twice before using the exponential shift. From (14) it follows that

(15) $$(D + 4)^2 y_p = 6e^{-4x},$$

the constants of integration being disregarded because only a particular solution is sought. Equation (15) yields

$$e^{4x}(D + 4)^2 y_p = 6,$$
$$D^2(y_p e^{4x}) = 6,$$
$$y_p e^{4x} = 3x^2,$$
$$y_p = 3x^2 e^{-4x}.$$

Thus the general solution of (14) is seen to be

$$y = c_1 + c_2 x + (c_3 + c_4 x + 3x^2)e^{-4x}.$$

The exponential shift is particularly helpful when applied in connection with terms for which the values of m' (using the notation of Chapter 9) are repetitions of values of m.

EXERCISES

In Exs. 1–12 use the exponential shift to find a particular solution.

1. $(D - 3)^2 y = e^{3x}$.   ANS. $y = \frac{1}{2}x^2 e^{3x}$.

2. $(D - 1)^2 y = e^x$.

3. $(D + 2)^2 y = 12xe^{-2x}$.   ANS. $y = 2x^3 e^{-2x}$.

4. $(D + 1)^2 y = 3xe^{-x}$.

5. $(D - 2)^3 y = 6xe^{2x}$.   ANS. $y = \frac{1}{4}x^4 e^{2x}$.

6. $(D + 4)^3 y = 8xe^{-4x}$.

7. $(D + 3)^3 y = 15x^2 e^{-3x}$.   ANS. $y = \frac{1}{4}x^5 e^{-3x}$.

8. $(D - 4)^3 y = 15x^2 e^{4x}$.

9. $D^2(D - 2)^2 y = 16e^{2x}$.   ANS. $y = 2x^2 e^{2x}$.

10. $D^2(D + 3)^2 y = 9e^{-3x}$.

11. $(D^2 - D - 2)y = 18xe^{-x}$.   ANS. $y = -(3x^2 + 2x)e^{-x}$.

12. $(D^2 - D - 2)y = 36xe^{2x}$.

In Exs. 13–18 find a particular solution, using the exponential shift in part of your work, as in Example (b) above.

13. $(D - 2)^2 y = 20 - 3xe^{2x}$.   ANS. $y = 5 - \frac{1}{2}x^3 e^{2x}$.

14. $(D - 2)^2 y = 4 - 8x + 6xe^{2x}$.

15. $y'' - 9y = 9(2x - 3 + 4xe^{3x})$.   ANS. $y = 3 - 2x + (3x^2 - x)e^{3x}$.

16. $y'' + 4y' + 4y = 4x - 6e^{-2x} + 3e^x$.

17. $(D + 1)^2 y = e^{-x} + 3x$.   ANS. $y = \frac{1}{2}x^2 e^{-x} + 3x - 6$.

18. $(D^2 - 4)y = 16xe^{-2x} + 8x + 4$.   ANS. $y = -(2x + 1)(xe^{-2x} + 1)$.

In Exs. 19–28 find the general solution.

19. $y'' - 4y = 8xe^{2x}$.   ANS. $y = c_1 e^{-2x} + (c_2 - \frac{1}{2}x + x^2)e^{2x}$.

20. $y'' - 9y = -72xe^{-3x}$.

21. $D(D + 1)^2 y = e^{-x}$.   ANS. $y = c_1 + (c_2 + c_3 x - \frac{1}{2}x^2)e^{-x}$.

22. $D^2(D - 2)^2 y = 2e^{2x}$.

23. $y'' + 2y' + y = 48e^{-x} \cos 4x$.   ANS. $y = (c_1 + c_2 x - 3 \cos 4x)e^{-x}$.

24. $y'' + 4y' + 4y = 18e^{-2x} \cos 3x$.

25. $(D - 1)^2 y = e^x \sec^2 x \tan x$.   ANS. $y = e^x(c_1 + c_2 x + \frac{1}{2} \tan x)$.

26. $(D^2 + 4D + 4)y = -x^{-2}e^{-2x}$.   ANS. $y = e^{-2x}(c_1 + c_2 x + \ln x)$.

27. $(D - a)^2 y = e^{ax} f''(x)$.   ANS. $y = e^{ax}[c_1 + c_2 x + f(x)]$.

28. $(D^2 + 7D + 12)y = e^{-3x} \sec^2 x(1 + 2 \tan x)$.

     ANS. $y = c_1 e^{-4x} + e^{-3x}(c_2 + \tan x)$.

47. The operator $1/f(D)$.

In seeking a particular solution of

(1) $$f(D)y = R(x)$$

it is natural to write

(2)
$$y = \frac{1}{f(D)} R(x)$$

and to try to define an operator $1/f(D)$ so that the function y of (2) will have meaning and will satisfy equation (1).

Instead of building a theory of such inverse differential operators, we shall adopt the following method of attack. Purely formal (unjustified) manipulations of the symbols will be performed, thus leading to a tentative evaluation of

$$\frac{1}{f(D)} R(x).$$

After all, the only thing which we require of our evaluation is that

(3)
$$f(D) \cdot \frac{1}{f(D)} R(x) = R(x).$$

Hence the burden of proof will be placed on a direct verification of the condition (3) in each instance.

48. Evaluation of $[1/f(D)]e^{ax}$. We proved (pages 110–111) with slightly different notation that

(1)
$$f(D)e^{ax} = e^{ax}f(a)$$

and

(2)
$$(D - a)^n(x^n e^{ax}) = n!e^{ax}.$$

Equation (1) suggests

(3)
$$\frac{1}{f(D)} e^{ax} = \frac{e^{ax}}{f(a)}, \quad f(a) \neq 0.$$

Now from (1) above it follows that

$$f(D) \frac{e^{ax}}{f(a)} = \frac{f(a)e^{ax}}{f(a)} = e^{ax}.$$

Hence (3) is correct.

Now suppose that $f(a) = 0$. Then $f(D)$ contains the factor $(D - a)$. Suppose that the factor occurs precisely n times in $f(D)$; that is, let

$$f(D) = \varphi(D)(D - a)^n; \quad \varphi(a) \neq 0.$$

With the aid of (2) we obtain

$$\varphi(D)(D - a)^n(x^n e^{ax}) = \varphi(D)n!e^{ax},$$

from which, by (1), it follows that

(4) $$\varphi(D)(D - a)^n(x^n e^{ax}) = n!\varphi(a)e^{ax}.$$

Therefore we write

(5) $$\frac{1}{\varphi(D)(D - a)^n} e^{ax} = \frac{x^n e^{ax}}{n!\varphi(a)}, \quad \varphi(a) \neq 0,$$

which is easily verified. Indeed,

$$\varphi(D)(D - a)^n \frac{x^n e^{ax}}{n!\varphi(a)} = \frac{n!\varphi(a)e^{ax}}{n!\varphi(a)} = e^{ax}.$$

Note that formula (3) is included in formula (5) as the special case, $n = 0$. See also Ex. 19, page 155.

EXAMPLE (a): Solve the equation

(6) $$(D^2 + 1)y = e^{2x}.$$

Here the roots of the auxiliary equation are $m = \pm i$. Further, $f(D) = (D^2 + 1)$ and $f(2) \neq 0$. Hence, using (3) above

$$y_p = \frac{1}{D^2 + 1} e^{2x} = \frac{e^{2x}}{2^2 + 1} = \frac{1}{5} e^{2x},$$

so that the solution of (6) is

$$y = c_1 \cos x + c_2 \sin x + \frac{1}{5} e^{2x}.$$

EXAMPLE (b): Solve the equation

(7) $$D^2(D - 1)^3(D + 1)y = e^x.$$

Here $m = 0, 0, 1, 1, 1, -1$. To get a particular solution of (7) we use formula (5) with $a = 1$, $n = 3$, $\varphi(D) = D^2(D + 1)$. Then $\varphi(1)! = 1^2 \cdot 2$ and a particular solution of (7) is given by

$$y_p = \frac{1}{(D - 1)^3 D^2(D + 1)} e^x = \frac{x^3 e^x}{3!1^2 \cdot 2} = \frac{1}{12} x^3 e^x.$$

Then the general solution of (7) is

$$y = c_1 + c_2x + c_3e^{-x} + (c_4 + c_5x + c_6x^2 + \tfrac{1}{12}x^3)e^x.$$

49. Evaluation of $(D^2 + a^2)^{-1} \sin ax$ and $(D^2 + a^2)^{-1} \cos ax$.
No special device is needed for the evaluation of $(D^2 + a^2)^{-1} \sin bx$
when $b \neq a$. In fact

$$\frac{1}{D^2 + a^2} \sin bx = \frac{\sin bx}{a^2 - b^2}; b \neq a,$$

as indicated in Ex. 1, page 145, and a similar result holds for the
expression $(D^2 + a^2)^{-1} \cos bx$, when $b \neq a$.

Consider next the evaluation of

(1) $$\frac{1}{D^2 + a^2} \sin ax.$$

The formulas of the preceding section can be put to good use here,
since

$$\sin ax = \frac{e^{aix} - e^{-aix}}{2i}.$$

Then

$$\frac{1}{D^2 + a^2} \sin ax = \frac{1}{2i} \frac{1}{(D - ai)(D + ai)} (e^{aix} - e^{-aix})$$
$$= \frac{1}{2i} \left(\frac{xe^{aix}}{1!2ai} - \frac{xe^{-aix}}{1!(-2ai)}\right)$$
$$= -\frac{x}{2a} \frac{e^{aix} + e^{-aix}}{2},$$

so that

(2) $$\frac{1}{D^2 + a^2} \sin ax = -\frac{x}{2a} \cos ax.$$

The verification of (2) is left as an exercise.

Another useful result,

(3) $$\frac{1}{D^2 + a^2} \cos ax = \frac{x}{2a} \sin ax,$$

can be obtained in the same way.

ORAL EXERCISES

Give the general solution of each equation.

1. $(D^2 - 1)y = e^{2x}$.   ANS. $y = c_1 e^x + c_2 e^{-x} + \frac{1}{3} e^{2x}$.
2. $(D^2 - 1)y = e^x$.   ANS. $y = c_1 e^x + c_2 e^{-x} + \frac{1}{2} x e^x$.
3. $(D^2 + 1)y = \sin x$.   ANS. $y = c_1 \cos x + c_2 \sin x - \frac{1}{2} x \cos x$.
4. $(D^2 + 4)y = \cos 2x$.   ANS. $y = c_1 \cos 2x + c_2 \sin 2x + \frac{1}{4} x \sin 2x$.
5. $(D^2 + 9)y = e^{2x}$.   6. $(D^2 + 4)y = e^{3x}$.
7. $(4D^2 + 1)y = e^{-2x}$.   8. $D(D - 2)y = e^{-x}$.
9. $D(D - 2)^2 y = e^{2x}$.   10. $D(D + 3)^2 y = e^{-3x}$.
11. $(D^2 + 4)y = \cos 3x$.   12. $(D^2 + 9)y = \cos 3x$.
13. $(D^2 + 4)y = \sin 2x$.   14. $(D^2 + 36)y = \sin 6x$.
15. $(D^2 + 9)y = \sin 3x$.   16. $(D^2 + 36)y = \cos 6x$.

EXERCISES

1. Verify formula (2) of Section 49 above.
2. Obtain and verify formula (3) of Section 49 above.

In Exs. 3–18 find the general solution.

3. $(D^2 + 3D - 4)y = 12e^{2x}$.   ANS. $y = c_1 e^{-4x} + c_2 e^x + 2e^{2x}$.
4. $(D^2 + 3D - 4)y = 21e^{3x}$.
5. $(D^2 + 3D - 4)y = 15e^x$.   ANS. $y = c_1 e^{-4x} + (c_2 + 3x)e^x$.
6. $(D^2 + 3D - 4)y = 20e^{-4x}$.
7. $(D^2 - 3D + 2)y = e^x + e^{2x}$.   ANS. $y = (c_1 - x)e^x + (c_2 + x)e^{2x}$.
8. $(4D^2 - 1)y = e^{x/2} + 12e^x$.
9. $D^2(D - 2)^3 y = 48e^{2x}$.
     ANS. $y = c_1 + c_2 x + (c_3 + c_4 x + c_5 x^2 + 2x^3)e^{2x}$.
10. $(D^4 - 18D^2 + 81)y = 36e^{3x}$.
11. $(D^2 + 16)y = 14 \cos 3x$.   ANS. $y = c_1 \cos 4x + c_2 \sin 4x + 2 \cos 3x$.
12. $(4D^2 + 1)y = 33 \sin 3x$.
13. $y'' + 16y = 24 \sin 4x$.   ANS. $y = (c_1 - 3x)\cos 4x + c_2 \sin 4x$.
14. $y'' + 16y = 48 \cos 4x$.
15. $y'' + y = 12 \cos 2x - \sin x$.
     ANS. $y = (c_1 + \frac{1}{2}x)\cos x + c_2 \sin x - 4 \cos 2x$.
16. $y'' + y = \sin 3x + 4 \cos x$.
17. $(D^2 - 2D + 5)y = e^x \cos 2x$.   Hint: use the exponential shift followed by formula (3) of Section 49.
     ANS. $y = e^x(c_1 \cos 2x + c_2 \sin 2x) + \frac{1}{4}x e^x \sin 2x$.
18. $(D^2 + 2D + 5)y = e^{-x} \sin 2x$.
     ANS. $y = e^{-x}(c_1 \cos 2x + c_2 \sin 2x) - \frac{1}{4}x e^{-x} \cos 2x$.
19. Prove that if $f(x) = (x - a)^n \varphi(x)$, then $f^{(n)}(a) = n! \varphi(a)$. Then use equation (5) of Section 48 above to prove that

$$\frac{1}{f(D)} e^{ax} = \frac{x^n e^{ax}}{f^{(n)}(a)},$$

where n is the smallest nonnegative integer for which $f^{(n)}(a) \neq 0$. See C. A. Hutchinson, "Another Note on Linear Operators," *Amer. Math. Monthly,* **46,** 161 (1939).

In Exs. 20–23 use the formula of Ex. 19 above.

20. Ex. 5.   **21.** Ex. 6.
22. Ex. 9.   **23.** Ex. 10.

In Exs. 24–29 verify the formulas* stated.

24. $\dfrac{1}{f(D)} \sin ax = \dfrac{f(-D) \sin ax}{f(ai)f(-ai)}; f(ai)f(-ai) \neq 0.$

25. $\dfrac{1}{f(D)} \cos ax = \dfrac{f(-D) \cos ax}{f(ai)f(-ai)}; f(ai)f(-ai) \neq 0.$

26. $\dfrac{1}{f(D)} \sinh ax = \dfrac{f(-D) \sinh ax}{f(a)f(-a)}; f(a)f(-a) \neq 0.$

27. $\dfrac{1}{f(D)} \cosh ax = \dfrac{f(-D) \cosh ax}{f(a)f(-a)}; f(a)f(-a) \neq 0.$

28. $\dfrac{1}{(D^2 + a^2)^n} \sin ax = \dfrac{x^n}{(2a)^n n!} \sin (ax - n\pi/2).$

29. $\dfrac{1}{(D^2 + a^2)^n} \cos ax = \dfrac{x^n}{(2a)^n n!} \cos (ax - n\pi/2).$

In Exs. 30–33 use the formulas of Exs. 24–25 above.

30. Ex. 1, page 140.   **31.** Ex. 11, page 140.
32. Ex. 12, page 140.   **33.** Ex. 32, page 141.

50. Evaluation of $[1/f(D)]x^n$. It is proved in more advanced books† that

$$\frac{1}{f(D)} x^n$$

is correctly evaluated by replacing $1/f(D)$ by its formal series expan-

---

* The formulas of Exs. 24–27 were obtained by C. A. Hutchinson, "An Operational Formula," *Amer. Math. Monthly,* **40,** 482–483 (1933); those of Exs. 28–29 were given by C. A. Hutchinson, "Note on an Operational Formula," *Amer. Math. Monthly,* **44,** 371–372 (1937).

† See E. L. Ince, *Ordinary Differential Equations,* London, Longmans, Green and Co., 1927, p. 140.

sion in ascending powers of D and then carrying out the indicated operations. By correctly evaluated it is meant that if y_p be the result of the evaluation, then $f(D)y_p = x^n$.

The extension of this method to the evaluation of $[1/f(D)]p(x)$, where $p(x)$ is a polynomial in x, should be evident. It is used in Example (c) below.

Two comments are in order here. First, if $f(D)$ has a factor D^k, $k > 0$, then negative powers of D will appear in the expansion. These are to be interpreted as iterated integrations, illustrated below:

$$D^{-1}x^3 = \frac{x^4}{4},$$

$$D^{-2}x^3 = D^{-1}\frac{x^4}{4} = \frac{x^5}{20}, \text{ etc.}$$

Note that in searching for a particular solution we disregard constants of integration. The presence of negative powers of D is easily avoided as is shown in Example (b) below.

Second, only a finite number of terms in the series expansion of $1/f(D)$ affect the result since, for $m > n$, $D^m x^n = 0$.

EXAMPLE (a): Find a particular solution of the equation

$$(D^2 + 1)y = x^2.$$

Now

$$\frac{1}{D^2 + 1} = 1 - D^2 + D^4 - \cdots,$$

so that

$$y_p = \frac{1}{D^2 + 1}x^2 = (1 - D^2)x^2 = x^2 - 2,$$

in which all terms involving $D^m x^2$ for $m > 2$ have been dropped since each is zero.

EXAMPLE (b): Solve the equation

(1) $$D^3(D^2 - 1)y = x^2.$$

First let us integrate each member of equation (1) three times, disregarding constants of integration, thus obtaining

$$(D^2 - 1)y = \frac{x^5}{60}.$$

Then

$$y_p = \frac{1}{D^2 - 1} \cdot \frac{x^5}{60} = (-1 - D^2 - D^4 - D^6 - \cdots)\frac{x^5}{60}$$

from which

$$y_p = -\frac{x^5}{60} - \frac{x^3}{3} - 2x.$$

The general solution of (1) is

$$y = c_1 e^x + c_2 e^{-x} + c_3 + c_4 x + c_5 x^2 - \frac{x^3}{3} - \frac{x^5}{60},$$

where the term $(-2x)$ from y_p has been absorbed into the complementary function.

If we do not wish to avoid negative powers of D, we can, from (1), write at once

$$y_p = \frac{1}{D^3(D^2 - 1)} x^2 = D^{-3}(-1 - D^2 - D^4 - D^6 - \cdots)x^2$$

$$= (-D^{-3} - D^{-1} - D - D^3 - \cdots)x^2.$$

Now $D^{-1}x^2 = x^3/3$, $D^{-2}x^2 = x^4/12$, $D^{-3}x^2 = x^5/60$, $Dx^2 = 2x$, and $D^3x^2 = 0$, so that

$$y_p = -\frac{x^5}{60} - \frac{x^3}{3} - 2x$$

as before.

EXAMPLE (c): Find a particular solution of the equation

(2) $$(D^2 + D - 2)y = 2x - x^3.$$

Here

$$y_p = \frac{1}{D^2 + D - 2}(2x - x^3).$$

By dividing $(-2 + D + D^2)$ into 1 (long division) it is readily found that

(3) $$y_p = (-\tfrac{1}{2} - \tfrac{1}{4}D - \tfrac{3}{8}D^2 - \tfrac{5}{16}D^3 - \cdots)(2x - x^3).$$

From (3) we conclude with a little labor that

(4) $$y_p = \tfrac{1}{2}x^3 + \tfrac{3}{4}x^2 + \tfrac{5}{4}x + \tfrac{11}{8}.$$

The formal character of the process we have just used makes imperative the verification of our final result by direct substitution into the original differential equation. That verification is left for the student.

The brevity of the solution above is due to the omission of all the actual work, the long division, and the reduction of (3) to (4). Before getting too enthusiastic about this method a student should solve equation (2) by the method of Chapter 9 and also supply the missing steps in the solution above. Then the two processes can be compared.

There does seem to be one type of equation for which the method of this section is a vast improvement over the previous attacks. See the next example.

EXAMPLE (d): Find a particular solution of the equation

$$(D^8 - 1)y = x^{15}.$$

Here

$$y_p = \frac{1}{D^8 - 1}\, x^{15} = (-1 - D^8 - \cdots)x^{15}.$$

But $D^8 x^{15} = 15!\,x^7/7!$. Hence*

$$y_p = -x^{15} - 15!\,x^7/7!.$$

51. Additional notes on the operational method. Since the equation

(1) $$(D - m)y = R(x)$$

is of the first order, an integrating factor e^{-mx} is available. It follows that a particular solution of (1) is

$$y_p = e^{mx}\!\int e^{-mx}R(x)dx,$$

---

* For those who must live life the hard way it is admitted that

$$15!/7! = 259\ 459\ 200.$$

where the constant of integration may be omitted. Thus it is seen that

(2) $$\frac{1}{D - m} R(x) = e^{mx} \int e^{-mx} R(x) dx.$$

Suppose $f(D) = (D - m_1)(D - m_2) \cdots (D - m_n)$ in which the factors are all distinct. Then there exists the partial fractions expansion

(3) $$\frac{1}{f(D)} = \frac{A_1}{D - m_1} + \frac{A_2}{D - m_2} + \cdots + \frac{A_n}{D - m_n},$$

the $A_1, A_2, \ldots, A_n$ being constants. It can be shown* that in $[1/f(D)]R(x)$ the operator $1/f(D)$ may be replaced by the right member in (3). Then formula (2), or any other suitable tool, may be used to evaluate each term of the type $A_k(D - m_k)^{-1}R(x)$.

Even if $f(D)$ involves repeated factors an evaluation similar to that above may be accomplished. The partial fractions expansion then requires the evaluation of terms of the kind $(D - m)^{-n}R(x)$ with $n > 1$. Put

$$y_p = (D - m)^{-n}R(x),$$

then

$$(D - m)^n y_p = R(x),$$

on which the exponential shift works neatly. Thus from

$$e^{-mx}(D - m)^n y_p = e^{-mx}R(x)$$

it follows that

$$D^n(e^{-mx}y_p) = e^{-mx}R(x)$$

so that the value of y_p can be obtained with n integrations.

At one stage of the derivation of the exponential shift formula we showed (page 147) that for any y

$$f(D)y = e^{ax}f(D + a)(e^{-ax}y).$$

Let us choose

$$y = e^{ax} \frac{1}{f(D + a)} V(x).$$

---

* E. L. Ince, *Ordinary Differential Equations*, London, Longmans, Green and Co., 1927, pp. 140–141.

Then

$$f(D)y = e^{ax}f(D + a)\left[\frac{1}{f(D + a)} V(x)\right]$$
$$= e^{ax}V(x).$$

Therefore

$$\frac{1}{f(D)} e^{ax}V(x) = y,$$

or

(4)
$$\frac{1}{f(D)} [e^{ax}V(x)] = e^{ax} \frac{1}{f(D + a)} V(x).$$

The relation (4) may be used to perform the exponential shift automatically in solving an equation such as

(5)
$$(D^2 - 2D + 5)y = e^x \cos 2x.$$

Here

$$y_p = \frac{1}{D^2 - 2D + 5} (e^x \cos 2x)$$

which, because of (4), can be written

$$y_p = e^x \frac{1}{(D + 1)^2 - 2(D + 1) + 5} \cos 2x$$

or

$$y_p = e^x \frac{1}{D^2 + 4} \cos 2x.$$

Then, using (3) page 154, we get

$$y_p = \tfrac{1}{4}xe^x \sin 2x.$$

EXERCISES

In each exercise find a particular solution and verify your result.

1. $(D^2 - 1)y = x^3$.
2. $(D^2 - 1)y = x^4$.   ANS. $y = -x^3 - 6x$.
3. $(4D^2 + 1)y = x^3$.   ANS. $y = -x^4 - 12x^2 - 24$.
4. $(4D^2 + 1)y = x^4$.   ANS. $y = x^3 - 24x$.
5. $(D - 1)^2y = x^2$.   ANS. $y = x^4 - 48x^2 + 384$.
     ANS. $y = x^2 + 4x + 6$.

6. $(D + 1)^2 y = x^2 + 3x + 3.$ ANS. $y = x^2 - x + 3.$

7. $(D - 1)^2 y = x^3 - 4x^2.$ ANS. $y = x^3 + 2x^2 + 2x.$

8. $(D + 1)^2 y = x^3 + 6x^2.$ ANS. $y = x^3 - 6x + 12.$

9. $D(D^2 + 4)y = 4x^3 + 2x.$ ANS. $y = \frac{1}{4}x^4 - \frac{1}{2}x^2.$

10. $D^2(D^2 + 4)y = 12x.$ ANS. $y = \frac{1}{2}x^3.$

11. $D^2(D + 1)y = 12x - 2.$ ANS. $y = 2x^3 - 7x^2.$

12. $D^2(D - 1)y = 12x - 2.$ ANS. $y = -2x^3 - 5x^2.$

13. $(D^2 - 3D + 2)y = 6x^2 - 6x - 11.$ ANS. $y = 3x^2 + 6x + \frac{1}{2}.$

14. $(D^2 - 3D + 2)y = 2x^3 - 9x^2 + 2x - 16.$ ANS. $y = x^3 - 2x - 11.$

15. $(D^6 - 1)y = x^{10}.$ ANS. $y = -x^{10} - \dfrac{10!}{4!} x^4.$

16. $(D^3 + 3D^2 - 4)y = 16x^3 + 20x^2.$ ANS. $y = -4x^3 - 5x^2 - 18x - \frac{27}{2}.$

MISCELLANEOUS EXERCISES

In Exs. 1–18 find a particular solution.

1. $(D^2 - 4D + 4)y = 6x^2e^{2x}.$ ANS. $y = \frac{1}{2}x^4e^{2x}.$

2. $(D - 3)^2 y = e^{3x}.$ ANS. $y = \frac{1}{2}x^2e^{3x}.$

3. $D(D - 2)y = e^{2x}.$ ANS. $y = \frac{1}{2}xe^{2x}.$

4. $D^2(D + 1)y = e^{-x}.$ ANS. $y = xe^{-x}.$

5. $(D^2 + 4)y = 8x^5.$ ANS. $y = 2x^5 - 10x^3 + 15x.$

6. $(D^2 + 4)y = 16xe^{2x}.$ ANS. $y = (2x - 1)e^{2x}.$

7. $(D^2 + 4D + 5)y = 4e^{-2x} \cos x.$ ANS. $y = 2xe^{-2x} \sin x.$

8. $(D^2 - D - 2)y = 4x^2 - 3e^{-x}.$ ANS. $y = xe^{-x} - 2x^2 + 2x - 3.$

9. $(D^2 - 4D + 13)y = 24e^{2x} \sin 3x.$ ANS. $y = -4xe^{2x} \cos 3x.$

10. $(D^2 - 4D + 13)y = 24e^{2x} \sin x.$ ANS. $y = 3e^{2x} \sin x.$

11. $(D^2 - 3D + 2)y = (x - 2)e^x.$ ANS. $y = -\frac{1}{2}(x^2 - 2x)e^x.$

12. $(D^2 - 3D + 2)y = 72xe^{-x}.$ ANS. $y = 2(6x + 5)e^{-x}.$

13. $(D^2 + 4)y = 12(\sin x + \sin 2x).$ ANS. $y = 4 \sin x - 3x \cos 2x.$

14. $(D^2 + 4)y = 20(e^x - \cos 2x).$ ANS. $y = 4e^x - 5x \sin 2x.$

15. $(D^2 + 16)y = 8(x + \sin 4x).$ ANS. $y = x(\frac{1}{2} - \cos 4x).$

16. $(D^2 + 4)y = 8 \sin x \cos x.$ ANS. $y = -x \cos 2x.$

17. $(D^2 + 4)y = 8 \cos^2 x.$ ANS. $y = 1 + x \sin 2x.$

18. $(D^4 - 1)y = x^6.$ ANS. $y = -x^6 - 360x^2.$

In Exs. 19–28 find the general solution.

19. $(D^2 - 4D + 13)y = 24e^{2x} \cos x.$
           ANS. $y = e^{2x}(c_1 \cos 3x + c_2 \sin 3x + 3 \cos x).$

20. $(D^2 - 4D + 13)y = 24e^{2x} \cos 3x.$
           ANS. $y = e^{2x}(c_1 \cos 3x + c_2 \sin 3x + 4x \sin 3x).$

21. $(D^2 + 25)y = \sin 5x$ ANS. $y = c_1 \cos 5x + c_2 \sin 5x - 0.1x \cos 5x.$

22. $D(D^2 + 1)y = \sin x.$ ANS. $y = c_1 + c_2 \cos x + (c_3 - \frac{1}{2}x)\sin x.$

23. $D^2(D^2 + 1)y = \sin x$.   ANS. $y = c_1 + c_2x + (c_3 + \frac{1}{2}x)\cos x + c_4 \sin x$.
24. $(D^2 - 3D + 2)y = x^2 - 2x$.
25. Ex. 8, page 140.
26. Ex. 10, page 140.
27. Ex. 18, page 141.
28. Ex. 19, page 141.

In Exs. 29–34 find the particular solution indicated.

29. $(D^2 + 1)y = 4e^x$; when $x = 0$, $y = 0$ and $y' = 0$.
ANS. $y = 2(e^x - \cos x - \sin x)$.
30. $(D^2 + 4)y = 2x - 8$; when $x = 0$, $y = 1$ and $y' = 0$.
ANS. $4y = 12 \cos 2x - \sin 2x + 2x - 8$.
31. $(D^2 + 3D + 2)y = 4x^2$; when $x = 0$, $y = 0$ and $y' = 0$.
ANS. $y = 2x^2 - 6x + 7 - 8e^{-x} + e^{-2x}$.
32. $(D^2 - 1)y = \sin 2x$; when $x = 0$, $y = 0$ and $y' = 1$.
ANS. $10y = 7(e^x - e^{-x}) - 2 \sin 2x$;
or $5y = 7 \sinh x - \sin 2x$.
33. $(D^2 + 2D)y = 2x$; when $x = 0$, $y = 0$ and when $x = 1$, $y = 0$.
ANS. $2y = x^2 - x$.
34. The equation of Ex. 33 with the conditions that: when $x = 0$, $y = 0$ and $y' = 0$.   ANS. $4y = 2x^2 - 2x + 1 - e^{-2x}$.

In Exs. 35–37 obtain from the particular solution indicated the value of y and the value of y' at $x = 1$.

35. $y'' + 2y' + y = x + 2$; when $x = 0$, $y = 1$ and $y' = 0$.
ANS.   At $x = 1$, $y = (e + 1)/e$, $y' = (e - 1)/e$.
36. $y'' + 2y' + y = x + 2$; when $x = 0$, $y = 0$ and $y' = 0$.
ANS.   At $x = 1$, $y = (e - 1)/e$, $y' = 1$.
37. $(D^2 + 1)y = 3$; when $x = \pi/2$, $y = 0$ and $y' = 0$.
ANS.   At $x = 1$, $y = 0.4756$ and $y' = -1.6209$.

Chapter 11

Variation of Parameters
and Other Methods

52. Variation of parameters. In this chapter three methods will be presented, any one of which will lead to the general solution of a linear differential equation with constant coefficients.

This time all that need be assumed about the right-hand member $R(x)$ in the equation

$$(1) \qquad\qquad f(D)y = R(x)$$

is that $R(x)$ be sufficiently well behaved so that the integrals we encounter will exist.

For equation (1), once the roots of the auxiliary equation $f(m) = 0$ are known, the complementary function is written down by inspection. Suppose, for instance, that (1) is of second order and its complementary function is given by

$$(2) \qquad\qquad y_c = c_1\varphi_1(x) + c_2\varphi_2(x),$$

where c_1 and c_2 are arbitrary constants (or parameters) and the $\varphi_1(x)$ and $\varphi_2(x)$ are, of course, known functions.

Then the method of variation of parameters is as follows. First replace the constants c_1 and c_2 by unknown functions of x, say A and B. That is, put

$$(3) \qquad\qquad y = A\varphi_1(x) + B\varphi_2(x),$$

where A and B should now be looked upon as two new dependent variables. Here A and B replace the parameters c_1 and c_2 of (2), and now A and B are being permitted to vary. That is where the method got its name.

164

Now three dependent variables A, B, and y are present. They must satisfy equations (1) and (3). But, in general, three variables can be made to satisfy three equations. Hence we are free to impose one more condition upon A, B, and y.

From (3) it follows that

(4) $$y' = A\varphi_1'(x) + B\varphi_2'(x) + A'\varphi_1(x) + B'\varphi_2(x).$$

Now let us impose a third condition by demanding that

(5) $$A'\varphi_1(x) + B'\varphi_2(x) = 0.$$

Then (4) becomes

(6) $$y' = A\varphi_1'(x) + B\varphi_2'(x),$$

from which

(7) $$y'' = A\varphi_1''(x) + B\varphi_2''(x) + A'\varphi_1'(x) + B'\varphi_2'(x),$$

involving nothing higher than first order derivatives of A and B.

Finally (3), (6), and (7) can be used to eliminate y from (1) and thus get an equation in A' and B' to go with (5) above. Thus A' and B' can be found and then we can determine A and B by integration. Once A and B are known, equation (3) gives us the desired y. See the examples below.

The method is easily extended to equations of order higher than two but no essentially new ideas appear and the details can get tedious. In this section only second-order equations will be treated.

EXAMPLE (a): Solve the equation

(8) $$(D^2 + 1)y = \sec x \tan x.$$

Of course,

$$y_c = c_1 \cos x + c_2 \sin x.$$

Let us seek a particular solution by the method of variation of parameters. Put

(9) $$y = A \cos x + B \sin x,$$

from which

$$y' = -A \sin x + B \cos x + A' \cos x + B' \sin x.$$

Next set

(10) $$A' \cos x + B' \sin x = 0,$$

so that

$$y' = -A \sin x + B \cos x.$$

Then

(11) $$y'' = -A \cos x - B \sin x - A' \sin x + B' \cos x.$$

Next we eliminate y by combining equations (9) and (11) with the original equation (8). Thus we get the relation

(12) $$-A' \sin x + B' \cos x = \sec x \tan x.$$

From (12) and (10) A' is easily eliminated. The result is

$$B' = \tan x,$$

so that

(13) $$B = \ln \sec x,$$

in which the arbitrary constant has been disregarded because we are seeking only a particular solution to add to our previously determined complementary function y_c.

From equations (12) and (10) it also follows easily that

$$A' = -\sin x \sec x \tan x,$$

or

$$A' = -\tan^2 x.$$

Then

$$A = -\int \tan^2 x \, dx = \int (1 - \sec^2 x) dx,$$

so that

(14) $$A = x - \tan x,$$

again disregarding the arbitrary constant.

Returning to equation (9) with the known A from (14) and B from (13), we write the particular solution

$$y_p = (x - \tan x) \cos x + \sin x \ln \sec x,$$

or

$$y_p = x \cos x - \sin x + \sin x \ln \sec x.$$

Then the general solution of (8) is

$$(15) \qquad y = c_1 \cos x + c_3 \sin x + x \cos x + \sin x \ln \sec x,$$

where the term $(-\sin x)$ in y_p has been absorbed in the complementary function term $c_3 \sin x$, since c_3 is an arbitrary constant.

The solution (15) can, as usual, be verified by direct substitution into the original differential equation.

EXAMPLE (b): Solve the equation

$$(16) \qquad\qquad (D^2 - 3D + 2)y = \frac{1}{1 + e^{-x}}.$$

Here

$$y_c = c_1 e^x + c_2 e^{2x},$$

so we put

$$(17) \qquad\qquad y = A e^x + B e^{2x}.$$

Since

$$y' = A e^x + 2B e^{2x} + A' e^x + B' e^{2x},$$

we impose the condition

$$(18) \qquad\qquad A' e^x + B' e^{2x} = 0.$$

Then

$$(19) \qquad\qquad y' = A e^x + 2B e^{2x},$$

from which it follows that

$$(20) \qquad y'' = A e^x + 4B e^{2x} + A' e^x + 2B' e^{2x}.$$

Combining (17), (19), (20), and the original equation (16), we find that

$$(21) \qquad\qquad A' e^x + 2B' e^{2x} = \frac{1}{1 + e^{-x}}.$$

Elimination of B' from equations (18) and (21) yields

$$A' e^x = - \frac{1}{1 + e^{-x}},$$

or

$$A' = -\frac{e^{-x}}{1 + e^{-x}}.$$

Then

$$A = \ln (1 + e^{-x}).$$

Similarly,

$$B'e^{2x} = \frac{1}{1 + e^{-x}}$$

so that

$$B = \int \frac{e^{-2x}}{1 + e^{-x}}\, dx = \int \left[e^{-x} - \frac{e^{-x}}{1 + e^{-x}} \right] dx,$$

or

$$B = -e^{-x} + \ln (1 + e^{-x}).$$

Then, from (17),

$$y_p = e^x \ln (1 + e^{-x}) - e^x + e^{2x} \ln (1 + e^{-x}).$$

The term $(-e^x)$ in y_p can be absorbed into the complementary function. The general solution of equation (16) is then seen to be

$$y = c_3 e^x + c_2 e^{2x} + (e^x + e^{2x}) \ln (1 + e^{-x}).$$

Equation (16) can equally well be solved without variation of parameters by a judicious use of the exponential shift of Section 46.

53. Solution of $y'' + y = f(x)$.   Consider next the equation

(1) $$(D^2 + 1)y = f(x)$$

in which all that we require of $f(x)$ is that it be integrable in the interval on which we seek a solution.   For instance, $f(x)$ may be any continuous function or any function with only a finite number of finite discontinuities on the interval $a \leqq x \leqq b$.

The method of variation of parameters will now be applied to the solution of (1).   Put

(2) $$y = A \cos x + B \sin x.$$

Then

$$y' = -A \sin x + B \cos x + A' \cos x + B' \sin x$$

and if we choose

(3) $A' \cos x + B' \sin x = 0,$

we obtain

(4) $y'' = -A \cos x - B \sin x - A' \sin x + B' \cos x.$

From (1), (2), and (4) it follows that

(5) $-A' \sin x + B' \cos x = f(x).$

Equations (3) and (5) may be solved for A' and B', yielding

$$A' = -f(x) \sin x, \quad B' = f(x) \cos x.$$

We may now write

(6) $A = -\int_a^x f(\beta) \sin \beta \, d\beta,$

(7) $B = \int_a^x f(\beta) \cos \beta \, d\beta,$

for any x in $a \leqq x \leqq b$. It is here that we use the integrability of $f(x)$ on the interval $a \leqq x \leqq b$.

The A and B of (6) and (7) may be inserted in (2) to give us the particular solution

$$y_p = -\cos x \int_a^x f(\beta) \sin \beta \, d\beta + \sin x \int_a^x f(\beta) \cos \beta \, d\beta$$

$$= \int_a^x f(\beta)[\sin x \cos \beta - \cos x \sin \beta] d\beta.$$

Hence we have

(8) $y_p = \int_a^x f(\beta) \sin (x - \beta) d\beta,$

and we can now write the general solution of equation (1):

(9) $y = c_1 \cos x + c_2 \sin x + \int_a^x f(\beta) \sin (x - \beta) d\beta.$

The solution (9) is of much value in more advanced mathematics and its applications. The student should keep in mind, however, that the integral in (9) will be nonelementary unless $f(x)$ is carefully chosen to avoid that complication.

Direct verification that the y_p of (8) satisfies equation (1) is simple for the student who knows Leibnitz' rule for differentiation of a definite integral (a topic often included in advanced calculus).

54. A general second-order linear equation.
The method used in Section 52 applies equally well to the equation

(1) $$y'' + p(x)y' + q(x)y = f(x),$$

where $p(x)$ and $q(x)$ need not be constants, just so long as we know two linearly independent solutions $y = y_1(x)$ and $y = y_2(x)$ of the corresponding homogeneous equation

(2) $$y'' + p(x)y' + q(x)y = 0.$$

Let the Wronskian (page 100) of $y_1(x)$ and $y_2(x)$ be denoted by $W(x)$,

(3) $$W(x) = \begin{vmatrix} y_1(x) & y_2(x) \\ y_1'(x) & y_2'(x) \end{vmatrix},$$

and let $W(x) \neq 0$ on the interval $a \leqq x \leqq b$. Then the method of variation of parameters yields the following particular solution of equation (1),

(4) $$y_p = \int_a^x \frac{f(\beta)[y_1(\beta)y_2(x) - y_1(x)y_2(\beta)]d\beta}{W(\beta)}.$$

The general solution of (1) is, of course,

(5) $$y = c_1 y_1(x) + c_2 y_2(x) + y_p(x).$$

Since we have, as yet, no methods for obtaining y_1 and y_2 unless equation (1) has constant coefficients, the solution (5) is at present of purely theoretical interest to us. In general, power series methods are used to find y_1 and y_2 when equation (1) has variable coefficients.

For the Wronskian (3) of any two linearly independent solutions y_1 and y_2 of equation (1), it is not difficult* to derive Abel's formula

$$(6) \qquad\qquad W(x) = ce^{-\int p(x)dx},$$

where c is constant.

EXERCISES

In Exs. 1–20 use the method of variation of parameters, Section 52.

1. $(D^2 + 1)y = \csc x \cot x$.
    ANS. $y = c_1 \cos x + c_2 \sin x - x \sin x - \cos x \ln \sin x$.

2. $(D^2 + 1)y = \cot x$.   ANS. $y = y_c - \sin x \ln(\csc x + \cot x)$.

3. $(D^2 + 1)y = \sec x$.
    ANS. $y = c_1 \cos x + c_2 \sin x + x \sin x + \cos x \ln \cos x$.

4. $(D^2 + 1)y = \sec^2 x$.   ANS. $y = y_c - 1 + \sin x \ln (\sec x + \tan x)$.

5. $(D^2 + 1)y = \sec^3 x$.   ANS. $y = y_c + \frac{1}{2} \sec x$.

6. $(D^2 + 1)y = \sec^4 x$.
    ANS. $y = y_c - \frac{1}{2} + \frac{1}{6} \sec^2 x + \frac{1}{2} \sin x \ln (\sec x + \tan x)$.

7. $(D^2 + 1)y = \tan x$.   ANS. $y = y_c - \cos x \ln (\sec x + \tan x)$.

8. $(D^2 + 1)y = \tan^2 x$.
    ANS. $y = y_1 - 1$, where y_1 is the solution of Ex. 4 above.

9. $(D^2 + 1)y = \sec x \csc x$.
    ANS. $y = y_c - \cos x \ln (\sec x + \tan x) - \sin x \ln (\csc x + \cot x)$.

10. $(D^2 + 1)y = \sec^2 x \csc x$.   ANS. $y = y_c - \sin x \ln (\csc 2x + \cot 2x)$.

11. $(D^2 - 2D + 1)y = e^{2x}(e^x + 1)^{-2}$.   ANS. $y = y_c + e^x \ln (1 + e^x)$.

12. $(D^2 - 3D + 2)y = e^{2x}/(1 + e^{2x})$.
    ANS. $y = y_c + e^x \text{ Arctan } (e^{-x}) - \frac{1}{2}e^{2x} \ln (1 + e^{-2x})$.

13. $(D^2 - 3D + 2)y = \cos (e^{-x})$.   ANS. $y = y_c - e^{2x} \cos (e^{-x})$.

14. $(D^2 - 1)y = 2(1 - e^{-2x})^{-1/2}$.
    ANS. $y = c_1 e^x + c_2 e^{-x} - e^x \text{ Arcsin } (e^{-x}) - (1 - e^{-2x})^{1/2}$.

15. $(D^2 - 1)y = e^{-2x} \sin e^{-x}$.   ANS. $y = y_c - \sin e^{-x} - e^x \cos e^{-x}$.

16. $(D^2 - 5D + 4)y = 6/(1 + e^{-2x})$.
    ANS. $y = y_c + 2e^x \text{ Arctan } e^{-x} - e^{2x} + e^{4x} \ln (1 + e^{-2x})$.

17. $(D^2 - 1)y = (1 + e^{-x})^{-2}$.
    ANS. $y = y_c - 1 + xe^{-x} + e^{-x} \ln (1 + e^{-x})$.

18. $(D - 1)(D - 3)y = \cos e^{-x}$.
    ANS. $y = y_c + e^{3x} \sin e^{-x} - e^{2x} \cos e^{-x}$.

---

* See, for example, E. D. Rainville, *Intermediate Differential Equations*, New York, John Wiley & Sons, 1943, p. 48.

19. $(D^2 - 3D + 2)y = 15(1 + e^{-x})^{1/2}$.

ANS. $y = c_1e^x + c_2e^{2x} + 4(e^x + e^{2x})(1 + e^{-x})^{3/2}$; or

$$y = y_c + 4e^{2x}(1 + e^{-x})^{5/2}.$$

20. $(D^2 - 3D + 2)y = (1 + e^{-2x})^{-1/2}$.

ANS. $y = y_c + e^x \ln [e^{-x} + (1 + e^{-2x})^{1/2}] - e^{2x}(1 + e^{-2x})^{1/2}$.

In Exs. 21–28 use the exponential shift once or twice, as needed, to solve the equation without variation of parameters.

21. Ex. 11.   **22.** Ex. 12.
23. Ex. 13.   **24.** Ex. 15.
25. Ex. 16.   **26.** Ex. 17.
27. Ex. 18.   **28.** Ex. 19.
29. Use variation of parameters to obtain the solution (4), Section 54.
30. Use variation of parameters to solve the equation

$$y'' + 4y' + 4y = f(x).$$

ANS. $y = c_1e^{-2x} + c_2xe^{-2x} + \displaystyle\int_0^x f(\beta)(x - \beta)e^{-2(x-\beta)}d\beta.$

55. Reduction of order by using factors of the operator.

Consider the equation

(1) $(D - a)(D - b)y = R(x)$.

The change of dependent variable

(2) $(D - b)y = w$

leads us to the equation

(3) $(D - a)w = R(x)$

which is linear of the first order.   Then (3) can be written in standard form (page 40)

$$dw - aw \, dx = R(x)dx$$

and so solved with the aid of the integrating factor e^{-ax}.

Once w is known we revert to equation (2) to find y.   Equation (2) is also of the first order, so it can be solved just as (3) was solved.

The problem of solving the equation (1) of order two is thus replaced by a succession of two problems, each that of solving an equation of order one.   In general this device permits us to replace a linear equation of order n (with constant coefficients) by n successive linear equations of order one.   The only difficulty is that of performing the integrations which occur.   In practice that difficulty is often quite serious.

EXAMPLE: Solve the equation*

(4) $$(D^2 - 1)y = \frac{2}{e^x + e^{-x}}.$$

Thinking of equation (4) in the form

$$(D + 1)(D - 1)y = \frac{2}{e^x + e^{-x}},$$

we put

(5) $$(D - 1)y = w.$$

Then we need to solve

$$(D + 1)w = \frac{2}{e^x + e^{-x}}$$

which may be written

(6) $$dw + w\,dx = \frac{2dx}{e^x + e^{-x}}.$$

An integrating factor for (6) is e^x.   Therefore

$$e^x\,dw + we^x\,dx = \frac{2e^x\,dx}{e^x + e^{-x}}$$

is exact.   Hence

$$e^x w = \int \frac{2e^x\,dx}{e^x + e^{-x}} = \int \frac{2e^{2x}}{e^{2x} + 1}\,dx,$$

from which

$$e^x w = \ln (e^{2x} + 1),$$

the arbitrary constant being disregarded as usual when searching for a particular solution.

Next the expression for w is inserted in equation (5) which then becomes

$$(D - 1)y = e^{-x} \ln (e^{2x} + 1),$$

or

---

* Equation (4) may be written $(D^2 - 1)y = \text{sech } x$, but the form here is convenient for the integrations which arise.

$$dy - y\, dx = e^{-x} \ln (e^{2x} + 1)dx.$$

Here an integrating factor is e^{-x}, so we write

$$e^{-x}\, dy - ye^{-x}\, dx = e^{-2x} \ln (e^{2x} + 1)dx,$$

or

$$e^{-x}y = \int e^{-2x} \ln (e^{2x} + 1)dx.$$

Integration by parts can be used to reduce the above to the form

(7) $$\qquad e^{-x}y = -\tfrac{1}{2}e^{-2x} \ln (e^{2x} + 1) + \int \frac{dx}{e^{2x} + 1}.$$

Then we write

$$e^{-x}y = -\tfrac{1}{2}e^{-2x} \ln (e^{2x} + 1) + \int \left[1 - \frac{e^{2x}}{e^{2x} + 1} \right] dx$$

and thus find that

$$e^{-x}y = -\tfrac{1}{2}e^{-2x} \ln (e^{2x} + 1) + x - \tfrac{1}{2} \ln (e^{2x} + 1),$$

or

(8) $$\qquad y = xe^x - \tfrac{1}{2}(e^x + e^{-x}) \ln (e^{2x} + 1).$$

Equation (8) is a particular solution of the original equation (4). The general solution of the differential equation (4) is therefore

$$y = c_1 e^x + c_2 e^{-x} + xe^x - \tfrac{1}{2}(e^x + e^{-x}) \ln (e^{2x} + 1).$$

56. A third method: change of dependent variable. Consider the general second-order linear equation

(1) $$\qquad\qquad y'' + py' + qy = R.$$

Suppose we know a solution $y = y_1$ of the corresponding homogeneous equation

(2) $$\qquad\qquad y'' + py' + qy = 0.$$

Then the introduction of a new dependent variable v by the substitution

(3) $$\qquad\qquad y = y_1 v$$

will lead to a solution of equation (1) in the following way.

From (3) it follows that

$$y' = y_1 v' + y_1' v,$$
$$y'' = y_1 v'' + 2y_1' v' + y_1'' v,$$

so that substitution of (3) into (1) yields

$$y_1 v'' + 2y_1' v' + y_1'' v + py_1 v' + py_1' v + qy_1 v = R,$$

or

(4) $$y_1 v'' + (2y_1' + py_1)v' + (y_1'' + py_1' + qy_1)v = R.$$

But $y = y_1$ is a solution of (2).   That is,

$$y_1'' + py_1' + qy_1 = 0$$

and equation (4) reduces to

(5) $$y_1 v'' + (2y_1' + py_1)v' = R.$$

Now let $v' = w$ so that equation (5) becomes

(6) $$y_1 w' + (2y_1' + py_1)w = R,$$

a linear equation of the first order in w.

By the usual method (integrating factor) we can find w from (6). Then we can get v from $v' = w$ by an integration.   Finally $y = y_1 v$.

Note that the method is not restricted to equations with constant coefficients.   It depends only upon our knowing a particular solution of equation (2); that is, upon our knowledge of the complementary function.   For practical purposes the method depends also upon our being able to effect the integrations which arise.

EXAMPLE: Solve the equation

(7) $$(D^2 + 1)y = \csc x.$$

The complementary function is

(8) $$y_c = c_1 \cos x + c_2 \sin x.$$

We may use any special case of (8) as the y_1 in the theory above. Let us then put

$$y = v \sin x.$$

We find that

$$y' = v' \sin x + v \cos x$$

and

$$y'' = v'' \sin x + 2v' \cos x - v \sin x.$$

The equation for v is

$$v'' \sin x + 2v' \cos x = \csc x,$$

or

(9) $$v'' + 2v' \cot x = \csc^2 x.$$

Put $v' = w$, then equation (9) becomes

$$w' + 2w \cot x = \csc^2 x,$$

or

$$dw + 2w \cot x \, dx = \csc^2 x \, dx,$$

for which an integrating factor is $\sin^2 x$. Thus

(10) $$\sin^2 x \, dw + 2w \sin x \cos x \, dx = dx$$

is exact. From (10) we get

$$w \sin^2 x = x,$$

seeking, as usual, only a particular solution.

Then

$$w = x \csc^2 x$$

or

$$v' = x \csc^2 x.$$

Hence

$$v = \int x \csc^2 x \, dx,$$

or

$$v = -x \cot x + \ln \sin x,$$

a result easily obtained by integration by parts.

Now

$$y = v \sin x,$$

so the particular solution which we sought is

$$y_p = -x \cos x + \sin x \ln \sin x.$$

Finally, the complete solution of (7) is seen to be

$$y = c_1 \cos x + c_2 \sin x - x \cos x + \sin x \ln \sin x.$$

EXERCISES

In Exs. 1–4 use the method of Section 55.

1. $(D^2 + 2D + 1)y = (e^x - 1)^{-2}$.

> ANS. $y = e^{-x}[c_1 + c_2 x - \ln (1 - e^{-x})]$.

2. $(D^2 + 2D + 1)y = (e^x + 1)^{-2}$.

> ANS. $y = e^{-x}[c_1 + c_2 x + \ln (1 + e^{-x})]$.

3. $(D - 1)(D - 3)y = \sin e^{-x}$.

> ANS. $y = y_c - e^{2x} \sin e^{-x} - e^{3x} \cos e^{-x}$.

4. $(D^2 - 1)y = 2e^x(1 + e^x)^{-2}$.

> ANS. $y = y_c + 1 + xe^x - (e^x + e^{-x}) \ln (1 + e^x)$.

In Exs. 5–9 use the method of Section 56.

5. Use the substitution $y = v \cos x$ to solve the equation of the example of Section 56.

6. $(D^2 + 1)y = \sec x$. \qquad ANS. See Ex. 3, page 171.

7. $(D^2 + 1)y = \sec^3 x$. Use $y = v \sin x$. \qquad ANS. See Ex. 5, page 171.

8. $(D^2 + 1)y = \csc^3 x$, taking a hint from Ex. 7 above. Use $y = v \cos x$, since $\cos x$ is complementary to $\sin x$ just as $\csc x$ is complementary to $\sec x$. \qquad ANS. $y = y_c + \frac{1}{2} \csc x$.

9. $(D^2 - 3D + 2)y = (1 + e^{-2x})^{-1/2}$. \qquad ANS. See Ex. 20, page 172.

10. $y'' + 4y' + 4y = x^{-2}e^{-2x}$. Use the exponential shift.

> ANS. $y = e^{-2x}(c_1 + c_2 x - \ln x)$.

11. In the example of Section 55 perform the integration needed in equation (7) by using the trick below:

$$\int \frac{dx}{e^{2x} + 1} = \int \frac{e^{-2x}\, dx}{1 + e^{-2x}} = -\tfrac{1}{2} \ln (1 + e^{-2x}).$$

Thus obtain for equation (4) a particular solution in the form

$$y = -\tfrac{1}{2}e^{-x} \ln (e^{2x} + 1) - \tfrac{1}{2}e^x \ln (1 + e^{-2x})$$

and show that this solution is equivalent to that given in equation (8).

MISCELLANEOUS EXERCISES

1. $(D^2 - 1)y = 2e^{-x}(1 + e^{-2x})^{-2}$.

> ANS. $y = y_c - xe^{-x} - \tfrac{1}{2}e^{-x} \ln (1 + e^{-2x})$.

2. $(D^2 - 1)y = (1 - e^{2x})^{-3/2}$. \qquad ANS. $y = y_c - (1 - e^{2x})^{1/2}$.

3. $(D^2 - 1)y = e^{2x}(3 \tan e^x + e^x \sec^2 e^x)$. \qquad ANS. $y = y_c + e^x \ln \sec e^x$.

4. $(D^2 + 1)y = \sec^2 x \tan x$.

> ANS. $y = y_c + \tfrac{1}{2} \tan x + \tfrac{1}{2} \cos x \ln (\sec x + \tan x)$.

5. Do Ex. 4 by another method.

6. $(D^2 + 1)y = \csc x$.   Use variation of parameters.

          ANS.   See the example of Section 56.

7. $(D^2 - 3D + 2)y = \sec^2(e^{-x})$.

          ANS. $y = c_1 e^x + c_2 e^{2x} + e^{2x} \ln \sec(e^{-x})$.

8. Do Ex. 7 by another method.

9. $(D^2 - 1)y = 2/(1 + e^x)$.

          ANS. $y = y_c - 1 - x e^x + (e^x - e^{-x}) \ln(1 + e^x)$.

10. $(D^3 + D)y = \sec^2 x$.   Hint: integrate once first.

          ANS. $y = c_1 + c_2 \cos x + c_3 \sin x - \cos x \ln(\sec x + \tan x)$.

11. $(D^2 - 1)y = 2/(e^x - e^{-x})$.

          ANS. $y = y_c - x e^{-x} + \frac{1}{2}(e^x - e^{-x}) \ln(1 - e^{-2x})$.

12. $(D^2 - 3D + 2)y = \sin e^{-x}$.   ANS. $y = y_c - e^{2x} \sin e^{-x}$.

13. $(D^2 - 1)y = 1/(e^{2x} + 1)$.   ANS. $y = y_c - \frac{1}{2} + \cosh x \operatorname{Arctan} e^{-x}$.

14. $y'' + y = \sec^3 x \tan x$.   ANS. $y = y_c + \frac{1}{6} \sec x \tan x$.

15. $y'' + y = \sec x \tan^2 x$.   Verify your answer.

16. $y'' + 4y' + 3y = \sin e^x$.   ANS. $y = y_c - e^{-2x} \sin e^x - e^{-3x} \cos e^x$.

17. $y'' + y = \csc^3 x \cot x$.   ANS. $y = y_c + \frac{1}{6} \cot x \csc x$.

Chapter 12

Applications

57. Vibration of a spring.   Consider a steel spring attached to a rigid support and hanging downward without obstruction.   The spring will obey Hooke's law: if the spring is stretched or compressed, its change in length will be proportional to the force exerted upon the spring and, when that force is removed, the spring will return to its original position with its length and other physical properties unchanged.*

According to Hooke's law there is associated with each spring a numerical constant, the ratio of the force exerted to the displacement produced by that force.   Suppose a force of magnitude f pounds stretches the spring s feet.   Then the relation

$$(1) \qquad\qquad f = ks$$

defines the spring constant k in the units pounds per foot.

FIGURE 16   FIGURE 17

A body B weighing w pounds is attached to the lower end of the spring (Figure 16) and brought to the point of equilibrium where it can remain at rest.   Then suppose that B is pulled down x_0 feet below the point of equilibrium and suddenly released.   Our first problem is to determine the motion of B.

---

* This is not a complete statement of the situation, of course.   We have left the realm of exact science.   Hooke's law is a marvelously close approximation to the truth for a large class of materials of which steel is merely an example. Throughout this chapter we shall use the customary approximations of careful engineering practice without further comment.   The student who wishes to go into various fine points not mentioned here can consult advanced works in theoretical engineering or in applied mathematics or physics.

Let us measure time t in seconds starting with $t = 0$ at the time B is released. Let us also indicate the position of the body B at time t by x, in feet, measured positive downward from the point of equilibrium E (Figure 17). Then the statement that B was released (that is, without imparted velocity) from a position x_0 feet below E can be expressed mathematically by saying that

(2)   when $t = 0$, $x = x_0$ and $\dfrac{dx}{dt} = 0$.

We have used the fact that the motion of B takes place in a straight (vertical) line so that the velocity v is given by

$$v = \frac{dx}{dt}.$$

Let $g = 32$ feet per second per second* be the magnitude of the acceleration due to gravity. Then B has mass w/g (lb) (sec²) per ft or w/g slugs.

The resultant force F acting upon B at any time is, according to Newton's law,

(3) $F = \dfrac{w}{g} \dfrac{d^2x}{dt^2}$

with F measured positive when it tends to move B in the positive x direction (downward). Let us neglect the force due to air resistance. Then the resultant force acting upon B is the one which by Hooke's law has magnitude $k|x|$, where k is the spring constant. This force is tending to restore equilibrium, to pull B back toward E. Therefore it is opposite in sign to x, so that

$$F = -kx,$$
or
(4) $\dfrac{w}{g} \dfrac{d^2x}{dt^2} = -kx.$

The problem of determining the motion of B is now seen to be one of solving a differential equation with associated boundary conditions. The displacement x from the equilibrium point E (x posi-

---

* The figure 32 is convenient and is in error less than ½ per cent.

tive downward) must be a function of the time t such that x satisfies the differential equation

$$(5) \qquad \frac{w}{g}\frac{d^2x}{dt^2} + kx = 0$$

and the associated conditions

$$(6) \qquad \text{when } t = 0,\ x = x_0 \text{ and } \frac{dx}{dt} = 0.$$

Let us solve the boundary value problem consisting of (5) and (6). Let $kg/w = \beta^2$. Then (5) may be written

$$\frac{d^2x}{dt^2} + \beta^2 x = 0$$

and we know its general solution to be

$$(7) \qquad x = c_1 \cos \beta t + c_2 \sin \beta t,$$

where c_1 and c_2 are arbitrary constants. Those constants must be determined so as to make the function x satisfy the conditions (6). From (7) it follows that

$$(8) \qquad v = \frac{dx}{dt} = -c_1 \beta \sin \beta t + c_2 \beta \cos \beta t.$$

Let $t = 0$ in (7) and (8). Then, using the conditions (6), we get

$$x_0 = c_1 \cdot 1 + c_2 \cdot 0$$

and

$$0 = -c_1\beta \cdot 0 + c_2\beta \cdot 1$$

so that $c_1 = x_0$ and $c_2 = 0$.

With c_1 and c_2 known the relation (7) becomes

$$(9) \qquad x = x_0 \cos \beta t$$

where $\beta = \sqrt{kg/w}$. Equation (9) is the solution we have been seeking. That it satisfies (5) and (6) is easily verified.

The motion described by (9) is called simple harmonic motion. It is periodic with period $2\pi/\beta$ or $2\pi(kg/w)^{-1/2}$. Its amplitude, the maximum deviation from the point of equilibrium, is $|x_0|$.

Variations of the above problem are obtainable by altering the boundary conditions as in the example below.   Note also that the method of solution may be varied a little, replacing (7) by

$$(10) \qquad\qquad x = c_3 \sin (\beta t + c_4),$$

or by

$$(11) \qquad\qquad x = c_5 \cos (\beta t + c_6).$$

Equations (10) and (11) have the advantage that each exhibits the amplitude explicitly as is indicated in the exercises below.

EXAMPLE: A spring is such that it would be stretched 3 inches by a 6-pound weight.   Let a 12-pound weight B be attached to the spring and pulled down 4 inches below the equilibrium point.   If B is started with an upward velocity of 2 feet per second, describe the motion of B.

First we determine the spring constant by using the fact that when $f = 6$ (lb), $s = \frac{3}{12} = \frac{1}{4}$ (ft).   Thus $6 = \frac{1}{4}k$ so that $k = 24$ (lb per ft).

With the notation of this section the problem to be solved may be expressed by

$$(12) \qquad\qquad \frac{12}{32}\frac{d^2x}{dt^2} + 24x = 0$$

together with the conditions

$$(13) \qquad\qquad \text{when } t = 0,\ x = \tfrac{1}{3},\ \text{and}\ v = -2.$$

Note that the upward velocity (decreasing x) is negative and that the initial value of x must be expressed in feet to be consistent with our use of $g = 32$ (ft per sec per sec).

From (12) we get

$$\frac{d^2x}{dt^2} + 64x = 0$$

so that

$$x = c_1 \cos 8t + c_2 \sin 8t.$$

Then

$$v = -8c_1 \sin 8t + 8c_2 \cos 8t.$$

Hence the conditions on x and v at $t = 0$ lead us to the values $c_1 = \frac{1}{3}$ and $c_2 = -\frac{1}{4}$. Therefore the desired solution is

$$(14) \qquad x = \tfrac{1}{3} \cos 8t - \tfrac{1}{4} \sin 8t.$$

See also Ex. 1 below.

A detailed discussion of the motion is straightforward once (14) has been obtained. In particular it can be shown that the amplitude of the motion is $A = \frac{5}{12}$ (ft); that is, B oscillates between points 5 inches above and below E. The period is $\pi/4$ (sec).

58. Damped vibrations. The vibration of a spring with a suspended weight is usually retarded by damping forces, of which air resistance is an example. It has been shown by experiment that in many instances such retarding forces are fairly well approximated by a term proportional to the velocity. This retarding force will act upward when B is moving downward $(v > 0)$ and downward when B is moving upward $(v < 0)$. It has a sign opposite to the sign of v.

Thus with such a resisting medium taken into consideration the resultant force F of Section 57 must be replaced by

$$(1) \qquad F = -kx - bv,$$

where b is a positive constant determined experimentally.

Since

$$F = \frac{w}{g} \frac{d^2x}{dt^2},$$

the differential equation of motion under our present assumptions is seen to be

$$(2) \qquad \frac{w}{g} \frac{d^2x}{dt^2} + b \frac{dx}{dt} + kx = 0.$$

In equation (2) put $\beta^2 = kg/w$ and $2\alpha = bg/w$ in order to simplify the writing. Then (2) becomes

$$(3) \qquad \frac{d^2x}{dt^2} + 2\alpha \frac{dx}{dt} + \beta^2 x = 0,$$

which has the auxiliary equation

$$m^2 + 2\alpha m + \beta^2 = 0$$

with roots $m = -\alpha \pm \sqrt{\alpha^2 - \beta^2}$. Often α is small compared to β. Let us assume $\alpha < \beta$ and put

$$\beta^2 - \alpha^2 = \gamma^2$$

so that we have

$$m = -\alpha \pm i\gamma.$$

Then the general solution of (3) is

(4) $$x = e^{-\alpha t}(c_1 \cos \gamma t + c_2 \sin \gamma t)$$

and the arbitrary constants c_1 and c_2 are available for the satisfaction of boundary conditions similar to those of Section 57. The factor $e^{-\alpha t}$ is called the *damping factor*. Since $\alpha > 0$ the damping factor approaches zero as $t \to \infty$.

EXAMPLE: Solve the problem of the example of Section 57 with an added damping force of magnitude $0.6|v|$. Such a damping force can be realized by immersing the weight B in a thick liquid.

The problem consists in solving the differential equation

(5) $$\frac{12}{32} \frac{d^2x}{dt^2} + 0.6 \frac{dx}{dt} + 24x = 0$$

together with the conditions

(6) when $t = 0$, $x = \frac{1}{3}$ and $v = -2$.

For (5) the auxiliary equation is

$$m^2 + 1.6m + 64 = 0$$

so that $m = -0.80 \pm 8.0i$, in which only two significant figures are retained because of the rough nature of the data and the value of g used. Then

$$x = e^{-0.8t}(c_1 \cos 8t + c_2 \sin 8t)$$

from which

$$v = e^{-0.8t}[(8c_2 - 0.8c_1) \cos 8t - (8c_1 + 0.8c_2) \sin 8t].$$

Because of the conditions (6) we get

$$\frac{1}{3} = c_1,$$
$$-2 = 8c_2 - 0.8c_1.$$

Then $c_1 = 0.33$ and $c_2 = -0.22$.

The desired solution is

(7) $x = e^{-0.8t}(0.33 \cos 8t - 0.22 \sin 8t)$,

a portion of its graph being shown in Figure 18.

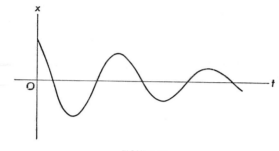

FIGURE 18

EXERCISES

In these exercises the notations and approximations (including $g = 32$ ft per sec per sec) of the text are used.

1. Show that the solution (14) of Section 57 can be put in the form

$$x = A \cos (8t + \varphi)$$

and that $A = 5/12$ (ft) and $\varphi = $ Arctan (3/4).

In Exs. 2–14 no damping force is present.

2. A spring is such than an 8-pound weight would stretch it 6 inches. Let a 4-pound weight be attached to the spring, pushed up 2 inches above its equilibrium point and then released. Describe the motion.
ANS. $x = -\frac{1}{6} \cos 11.3t$.

3. If the 4-pound weight of Ex. 2 starts at the same point, 2 inches above E, but with an upward velocity of 15 ft per sec, when will the weight reach its lowest point?   ANS. At $t = 0.4$ sec, approximately.

4. A spring is such that it is stretched 4 inches by a 10-pound weight. Suppose the 10-pound weight to be pulled down 5 inches below E and then given a downward velocity of 15 ft per sec. Describe the motion.
ANS. $x = 0.42 \cos 9.8t + 1.53 \sin 9.8t$
$= 1.59 \cos (9.8t - \varphi)$, where $\varphi = $ Arctan 3.64.

5. A spring is such that a 5-pound weight stretches it 6 inches. The 5-pound weight is attached, the spring reaches equilibrium, then the weight is pulled down 3 inches below the equilibrium point and started off with an upward velocity of 6 ft per sec. Find an equation giving the position of the weight at all subsequent times.
ANS. $x = \frac{1}{4}(\cos 8t - 3 \sin 8t)$.

6. A spring is such that it is stretched 4 inches by an 8-pound weight. Suppose the weight to be pulled down 6 inches below E and then given an upward velocity of 8 ft per sec. Describe the motion.
ANS. $x = 0.50 \cos 9.8t - 0.82 \sin 9.8t$.

7. Show that the answer to Ex. 6 can be written $x = 0.96 \cos (9.8t + \varphi)$ where $\varphi = $ Arctan 1.64.

8. A spring is stretched 1.5 inches by a 2-pound weight. Let the weight be pushed up 3 inches above E and then released. Describe the motion.
ANS. $x = -\frac{1}{4} \cos 16t$.

9. For the spring and weight of Ex. 8 let the weight be pulled down 4 inches below E and given a downward initial velocity of 8 ft per sec. Describe the motion. ANS. $x = \frac{1}{3} \cos 16t + \frac{1}{2} \sin 16t$.

10. Show that the answer to Ex. 9 can be written $x = 0.60 \sin (16t + \varphi)$ where $\varphi = $ Arctan $\frac{2}{3}$.

11. A spring is stretched 3 inches by a 5-pound weight. Let the weight be started from E with an upward velocity of 12 ft per sec. Describe the motion. ANS. $x = -1.06 \sin 11.3t$.

12. For the spring and weight of Ex. 11, let the weight be pulled down 4 inches below E and then given an upward velocity of 8 ft per sec. Describe the motion. ANS. $x = 0.33 \cos 11.3t - 0.71 \sin 11.3t$.

13. Find the amplitude of the motion in Ex. 12. ANS. 0.78 ft.

14. A 20-pound weight stretches a certain spring 10 inches. Let the spring first be compressed 4 inches, and then the 20-pound weight attached and given an initial downward velocity of 8 ft per sec. Find how far the weight would drop. ANS. 35 in.

15. For the example of Section 58 find the time and position of the first stop in the motion. ANS. $t = 0.3$ sec, $x = -0.3$ ft.

16. For the example of Section 58 find the time in which the damping factor $e^{-0.8t}$ drops to one-tenth of its initial value. ANS. 2.9 sec.

17. Put (7) of Section 58 into the form $x = Ae^{-0.8t} \cos (8t + \varphi)$.
ANS. $A = 0.40$, $\varphi = $ Arctan (0.67).

18. A spring is such that a 4-pound weight stretches it 0.64 feet. The 4-pound weight is pushed up $\frac{1}{3}$ foot above the point of equilibrium and then started with a downward velocity of 5 ft per sec. The motion takes place in a medium which furnishes a damping force of magnitude $\frac{1}{4}|v|$ at all times. Find the equation describing the position of the weight at time t. ANS. $x = \frac{1}{3}e^{-t}(2 \sin 7t - \cos 7t)$.

19. A spring is such that a 4-pound weight stretches it 0.32 feet. The weight is attached to the spring and moves in a medium which furnishes a damping force of magnitude $\frac{3}{2}|v|$. The weight is drawn down $\frac{1}{2}$ foot below the equilibrium point and given an initial upward velocity of 4 ft per sec. Find the position of the weight thereafter.

ANS. $x = \frac{1}{8}e^{-6t}(4 \cos 8t - \sin 8t)$.

20. A spring is such that a 4-pound weight stretches the spring 0.4 feet. The 4-pound weight is attached to the spring (suspended from a fixed support) and the system is allowed to reach equilibrium. Then the weight is started from equilibrium position with an imparted upward velocity of 2 ft per sec. Assume that the motion takes place in a medium which furnishes a retarding force of magnitude numerically equal to the speed, in feet per second, of the moving weight. Determine the position of the weight as a function of time.

ANS. $x = -\frac{1}{4}e^{-4t} \sin 8t$.

21. A spring is stretched 6 inches by a 3-pound weight. The 3-pound weight is attached to the spring and then started from equilibrium with an imparted upward velocity of 12 ft per sec. Air resistance furnishes a retarding force equal in magnitude to $0.03|v|$. Find the equation of motion. ANS. $x = -1.5e^{-0.16t} \sin 8t$.

22. A spring is stretched 10 inches by a 4-pound weight. The weight is started 6 inches below the equilibrium point with an upward velocity of 8 ft per sec. If a resisting medium furnishes a retarding force of magnitude $\frac{1}{4}|v|$, describe the motion.

ANS. $x = e^{-t}[0.50 \cos 6.1t - 1.23 \sin 6.1t]$.

23. For Ex. 22 find the times of the first three stops and the position (to the nearest inch) of the weight at each stop.

ANS. $t_1 = 0.3$ sec, $x_1 = -12$ in; $t_2 = 0.8$ sec, $x_2 = +6$ in; $t_3 = 1.3$ sec, $x_3 = -4$ in.

24. A spring is stretched 4 inches by a 2-pound weight. The 2-pound weight is started from the equilibrium point with a downward velocity of 12 ft per sec. If air resistance furnishes a retarding force of magnitude 0.02 of the velocity, describe the motion.

ANS. $x = 1.22e^{-0.16t} \sin 9.8t$.

25. For Ex. 24 find how long it takes the damping factor to drop to one-tenth its initial value. ANS. 14.4 sec.

26. For Ex. 24 find the position of the weight: (a) at the first stop; (b) at the second stop. ANS. (a) $x = 1.2$ ft; (b) $x = -1.1$ ft.

27. Determine the constants c_1 and c_2 so that

(4) $$x = e^{-\alpha t}(c_1 \cos \gamma t + c_2 \sin \gamma t)$$

will satisfy the conditions that when $t = 0$, $x = x_0$ and $v = v_0$.

ANS. $x = \gamma^{-1}e^{-\alpha t}[\gamma x_0 \cos \gamma t + (v_0 + \alpha x_0) \sin \gamma t]$.

28. Solve and interpret the following boundary value problem:

(A) $$\frac{w}{g}\frac{d^2x}{dt^2} + kx = 0$$

together with

(B) when $t = 0$, $x = x_0$ and $v = v_0$.

ANS. $x = x_0 \cos \beta t + (v_0/\beta) \sin \beta t$, where $\beta^2 = kg/w$.

29. Find the amplitude of the motion in Ex. 28 by determining the maximum value of x. ANS. $A = [x_0^2 + (v_0/\beta)^2]^{1/2}$.

30. Solve the problem of Ex. 28 using the form $x = c_3 \sin (\beta t + c_4)$ for the general solution of equation (A). See also Ex. 31 below.

ANS. $x = [x_0^2 + (v_0/\beta)^2]^{1/2} \sin(\beta t + \varphi)$, where $\tan \varphi = \beta x_0/v_0$.

31. Remove the amgibuity in the description of φ in Ex. 30 by bounding φ for each combination of algebraic signs of x_0 and v_0. For instance, show that if $x_0 > 0$ and $v_0 < 0$, then $\pi/2 < \varphi < \pi$.

32. Use the form $x = c_5 \cos (\beta t + c_6)$ for the general solution of equation (A) to solve the problem of Ex. 28.

ANS. $x = [x_0^2 + (v_0/\beta)^2]^{1/2} \cos(\beta t + \varphi)$, where $\tan \varphi = -v_0/(\beta x_0)$.

33. Remove the ambiguity in the description of φ in Ex. 32. For instance, show that if $x_0 < 0$ and $v_0 > 0$, then $\pi < \varphi < 3\pi/2$.

59. Critical damping. The problem in damped vibrations which was studied in Section 58 was reduced to the problem of solving the equation

(1) $$\frac{d^2x}{dt^2} + 2\alpha \frac{dx}{dt} + \beta^2 x = 0$$

together with certain initial conditions.

The auxiliary equation for (1) is

$$m^2 + 2\alpha m + \beta^2 = 0$$

and it has the roots

(2) $$m = -\alpha \pm \sqrt{\alpha^2 - \beta^2}.$$

The general solution of equation (1) will assume various forms according to whether the two values of m (a) involve imaginaries, (b) are equal, or (c) are real and distinct.

When $\alpha < \beta$ the roots of the auxiliary equation are imaginary and the solution of equation (1) takes the form

(3) $$x = e^{-\alpha t}(c_1 \cos \gamma t + c_2 \sin \gamma t),$$

or

$$x = Ae^{-\alpha t} \cos (\gamma t + \varphi),$$

in which $\gamma^2 = \beta^2 - \alpha^2$. The motion described by equation (3) is a damped oscillatory motion.

When $\alpha = \beta$ the values of m are real and equal and the solution of equation (1) assumes the form

(4) $$x = (c_3 + c_4 t)e^{-\alpha t}.$$

The motion described by (4) is not oscillatory; it is called *critically damped* motion.

When $\alpha > \beta$ the roots of the auxiliary equation are real and distinct. Then the solution of equation (1) becomes

(5) $$x = e^{-\alpha t}(c_5 e^{\delta t} + c_6 e^{-\delta t})$$

in which $\delta^2 = \alpha^2 - \beta^2$. The motion described by equation (5) is often called *overdamped* motion; the parameter α is larger than it needs to be in order to remove the oscillations.

In Figure 19 there is a representative graph of each type of motion mentioned above, a damped oscillatory motion, a critically damped one, and an overdamped one.

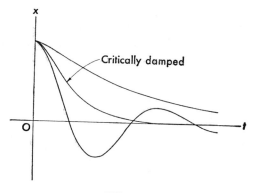

FIGURE 19

60. Forced vibrations. Suppose next that a spring is supported as in the previous section but that an additional vertical force is acting upon the weight attached to the spring. The additional force may, for example, be due to the presence of a magnetic field, to motion of the support, etc. The new, impressed force will depend upon time, and we may use $f(t)$ to represent the acceleration which it alone would impart to the weight B. Then the impressed force is $(w/g)f(t)$ and the differential equation with damping taken into consideration, is therefore

$$\text{(1)} \qquad \frac{w}{g}\frac{d^2x}{dt^2} + b\frac{dx}{dt} + kx = \frac{w}{g}f(t)$$

or

$$\text{(2)} \qquad \frac{d^2x}{dt^2} + 2\alpha\frac{dx}{dt} + \beta^2 x = f(t),$$

where again $2\alpha = bg/w$ and $\beta^2 = kg/w$.

For $f(t)$ the particular choices $f(t) = A \sin \omega t$, $f(t) = A \cos \omega t$, $f(t) = A_1 \cos \omega t + A_2 \sin \omega t$, or $f(t) = A \sin (\omega t + \sigma)$, in which A, ω, A_1, A_2, σ are constants, are of special interest in practical work. The fourth of these forms for $f(t)$ includes the others. In Chapter 14 the analogous electromotive forces impressed upon an electric circuit will be considered. Mathematically the problems are the same.

It will be seen in the next section that in undamped motion ($b = 0$) the case $\omega = \beta$ is of particular interest and importance. That case will be avoided in this section.

EXAMPLE: A spring is such that a 6-pound weight stretches the spring 2 inches. There is no appreciable damping present, but the spring and weight are subject to an impressed force such that the equation of motion is

$$\text{(3)} \qquad \frac{6}{32}\frac{d^2x}{dt^2} + 36x = -4.60 \sin 4t.$$

The weight B is pulled down 3 inches below the equilibrium point and then released. Describe the motion.

The problem is that of solving

$$\text{(4)} \qquad \frac{d^2x}{dt^2} + 192x = -24.5 \sin 4t$$

with the conditions

$$\text{(5)} \qquad \text{when } t = 0,\ x = 0.25 \text{ and } v = 0.$$

The general solution of (4) is easily found to be

$$\text{(6)} \qquad x = c_1 \cos 13.9t + c_2 \sin 13.9t - 0.14 \sin 4t.$$

Then

$$\text{(7)} \qquad v = 13.9(-c_1 \sin 13.9t + c_2 \cos 13.9t) - 0.56 \cos 4t.$$

Thus the conditions (5) lead to the equations

$$0.25 = c_1$$
$$0 = 13.9c_2 - 0.56,$$

so that $c_1 = 0.25$ and $c_2 = 0.04$.

Therefore the motion under consideration is described by the relation

(8) $\qquad x = 0.25 \cos 13.9t + 0.04 \sin 13.9t - 0.14 \sin 4t.$

61. Resonance. In the undamped forced vibrations of a spring, equations of the type

(1) $\qquad \dfrac{d^2x}{dt^2} + \beta^2 x = A \sin \omega t$

can arise, as was seen in Section 60. For equation (1) the roots of the auxiliary equation $m^2 + \beta^2 = 0$ are $m = \pm i\beta$. The right member of (1) is a solution of an equation whose auxiliary equation has roots $m' = \pm i\omega$. Therefore, using the method of undetermined coefficients as in Chapter 9, we can conclude that if $\omega^2 \neq \beta^2$, then (1) has a particular solution of the form

(2) $\qquad x_p = a_1 \sin \omega t.$

On the other hand, if $\omega^2 = \beta^2$, then equation (1) has no particular solution of the form (2) but it does have a particular solution of the form

(3) $\qquad x_p = b_1 t \cos \beta t.$

Thus, if $\omega^2 \neq \beta^2$, equation (1) has the general solution

(4) $\qquad x = c_1 \cos \beta t + c_2 \sin \beta t + Aq \sin \omega t$

where $q = 1/(\beta^2 - \omega^2)$. An important property of the solution (4) is that the numerical value of x is bounded. Indeed, since $|\sin y| \leqq 1$ and $|\cos y| \leqq 1$, it follows that $|x| \leqq |c_1| + |c_2| + |Aq|$. Thus there is a limit to the amplitude of the vibrations.

If $\omega = \beta$, then equation (1) has the general solution

(5) $\qquad x = c_1 \cos \beta t + c_2 \sin \beta t - \dfrac{A}{2\beta} t \cos \beta t.$

In (5) the terms $c_1 \cos \beta t$ and $c_2 \sin \beta t$ are bounded, but the term $\frac{1}{2}(A/\beta)t \cos \beta t$ is unbounded because of the factor t. When $\omega = \beta$ the resulting physical phenomenon (the building up of large amplitudes in the vibration) is called *resonance*.

In actual practice, of course, the amplitude does not exceed all bounds. The elastic limit will be reached and the spring will break, unless before that the weight meets with outside interference such as a floor.

EXERCISES

1. A certain straight-line motion is determined by the differential equation

$$\frac{d^2x}{dt^2} + 2\alpha \frac{dx}{dt} + 169x = 0$$

and the conditions that when $t = 0$, $x = 0$ and $v = 8$ ft per sec.
(a) Find the value of α which leads to critical damping, determine x in terms of t, and draw the graph for $0 \leqq t \leqq 0.2$.
ANS. $\alpha = 13(1/\text{sec})$, $x = 8te^{-13t}$.
(b) Use $\alpha = 12$. Find x in terms of t and draw the graph.
ANS. $x = 1.6e^{-12t} \sin 5t$.
(c) Use $\alpha = 14$. Find x in terms of t and draw the graph.
ANS. $x = 0.77(e^{-8.8t} - e^{-19.2t})$.

2. A spring is such that a 4-pound weight stretches it 6 inches. There is no appreciable damping present, but an impressed force $\frac{1}{2} \cos 8t$ is acting on the spring. If the 4-pound weight is started from the equilibrium point with an imparted upward velocity of 4 ft per sec, determine the position of the weight as a function of time.
ANS. $x = \frac{1}{4}(t - 2) \sin 8t$.

3. A spring is such that a 2-pound weight stretches it $\frac{1}{2}$ foot. An impressed force $\frac{1}{4} \sin 8t$ and a damping force of magnitude $|v|$ are both acting on the spring. The weight starts $\frac{1}{4}$ foot below the equilibrium point with an imparted upward velocity of 3 ft per sec. Find a formula for the position of the weight at time t.
ANS. $x = \frac{3}{32}e^{-8t}(3 - 8t) - \frac{1}{32} \cos 8t$.

4. A spring is such that a 16-pound weight stretches it 1.5 inches. The weight is pulled down to a point 4 inches below the equilibrium point and given an initial downward velocity of 4 ft per sec. There is no damping force present, but there is an impressed force of $360 \cos 4t$ pounds. Find the position and velocity of the weight at time $t = \pi/8$ seconds. ANS. At $t = \pi/8(\text{sec})$, $x = -\frac{8}{3}$ (ft), $v = -8$ (ft/sec).

5. A spring is such that a 4-pound weight stretches it 6 inches. The 4-pound weight is attached to the vertical spring and reaches its equilibrium point. The weight is then $(t = 0)$ drawn downward 3 inches and released. No damping force is present, but there is a simple harmonic exterior force equal to sin $8t$ impressed upon the whole system. Find the time for each of the first 4 stops following $t = 0$. Put the stops in chronological order.   ANS. $t = \pi/8, \frac{1}{2}, \pi/4, 3\pi/8$ (sec).

6. A spring is such that a 2-pound weight stretches it 6 inches. There is a damping force present, with magnitude the same as the magnitude of the velocity. An impressed force (2 sin $8t$) is acting on the spring. If, at $t = 0$, the weight is released from a point 3 inches below the equilibrium point, find its position for $t > 0$.

ANS. $x = (\frac{1}{2} + 4t)e^{-8t} - \frac{1}{4} \cos 8t$.

7. In the example of Section 60 change the conditions by imparting to the weight an initial downward velocity of 4 ft per sec.

ANS. $x = 0.25 \cos 13.9t + 0.33 \sin 13.9t - 0.14 \sin 4t$.

8. Show that the solution to Ex. 7 can be put in the form

$$x = 0.41 \cos (13.9t - \varphi) - 0.14 \sin 4t,$$

where $\varphi = $ Arctan (1.32). In this form the first term is called the natural component, and the second term the forced component, of the motion.

9. A spring is such that it is stretched 6 inches by a 12-pound weight (the spring of the example in Section 57). The 12-pound weight is pulled down 3 inches below the equilibrium point and then released. If no damping is present but there is an impressed force of magnitude 9 sin $4t$ pounds, describe the motion. Assume that the impressed force acts downward for very small t.   ANS. $x = \frac{1}{4} \cos 8t - \frac{1}{4} \sin 8t + \frac{1}{2} \sin 4t$.

10. Show that the answer to Ex. 9 can be written

$$x = \frac{1}{4} \sqrt{2} \cos (8t + \pi/4) + \frac{1}{2} \sin 4t.$$

11. Alter Ex. 9 by inserting a damping force of magnitude one-half that of the velocity and then determine x.

ANS. $x = e^{-2t/3}(0.30 \cos 8.0t - 0.22 \sin 8.0t) - 0.05 \cos 4t + 0.49 \sin 4t$.

12. A spring is such that a 2-pound weight stretches it $\frac{1}{2}$ foot. An impressed force $\frac{1}{4} \sin 8t$ is acting upon the spring. If the 2-pound weight is released from a point 3 inches below the equilibrium point, determine the equation of motion.   ANS. $x = \frac{1}{4}(1 - t) \cos 8t + \frac{1}{32} \sin 8t$ (ft).

13. For the motion of Ex. 12 find the first four times at which stops occur and find the position at each stop.   ANS. $t = \pi/8, \pi/4, 1, 3\pi/8$ (sec) and $x = -0.15, +0.05, +0.03, +0.04$ (ft), respectively.

14. Determine the position to be expected, if nothing such as breakage interferes, at the time of the 65th stop, when $t = 8\pi$ (sec), in Ex. 12.

ANS. $x = -6.0$ (ft).

15. Let the motion of Ex. 12 be retarded by a damping force of magnitude $0.6|v|$. Find the equation of motion.

ANS. $x = 0.30e^{-4.8t} \cos 6.4t + 0.22e^{-4.8t} \sin 6.4t - 0.05 \cos 8t$ (ft).

16. Show that (to the nearest 0.01 ft) whenever $t > 1$ (sec) the solution of Ex. 15 may be replaced by $x = -0.05 \cos 8t$.

17. Let the motion of Ex. 12 be retarded by a damping force of magnitude $|v|$. Find the equation of motion and also determine its form (to the nearest 0.01 ft) for $t > 1$ (sec).
ANS. $x = \frac{9}{32}(8t + 1)e^{-8t} - \frac{1}{32} \cos 8t$ (ft); for $t > 1$, $x = -\frac{1}{32} \cos 8t$.

18. Let the motion of Ex. 12 be retarded by a damping force of magnitude $\frac{5}{3}|v|$. Find the equation of motion.
ANS. $x = 0.30e^{-(8/3)t} - 0.03e^{-24t} - 0.02 \cos 8t$.

19. Interpret and solve the problem consisting of

(A) $$\frac{w}{g}\frac{d^2x}{dt^2} + kx = A\frac{w}{g}\sin \beta t; \beta^2 = kg/w,$$

together with the conditions: when $t = 0$, $x = x_0$ and $v = v_0$.
ANS. $x = x_0 \cos \beta t + \beta^{-2}(\frac{1}{2}A + \beta v_0) \sin \beta t - \frac{1}{2}\beta^{-1} At \cos \beta t$.

20. Interpret and solve the problem consisting of the differential equation

(A) $$\frac{w}{g}\frac{d^2x}{dt^2} + kx = \frac{w}{g}A \sin \omega t$$

with conditions

(B) when $t = 0$, $x = x_0$ and $v = v_0$,

under the restriction that $\omega^2 \neq \beta^2$ where $\beta^2 = kg/w$.
ANS. $x = x_0 \cos \beta t + \beta^{-1}(v_0 - Aq\omega) \sin \beta t + Aq \sin \omega t$, where $q = 1/(\beta^2 - \omega^2)$.

21. In equation (A) of Ex. 20 replace $\sin \omega t$ by $\cos \omega t$. Then find x.
ANS. $x = (x_0 - Aq) \cos \beta t + \beta^{-1}v_0 \sin \beta t + Aq \cos \omega t$.

22. In equation (A) of Ex. 20 replace $\sin \omega t$ by $\sin (\omega t + \sigma)$. Then find x.
ANS. $x = (x_0 - Aq \sin \sigma) \cos \beta t + \beta^{-1}(v_0 - Aq\omega \cos \sigma) \sin \beta t + Aq \sin (\omega t + \sigma)$.

23. Interpret and solve the problem consisting of the differential equation

(C) $$\frac{w}{g}\frac{d^2x}{dt^2} + b\frac{dx}{dt} + kx = \frac{w}{g}A \sin \omega t$$

with conditions

(B) when $t = 0$, $x = x_0$ and $v = v_0$.

Use the notations $2\alpha = bg/w$, $\beta^2 = kg/w$, $\gamma^2 = \beta^2 - \alpha^2$, and also $\delta = 1/[4\alpha^2\omega^2 + (\beta^2 - \omega^2)^2]$, and assume that $\beta > \alpha$.
ANS. $x = (x_0 + 2\alpha\delta\omega A)e^{-\alpha t} \cos \gamma t + \gamma^{-1}[v_0 + \alpha x_0 + \delta\omega A(\alpha^2 + \omega^2 - \gamma^2)]e^{-\alpha t} \sin \gamma t - 2\alpha\delta\omega A \cos \omega t + \delta(\beta^2 - \omega^2)A \sin \omega t$.

24. State in consistent units the dimensions of each variable and parameter entering Ex. 23.   Check the dimensions of each equation.

ANS.

w — lb	k — lb/ft	v_0 — ft/sec
g — ft/sec²	A — ft/sec²	α — 1/sec
x — ft	ω — 1/sec	β — 1/sec
t — sec	x_0 — ft	γ — 1/sec
b — (lb)(sec)/ft	v — ft/sec	δ — sec⁴.

62. The simple pendulum.

A rod of length L feet is suspended by one end so that it can swing freely in a vertical plane.   Let a weight B (the bob) of w pounds be attached to the free end of the rod, and let the weight of the rod be negligible compared to the weight of the bob.

Let θ (radians) be the angular displacement from the vertical, as shown in Figure 20, of the rod at time t (sec). The tangential component of the force w (lb) is $w \sin \theta$ and it tends to decrease θ.   Then, neglecting the weight of the rod and using $s = L\theta$ as a measure of arc length from the vertical position, we may conclude that

FIGURE 20

$$(1) \qquad \frac{w}{g}\frac{d^2s}{dt^2} = -w \sin \theta.$$

Since $s = L\theta$ and L is constant, (1) becomes

$$(2) \qquad \frac{d^2\theta}{dt^2} + \frac{g}{L}\sin \theta = 0.$$

The solution of equation (2) is not elementary; it involves an elliptic integral.   If θ is small, however, $\sin \theta$ and θ are nearly equal and (2) is closely approximated by the much simpler equation

$$(3) \qquad \frac{d^2\theta}{dt^2} + \beta^2\theta = 0;\ \beta^2 = g/L.$$

The solution of (3) with pertinent boundary conditions gives usable results whenever those conditions are such that θ remains small, say $|\theta| < 0.3$ (radians).   Recall also that in the derivation it was assumed that the effect of the weight of the rod is negligible compared to that of the weight of the bob.

EXERCISES

1. A clock has a 6-inch pendulum. The clock ticks once for each time that the pendulum completes a swing, returning to its original position. How many times does the clock tick in 30 seconds?   ANS.   38 times.

2. A 6-inch pendulum is released from rest at an angle one-tenth of a radian from the vertical. Using $g = 32$ (ft per sec per sec), describe the motion.
ANS. $\theta = 0.1 \cos 8t$ (radians).

3. For the pendulum of Ex. 2 find the maximum angular speed and its first time of occurrence.   ANS.   0.8 (rad per sec) at 0.2 sec.

4. A 6-inch pendulum is started with a velocity of one radian per second, toward the vertical, from a position one-tenth radian from the vertical. Describe the motion.   ANS. $\theta = \frac{1}{10} \cos 8t - \frac{1}{8} \sin 8t$ (radians).

5. For Ex. 4 find to the nearest degree the maximum angular displacement from the vertical.   ANS. $9°$.

6. Interpret as a pendulum problem and solve the boundary value problem:

(A) $$\frac{d^2\theta}{dt^2} + \beta^2\theta = 0; \ \beta^2 = g/L,$$

(B) $$\text{when } t = 0, \ \theta = \theta_0 \text{ and } \omega = \frac{d\theta}{dt} = \omega_0.$$

ANS. $\theta = \theta_0 \cos \beta t + \beta^{-1} \omega_0 \sin \beta t$ (radians).

7. Find the maximum angular displacement from the vertical for the pendulum of Ex. 6.   ANS. $\theta_{\max} = (\theta_0{}^2 + \beta^{-2} \omega_0{}^2)^{1/2}$.

MISCELLANEOUS EXERCISES

1. A spring is stretched 6 inches by a 4-pound weight. Let the weight be pulled down 6 inches below equilibrium and given an initial upward velocity of 7 ft per sec. Assuming a damping force twice the magnitude of the velocity, describe the motion and sketch the graph for $0 \leq t \leq 0.3$ (sec) at intervals of 0.05 sec.   ANS. $x = \frac{1}{2}e^{-8t}(1 - 6t)$.

2. A spring is stretched 1.5 inches by a 4-pound weight. Let the weight be pulled down 3 inches below equilibrium and released. If there is an impressed force $8 \sin 16t$ acting upon the spring, but no damping force is present, describe the motion.
ANS. $x = \frac{1}{4}(1 - 8t) \cos 16t + \frac{1}{8} \sin 16t$.

3. For the motion of Ex. 2 find the first four times at which stops occur and find the position at each stop.
ANS. $t = \frac{1}{8}, \ \pi/16, \ \pi/8, \ 3\pi/16$ (sec) and
$x = +0.11, \ +0.14, \ -0.54, \ +0.93$ (ft), respectively.

4. An object weighing w pounds is dropped from a height h feet above the earth. At time t (sec) after the object is dropped let its distance from the starting point be x (ft), measured positive downward. Assuming air resistance to be negligible, show that x must satisfy the equation

$$\frac{w}{g}\frac{d^2x}{dt^2} = w$$

so long as $x < h$. Find x.   ANS. $x = \frac{1}{2}gt^2$.

5. Let the weight of Ex. 4 be given an initial velocity v_0. Let v be the velocity at time t. Determine v and x.

ANS. $v = gt + v_0$, $x = \frac{1}{2}gt^2 + v_0t$.

6. From the results in Ex. 5 find a relation which does not contain t explicitly.   ANS. $v^2 = v_0^2 + 2gx$.

7. If air resistance furnishes an additional force proportional to the velocity in the motion studied in Ex. 4 and 5 above show that the equation of motion becomes

(A) $$\frac{w}{g}\frac{d^2x}{dt^2} + b\frac{dx}{dt} = w.$$

Solve equation (A) together with the conditions

(B)   when $t = 0$, $x = 0$ and $v = v_0$.

Use $a = bg/w$.   ANS. $x = a^{-1}gt + a^{-2}(av_0 - g)(1 - e^{-at})$.

8. In order to compare the results of Ex. 5 and Ex. 7 when $a = bg/w$ is small, use the power series for e^{-at} in the answer for Ex. 7 and discard all terms involving a^n for $n \geq 3$.

ANS. $x = \frac{1}{2}gt^2 + v_0t - \frac{1}{6}at^2(3v_0 + gt) + \frac{1}{24}a^2t^3(4v_0 + gt)$.

9. The equation of motion of the vertical fall of a man with a parachute may be roughly approximated by equation (A) of Ex. 7. Suppose a 180-pound man drops from a great height and attains a velocity of 20 miles per hour after a long time. Determine the implied coefficient b of equation (A).   ANS.   6.1 (lb)(sec) per (ft).

10. A particle is moving along the x-axis according to the law

$$\frac{d^2x}{dt^2} + 6\frac{dx}{dt} + 25x = 0.$$

If the particle started at $x = 0$ with an initial velocity of 12 (ft per sec) to the left, determine: (a) x in terms of t, (b) the times at which stops occur, and (c) the ratio between the numerical values of x at successive stops.

ANS.   (a) $x = -3e^{-3t}\sin 4t$,
       (b) $t = 0.23 + n\pi/4$, $n = 0, 1, 2, 3, \cdots$, (c) 0.095.

Chapter 13

Systems of Equations

63. Systems of equations. In solving systems of simultaneous linear equations the differential operator notation is a convenient tool. Consider the system

(1)
$$y'' - y + 5v' = x,$$
$$2y' - v'' + 4v = 2,$$

with independent variable x and dependent variables y and v. It is natural to attack the system (1) by eliminating one dependent variable so as to obtain a single equation for the other dependent variable. Using $D = d/dx$, write the system (1) in the form

(2)
$$(D^2 - 1)y + 5Dv = x,$$
$$2Dy - (D^2 - 4)v = 2.$$

Then elimination of one dependent variable is straightforward. We may, for instance, operate upon the first equation with $2D$ and on the second equation with $(D^2 - 1)$ and then subtract one from the other, thus obtaining

$$[10D^2 + (D^2 - 1)(D^2 - 4)]v = 2Dx - (D^2 - 1)2,$$

or

(3)
$$(D^4 + 5D^2 + 4)v = 4.$$

In a similar manner v may be eliminated; the resultant equation for y is

$$[(D^2 - 1)(D^2 - 4) + 10D^2]y = (D^2 - 4)x + 5D(2),$$

or

(4)
$$(D^4 + 5D^2 + 4)y = -4x.$$

From equations (3) and (4) it follows at once that

(5) $v = 1 + a_1 \cos x + a_2 \sin x + a_3 \cos 2x + a_4 \sin 2x$

and

(6) $y = -x + b_1 \cos x + b_2 \sin x + b_3 \cos 2x + b_4 \sin 2x.$

The a's and b's have yet to be adjusted so as to make (5) and (6) satisfy the original equations, rather than just the equations (3) and (4), which resulted from the original ones after certain eliminations were performed.

Combining (by substitution) the v of (5) and the y of (6) with the first equation of the system (2) leads to the identity

(7) $x - 2b_1 \cos x - 2b_2 \sin x - 5b_3 \cos 2x - 5b_4 \sin 2x$
       $- 5a_1 \sin x + 5a_2 \cos x - 10a_3 \sin 2x + 10a_4 \cos 2x \equiv x.$

That (7) be an identity in x demands that

$$(8) \qquad \begin{aligned} -2b_1 + 5a_2 &= 0, \\ -2b_2 - 5a_1 &= 0, \\ -5b_3 + 10a_4 &= 0, \\ -5b_4 - 10a_3 &= 0. \end{aligned}$$

Relations between the a's and b's equivalent to the relations (8) follow from substitution of the v of (5) and the y of (6) into the second equation of the system (2).

We conclude that the general solution of the system (2) is

(9) $v = 1 + a_1 \cos x + a_2 \sin x + a_3 \cos 2x + a_4 \sin 2x,$
       $y = -x + \frac{5}{2}a_2 \cos x - \frac{5}{2}a_1 \sin x + 2a_4 \cos 2x - 2a_3 \sin 2x,$

in which a_1, a_2, a_3, a_4 are arbitrary constants.

The equations (3) and (4) for v and y can be written with the aid of determinants. From the system (2) above we may write at once

$$\begin{vmatrix} (D^2 - 1) & 5D \\ 2D & -(D^2 - 4) \end{vmatrix} v = \begin{vmatrix} (D^2 - 1) & x \\ 2D & 2 \end{vmatrix},$$

which reduces to equation (3) above, if care is used in the interpretation of the right-hand member. The determinant on the right is to be interpreted as

$$(D^2 - 1)(2) - 2D(x),$$

not as the differential operator $2(D^2 - 1) - x(2D)$.

Determinants are extremely useful in any treatment of the theory of systems of linear equations. For many simple systems which arise in practice no such powerful tool is needed.

There are other techniques for treating a system such as (2) above. For example, we may first obtain (3) and from it v as in equation (5). Next we wish to find an equation giving y in terms of v; that is, we seek to eliminate from the system (2) those terms which involve derivatives of y. From (2) we obtain the two equations

(10) $$(2D^2 - 2)y + 10Dv = 2x,$$
(11) $$2D^2y - (D^3 - 4D)v = 0,$$

the latter by operating with D on each member of the second equation of the system (2). From (10) and (11) it follows at once that

$$2y - D^3v - 6Dv = -2x,$$

or

(12) $$y = -x + \tfrac{1}{2}D^3v + 3Dv.$$

The v of equation (5) may now be used in (12) to compute the y which was given in the solution (9) above. In this method of solution there is no need to obtain (4), (6), (7), or (8) above.

Both methods outlined above are available whenever the system is linear with constant coefficients. Such systems appear naturally in the study of electric networks in the next chapter.

Systems of nonlinear equations and systems of linear equations with variable coefficients will not be studied in this book.

EXERCISES

Obtain the general solution except where otherwise directed.

1. $v' - 2v + 2w' = 2 - 4e^{2x}$,
$\quad 2v' - 3v + 3w' - w = 0$.   ANS. $v = a_1e^x + a_2e^{-2x} + 5e^{2x} - 1$,
$\qquad\qquad w = \tfrac{1}{2}a_1e^x - a_2e^{-2x} - e^{2x} + 3$.

2. $y' - 2y - v' - v = 6e^{3x}$,
$\quad 2y' - 3y + v' - 3v = 6e^{3x}$; when $x = 0$, $y = 3$ and $v = 0$.
$\qquad\qquad$ ANS. $y = e^x(1 + 2x + 2e^{2x})$,
$\qquad\qquad\qquad v = e^x(1 - x - e^{2x})$.

3. $(D + 1)y - (D + 1)v = 0,$
$Dy + (D - 1)v = e^x.$

ANS. $y = e^x + a_1e^{-x} + a_2e^{x/2},$
$v = e^x - \frac{1}{2}a_1e^{-x} + a_2e^{x/2}.$

4. $2(D + 1)v + (D - 1)w = 3x,$
$(D + 1)v + (D + 1)w = 1.$

ANS. $v = x + c_1e^{-x} + c_2e^{-3x},$
$w = 1 - x - c_2e^{-3x}.$

5. $(3D + 2)v + (D - 6)w = 5e^x,$
$(4D + 2)v + (D - 8)w = 5e^x + 2x - 3.$

ANS. $v = a_1 \cos 2x + a_2 \sin 2x + 2e^x - 3x + 5,$
$w = a_2 \cos 2x - a_1 \sin 2x + e^x - x.$

6. $(D^2 + 6)y + Dv = 0,$
$(D + 2)y + (D - 2)v = 2.$

ANS. $y = c_1e^{3x} + c_2 \cos 2x + c_3 \sin 2x,$
$v = -1 - 5c_1e^{3x} + c_3 \cos 2x - c_2 \sin 2x.$

7. $D^2y - (2D - 1)v = 1,$
$(2D + 1)y + (D^2 - 4)v = 0.$

ANS. $v = 1 + a_1e^x + a_2e^{-x} + c_3 \cos x + a_4 \sin x,$
$y = 4 + a_1e^x - 3a_2e^{-x} + (a_3 - 2a_4) \cos x + (2a_3 + a_4) \sin x.$

8. $(D^2 - 3D)y - (D - 2)z = 14x + 7,$
$(D - 3)y + Dz = 1.$

ANS. $y = 2 + a_1e^x + a_2e^{3x} + a_3e^{-2x},$
$z = 7 + 7x + 2a_1e^x - \frac{5}{2}a_3e^{-2x}.$

9. $(D^3 + D^2 - 1)u + (D^3 + 2D^2 + 3D + 1)v = 3 - x,$
$(D - 1)u + (D + 1)v = 3 - x.$

ANS. $u = 2x + a_1 + a_2 \cos x + a_3 \sin x,$
$v = x + a_1 - a_3 \cos x + a_2 \sin x.$

10. $y'' - 3y' - v' + 2v = 14x + 3,$
$y' - 3y + v' = 1;$ when $x = 0,$ $y = 0,$ $y' = 0,$ $y'' = -9.$

ANS. $y = 2 - \frac{1}{2}e^x - \frac{1}{2}e^{3x} - e^{-2x},$
$v = 7x + 5 - e^x + \frac{5}{2}e^{-2x}.$

11. $(D^2 + 2)y - Dv = 2x + 5,$
$(D - 1)y + (D + 1)v = -2x - 1;$ when $x = 0,$
$y = 3, v = -3, v' = 5.$

ANS. $y = x + 2 + e^{-2x} + \sin x,$
$v = 1 - x - 3e^{-2x} - \cos x.$

12. $(D^2 + 1)y + 4(D - 1)v = 4e^x,$
$(D - 1)y + (D + 9)v = 0;$ when $x = 0,$ $y = 5,$ $y' = 0,$ $v = \frac{1}{2}.$

ANS. $y = 2e^x + 2e^{-x} + e^{-2x}(\cos x + 2 \sin x),$
$v = \frac{1}{2}e^{-x} + e^{-2x} \sin x.$

13. $\dfrac{d^2x}{dt^2} + x - 2\dfrac{dy}{dt} = 2t,$

$2\dfrac{dx}{dt} - x + \dfrac{dy}{dt} - 2y = 7.$

ANS. $x = 2t - 2 + b_1e^t + b_2e^{-t} + b_3e^{-2t},$
$y = -t - 1 + b_1e^t - b_2e^{-t} - \frac{5}{4}b_3e^{-2t}.$

14. $2(D + 1)y + (D - 1)w = x + 1$,
$(D + 3)y + (D + 1)w = 4x + 14$.

     ANS. $y = x + 2 + c_1 e^{-x} \cos 2x + c_2 e^{-x} \sin 2x$.

$w = x + 6 + (c_2 - c_1)e^{-x} \cos 2x - (c_1 + c_2)e^{-x} \sin 2x$.

15. $(D + 1)y + (D - 4)v = 6 \cos x$,
$(D - 1)y + (D^2 + 4)v = -6 \sin x$.

     ANS. $y = 3 \cos x + 3 \sin x + a_1 + a_2 \cos 3x + a_3 \sin 3x$,

$v = \frac{1}{4}a_1 - \frac{1}{5}(a_2 - 3a_3) \cos 3x - \frac{1}{5}(3a_2 + a_3) \sin 3x$.

16. $2Du + (D - 1)v + (D + 2)w = 0$,
$(D + 2)u + (2D - 3)v - (D - 6)w = 0$,
$2Du - (D + 3)v - Dw = 0$.

                 ANS. $u = 3c_1 e^{2x} + 3c_2 e^{-x} + 3c_3 e^{x/2}$,

$v = 4c_1 e^{2x} - 5c_2 e^{-x} + c_3 e^{x/2}$,

$w = -4c_1 e^{2x} - 4c_2 e^{-x} - c_3 e^{x/2}$.

17. $D^2 y + (D - 1)v = 0$,
$(2D - 1)y + (D - 1)w = 0$,
$(D + 3)y + (D - 4)v + 3w = 0$.

            ANS. $y = a_1 + a_2 e^x + 3a_3 e^{4x}$,

$v = b_2 e^x - a_2 x e^x - 16a_3 e^{4x}$,

$w = -a_1 + (b_2 - a_2)e^x - a_2 x e^x - 7a_3 e^{4x}$.

Chapter 14

Electric Circuits and Networks

64. Fundamental relations. The basic laws which govern the flow of electric current in a circuit or a network will be given here without derivation. The notation used is common to most texts in electrical engineering; it is:

t (sec) = time

q (coulombs) = quantity of electricity; e.g., charge on a capacitor

i (amperes) = current, time rate of flow of electricity

e (volts) = electromotive force or voltage

R (ohms) = resistance

L (henrys) = inductance

C (farads) = capacitance.

By the definition of q and i it follows that

$$i = \frac{dq}{dt}.$$

The current at each point in a network may be determined by solving the equations which result from applying Kirchhoff's laws:

(a) *The sum of the currents into (or away from) any point is zero,*

and

(b) *Around any closed path the sum of the instantaneous voltage drops in a specified direction is zero.*

A circuit is treated as a network containing only one closed path. Figure 21 exhibits an "*RLC* circuit" with some of the customary conventions for indicating various elements.

For a circuit Kirchhoff's current law (a) indicates merely that the current is the same throughout. That law plays a larger role in networks, as we shall see later.

In order to apply Kirchhoff's voltage law (b) it is necessary to have the contributions of each of the idealized elements in Figure 21. The *voltage drop* across the resistance is ***Ri,*** that across the inductance is $L\dfrac{di}{dt}$, while the capacitor contributes $\dfrac{1}{C}\,q$. The impressed electromotive force e ($e = E$, assumed constant in Figure 21) is contributing a *voltage rise*.

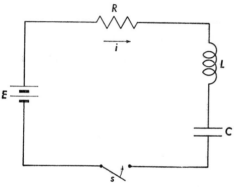

FIGURE 21

Assume that at time $t = 0$ the switch s shown in Figure 21 is to be closed. If the capacitor is initially without charge, then $q = 0$ at $t = 0$, while of course $i = 0$ at $t = 0$ since the circuit was not closed until $t = 0$. From Kirchhoff's law (b) we get the differential equation

$$(1) \qquad\qquad L\frac{di}{dt} + Ri + \frac{1}{C}\,q - E = 0,$$

in which

$$(2) \qquad\qquad\qquad i = \frac{dq}{dt}.$$

Equations (1) and (2) together with the initial conditions

$$(3) \qquad\qquad \text{when } t = 0,\ q = 0 \text{ and } i = 0$$

constitute the mathematical problem to be solved in connection with Figure 21. This problem is equivalent to one in damped vibrations. Indeed, the analogies between electrical and mechanical systems are quite useful in practice.*

65. Circuits. EXAMPLE (a): Consider a circuit with the schematic diagram shown in Figure 22. Here the impressed electromotive force is alternating. It is assumed that the switch s is closed at an instant ($t = 0$) when the applied voltage $E \sin \omega t$ is zero.

From Kirchhoff's voltage law it follows that, for $t > 0$,

$$(1) \qquad\qquad L \frac{di}{dt} + Ri = E \sin \omega t,$$

while

$$(2) \qquad\qquad \text{when } t = 0, \, i = 0.$$

FIGURE 22

Since L, R, E, and ω are constants, equation (1) may be integrated easily by methods developed earlier in this book. The general solution of (1) is

$$(3) \qquad i = a_1 e^{-Rt/L} + \frac{E}{Z^2} (R \sin \omega t - \omega L \cos \omega t),$$

where a_1 is an arbitrary constant and where $Z = (R^2 + \omega^2 L^2)^{1/2}$. The quantity Z is called the *steady-state impedance* of the circuit.

---

*See M. F. Gardner and J. L. Barnes, *Transients in Linear Systems*, New York, John Wiley & Sons, 1942, Vol. 1.

The steady-state impedance in the more general RLC circuit appears in the exercises below.

Since the i of equation (3) is to satisfy (2), it can be seen that $a_1 = E\omega L/Z^2$. Therefore the current in the circuit of Figure 22 is given by

$$(4) \qquad i = \frac{E}{Z^2}\,(R\,\sin\,\omega t - \omega L\,\cos\,\omega t + \omega L e^{-Rt/L}).$$

For sufficiently large t the last term on the right in (4) is negligible, while the first two terms do not change character with large t. Indeed, the current i may be split into two parts

$$(5) \qquad i = i_t + i_s,$$

where

$$(6) \qquad i_t = \frac{E\omega L}{Z^2}\,e^{-Rt/L},$$

is called the *transient current* and

$$(7) \qquad i_s = \frac{E}{Z^2}\,(R\,\sin\,\omega t - \omega L\,\cos\,\omega t)$$

is called the *steady-state current*. Equation (7) can also be put in the form

$$i_s = \frac{E}{Z}\,\sin\,(\omega t - \epsilon),$$

where $\epsilon = \text{Arctan}\,(\omega L/R)$.

It is of interest to know the maximum steady-state current, which is easily found to be

$$(8) \qquad \max\,(i_s) = \frac{E}{Z^2}\,\sqrt{R^2 + \omega^2 L^2} = \frac{E}{Z}.$$

EXAMPLE (b): Determine the current in the circuit shown in Figure 21, page 204.

This problem was set up in the previous section. The current i and the charge q are determined by

(9) $$L\frac{di}{dt} + Ri + \frac{1}{C}q = E,$$

(10) $$i = \frac{dq}{dt},$$

and

(11)   when $t = 0$, $q = 0$ and $i = 0$.

From (9) and (10) it follows that q must satisfy the equation

(12) $$L\frac{d^2q}{dt^2} + R\frac{dq}{dt} + \frac{1}{C}q = E.$$

A particular solution $q = CE$ is evident by inspection.

The auxiliary equation for (12) is

$$LCm^2 + RCm + 1 = 0,$$

from which

$$m = \frac{-RC \pm \sqrt{R^2C^2 - 4LC}}{2LC},$$

or

(13) $$m = -\frac{R}{2L} \pm \sqrt{\frac{R^2}{4L^2} - \frac{1}{LC}}.$$

The form of the solution of equation (12) will depend, as we already know, upon whether the roots (13) of the auxiliary equation are real and distinct, equal, or conjugate imaginary numbers. Hence we separate our treatment of this problem into three cases according to whether the expression

$$\frac{R^2}{4L^2} - \frac{1}{LC}$$

is > 0, $= 0$, or < 0.

Case 1: $\frac{R^2}{4L^2} - \frac{1}{LC} > 0$, or $4L/C < R^2$.

Let us put $\alpha = R/(2L)$ and $b = \sqrt{\frac{R^2}{4L^2} - \frac{1}{LC}}$. Then the roots (13) of the auxiliary equation become $m_1 = -\alpha + b$ and $m_2 = -\alpha - b$, where α and b are positive and where $b < \alpha$. Note that m_1 and m_2 are each negative.

For Case 1, then, the general solution of the differential equation (12) is

$$(14) \qquad q = a_1 e^{-(\alpha-b)t} + a_2 e^{-(\alpha+b)t} + EC,$$

where a_1 and a_2 are arbitrary constants.

Since $i = dq/dt$, we get

$$(15) \qquad i = -(\alpha - b)a_1 e^{-(\alpha-b)t} - (\alpha + b)a_2 e^{-(\alpha+b)t}.$$

But when $t = 0$, $q = 0$ and $i = 0$. Hence a_1 and a_2 may be determined from the equations

$$a_1 + a_2 = -EC,$$
$$(\alpha - b)a_1 + (\alpha + b)a_2 = 0.$$

Then $a_1 = -(\alpha + b)EC/(2b)$ and $a_2 = (\alpha - b)EC/(2b)$.

Thus, for Case 1,

$$(16) \qquad q = \frac{EC}{2b}[2b - (\alpha + b)e^{-(\alpha-b)t} + (\alpha - b)e^{-(\alpha+b)t}]$$

and

$$(17) \qquad i = \frac{(\alpha^2 - b^2)EC}{2b}[e^{-(\alpha-b)t} - e^{-(\alpha+b)t}].$$

Note that $\alpha^2 - b^2 = 1/(LC)$ so that (17) may be put in the more convenient form

$$i = \frac{Ee^{-\alpha t}}{2bL}(e^{bt} - e^{-bt}),$$

or

$$(18) \qquad i = \frac{E}{bL}e^{-\alpha t}\sinh bt.$$

Case 2: $\frac{R^2}{4L^2} - \frac{1}{LC} = 0$, or $R^2 = 4L/C$.

Here, with $\alpha = R/(2L)$ again, the roots of the auxiliary equation are $m_1 = -\alpha$ and $m_2 = -\alpha$. Hence

$$q = a_1 e^{-\alpha t} + a_2 t e^{-\alpha t} + EC,$$

so that
$$i = -\alpha a_1 e^{-\alpha t} + a_2 e^{-\alpha t} - \alpha a_2 t e^{-\alpha t}.$$

Once more using the initial conditions we find that
$$a_1 + EC = 0,$$
$$-\alpha a_1 + a_2 = 0.$$

Then

(19) $$q = EC(1 - e^{-\alpha t} - \alpha t e^{-\alpha t})$$

and
$$i = \alpha^2 ECt e^{-\alpha t},$$

or, since $\alpha^2 = 1/(LC)$,

(20) $$i = \frac{E}{L} t e^{-\alpha t}.$$

Case 3: $\dfrac{R^2}{4L^2} - \dfrac{1}{LC} < 0$, or $R^2 < 4L/C$.

This time let us put $\beta = \sqrt{\dfrac{1}{LC} - \dfrac{R^2}{4L^2}}$ and $\alpha = R/(2L)$. Then α and β are positive and the auxiliary equation has roots $m_1 = -\alpha + j\beta$ and $m_2 = -\alpha - j\beta$, where $j = \sqrt{-1}$.

Hence
$$q = EC + e^{-\alpha t}(a_1 \cos \beta t + a_2 \sin \beta t)$$
and
$$i = e^{-\alpha t}[(-\alpha a_1 + \beta a_2) \cos \beta t - (\alpha a_2 + \beta a_1) \sin \beta t].$$

Since $q = 0$ and $i = 0$, when $t = 0$, we find that $a_1 = -EC$ and $a_2 = -\alpha EC/\beta$.

Then

(21) $$q = \frac{EC}{\beta}[\beta - e^{-\alpha t}(\beta \cos \beta t + \alpha \sin \beta t)]$$

and
$$i = \frac{EC}{\beta}(\alpha^2 + \beta^2)e^{-\alpha t} \sin \beta t.$$

But $\alpha^2 + \beta^2 = 1/(LC)$, so finally

(22) $$i = \frac{E}{\beta L} e^{-\alpha t} \sin \beta t.$$

EXERCISES

1. Return to Example (a) of this section, but assume that the switch is closed when the impressed electromotive force is at its maximum. That is, use Figure 22, page 205, with the replacement $e = E \cos \omega t$ and close the switch at $t = 0$ again, assuming that $i = 0$ when $t = 0$. Find i, i_t, i_s, and max (i_s).

   ANS. $i = \dfrac{E}{Z^2}(\omega L \sin \omega t + R \cos \omega t - R e^{-Rt/L})$; $i_t = -\dfrac{ER}{Z^2} e^{-Rt/L}$;

   $i_s = EZ^{-2}(\omega L \sin \omega t + R \cos \omega t)$; max $(i_s) = E/Z$.

2. In the RL circuit of Figure 22, page 205, replace the alternating-current element with a direct-current element E. Assume that the switch s is closed at $t = 0$ and that $i = 0$ when $t = 0$. Determine the current i and note its steady-state and transient terms.

   ANS. $i = \dfrac{E}{R}(1 - e^{-Rt/L})$; $i_s = \dfrac{E}{R}$; $i_t = -\dfrac{E}{R} e^{-Rt/L}$.

3. Figure 23 shows an RC circuit with an alternating-current element inserted. Assume that the switch is closed at $t = 0$ at which time $q = 0$ and $i = 0$. Use the notation $Z^2 = R^2 + (\omega C)^{-2}$, where Z is the steady-state impedance of this circuit. Find i for $t > 0$.

   ANS. $i = EZ^{-2}[R \sin \omega t + (\omega C)^{-1} \cos \omega t - (\omega C)^{-1} e^{-t/(RC)}]$.

FIGURE 23

4. In Figure 23 replace the alternating-current element with a direct-current element $E = 50$ volts and use $R = 10$ ohms, $C = 4(10)^{-4}$ farad. Assume that when the switch s is closed (at $t = 0$) the charge on the capacitor is 0.015 coulomb. Find the initial current in the circuit and the current for $t > 0$.

   ANS. $i_0 = 1.25$ (amp), $i = 1.25 e^{-250t}$.

5. In Figure 23 replace $E \sin \omega t$ with $110 \cos 377t$ and use $R = 12$ ohms, $C = 3(10)^{-4}$ farad. Show that the impressed voltage $110 \cos 377t$ is ordinary 60-cycle alternating voltage. Assuming that $q = 0$ when $t = 0$, find the current i for $t > 0$.

ANS. $i = 5.94 \cos 377t - 4.38 \sin 377t + 3.23e^{-278t}$.

6. Figure 24 shows an RLC circuit with an alternating-current element. Show that the impressed electromotive force $E \sin 377t$ is ordinary 60-cycle alternating voltage. Using the values $E = 110$, $R = 100$, $L = 0.10$, $C = 5(10)^{-5}$, and assuming that when $t = 0$, $q = 0$ and $i = 0$, find the current i for $t > 0$.

ANS. $i = 1.08 \sin 377t + 0.16 \cos 377t - 1.17e^{-276t} + 1.01e^{-724t}$.

7. In Ex. 6 replace the 100-ohm resistance with a 10-ohm resistance, leaving everything else unchanged. Then compute the current i.

ANS. $i = 3.28 \sin 377t + 5.03 \cos 377t$
$- 5.03e^{-50t} \cos 444t - 3.34e^{-50t} \sin 444t$.

8. In Ex. 6 replace the 100-ohm resistance with a 40-ohm resistance, and the 0.10-henry inductance with a 0.02-henry inductance, leaving everything else unchanged. Then compute the current i.

ANS. $i = 1.20 \sin 377t + 1.36 \cos 377t - [1.36 + 1.82(10)^3t]e^{-1000t}$.

FIGURE 24

9. In Figure 24 replace the electromotive force by $e = E \cos 377t$. Use the values $E = 110$, $R = 100$, $L = 0.10$, $C = 5(10)^{-5}$, as in Ex. 6, and compute q and i for $t > 0$, assuming that when $t = 0$, $q = 0$ and $i = 0$.

ANS. $i = 1.08 \cos 377t - 0.16 \sin 377t + 0.86e^{-276t} - 1.94e^{-724t}$.

10. In Ex. 9 replace the 100-ohm resistance with a 10-ohm resistance, leaving the rest of the problem unchanged.

ANS. $i = 3.28 \cos 377t - 5.03 \sin 377t$
$- 3.28e^{-50t} \cos 444t + 6.37e^{-50t} \sin 444t$.

11. In Ex. 9 replace the 100-ohm resistance with a 40-ohm resistance and the 0.10-henry inductance with a 0.02-henry inductance, leaving the rest of the problem unchanged.

ANS. $i = 1.20 \cos 377t - 1.36 \sin 377t - [1.20 - 4.82(10)^3 t]e^{-1000t}$.

12. In Ex. 9 replace the 0.10-henry inductance with 0.01-henry inductance, leaving the rest of the problem unchanged.

ANS. $i = 0.88 \cos 377t - 0.44 \sin 377t + 0.26e^{-204t} - 1.14e^{-9800t}$.

13. In Figure 21, page 204, use the values $E = 60$ volts, $R = 8$ ohms, $L = 0.06$ henry, $C = 3(10)^{-4}$ farad, and assume that when $t = 0$, $q = 0$ and $i = 0$. Set up and solve the problem without using the formulas derived in this section. Find the current for $t > 0$.

ANS. $i = 4.42e^{-66.7t} \sin 226t$.

14. Solve Ex. 13 with the following replacements in the values of the circuit constants: $R = 30$ ohms, $C = 4(10)^{-4}$ farad, (L unchanged).

ANS. $i = 6.95e^{-250t} \sinh (144t)$.

15. Solve Ex. 13 with the following replacements in the values of the circuit constants: $R = 40$ ohms, $L = 0.02$ henry, $C = 5(10)^{-5}$ farad.

ANS. $i = 3000te^{-1000t}$.

16. In Ex. 15 find the maximum current.   ANS. $i_{max} = 3/e$ (amps).

In Exs. 17–20 the following notations are used to simplify the appearance of the formulas:

$$\alpha = \frac{R}{2L}, \; b^2 = \alpha^2 - \frac{1}{LC}, \; \beta^2 = \frac{1}{LC} - \alpha^2,$$

$$\gamma = \omega L - \frac{1}{\omega C}, \; Z^2 = R^2 + \gamma^2.$$

The quantity Z is called the *steady-state impedance* for an RLC circuit, such as that in Figure 24.

17. For the circuit of Figure 24 replace $E \sin 377t$ by $E \sin \omega t$ and also assume that the R, L, and C satisfy the inequality $4L < R^2 C$. Put $q = 0$ and $i = 0$ when $t = 0$. Determine q and i for $t > 0$.

ANS. $i = EZ^{-2}(R \sin \omega t - \gamma \cos \omega t)$

$$+ \tfrac{1}{2}Eb^{-1}Z^{-2}[\{\gamma(\alpha + b) - \omega R\}e^{-(\alpha-b)t}$$

$$+ \{\omega R - \gamma(\alpha - b)\}e^{-(\alpha+b)t}].$$

18. For the circuit of Figure 24 replace $E \sin 377t$ by $E \sin \omega t$ and also assume that the R, L, and C satisfy the inequality $R^2 C < 4L$. Put $q = 0$ and $i = 0$ when $t = 0$. Determine q and i for $t > 0$.

ANS. $i = EZ^{-2}(R \sin \omega t - \gamma \cos \omega t)$

$$+ E\beta^{-1}Z^{-2}e^{-\alpha t}\left[\beta\gamma \cos \beta t - \alpha\left(\gamma + \frac{2}{\omega C}\right)\sin \beta t\right].$$

19. For the circuit of Figure 24 replace $E \sin 377t$ by $E \sin \omega t$ and also assume that $4L = R^2 C$. Put $q = 0$ and $i = 0$ when $t = 0$. Determine q and i for $t > 0$.

ANS. $i = EZ^{-2}(R \sin \omega t - \gamma \cos \omega t)$

$$+ E\omega^{-1}Z^{-2}e^{-\alpha t}[\gamma\omega - \alpha(\gamma\omega + \alpha R)t].$$

20. Show that the answer to Ex. 19 can be put in the form

$$i = EZ^{-2}(R \sin \omega t - \gamma \cos \omega t) + EZ^{-2}e^{-\alpha t}[\gamma + (\alpha\gamma - R\omega)t].$$

66. Simple networks. In a network such as that in Figure 25 we apply both of Kirchhoff's laws (page 203) to get a system of equations to determine the currents present. Since there are four dependent variables present, i, i_1, i_2, q_1, we need four equations to determine them.

From the current law it follows that

(1) $i = i_1 + i_2.$

Application of the voltage law to the circuit on the left in Figure 25 yields

(2) $20i + 0.08 \dfrac{di_2}{dt} = 4.$

FIGURE 25

Using the voltage law on the outside circuit, we get

(3) $20i + 10i_1 + 5(10)^3 q_1 = 4.$

The definition of current as time rate of change of charge yields

$$(4) \qquad\qquad\qquad i_1 = \frac{dq_1}{dt}.$$

Still another equation may be obtained from the circuit on the right in Figure 25, namely,

$$(5) \qquad\qquad 10i_1 + 5(10)^3 q_1 - 0.08 \frac{di_2}{dt} = 0.$$

Equation (5) also follows at once from equations (2) and (3): it may be used instead of either (2) or (3).

Let us stipulate that the currents i, i_1, i_2 are each zero at the time $(t = 0)$ the switch is closed. Then equation (3) shows that the capacitor has at that time a charge of $8(10)^{-4}$ coulomb.

The system of four equations, (1)–(4), is to be solved for the charge q_1 and the currents i, i_1, i_2. The methods of Chapter 13 are available but this problem is so simple that no explicit use of differential operators is needed.

A single equation for q_1 can be found easily. From (3) we get i in terms of i_1 and q_1,

$$(6) \qquad\qquad i = -0.5i_1 - 2.5(10)^2 q_1 + 0.2.$$

Next we put this expression for i into equation (1) in order to obtain i_2 in terms of i_1 and q_1, thus arriving at

$$(7) \qquad\qquad i_2 = -1.5i_1 - 2.5(10)^2 q_1 + 0.2.$$

Finally, equations (6) and (7) may be combined with (2) to yield the desired equation in i_1 and q_1, namely,

$$0.12 \frac{di_1}{dt} + 30i_1 + 5(10)^3 q_1 = 0.$$

Therefore the charge q_1 must satisfy the equation

$$(8) \qquad\qquad 0.12 \frac{d^2 q_1}{dt^2} + 30 \frac{dq_1}{dt} + 5(10)^3 q_1 = 0.$$

By the usual methods the general solution of equation (8) is found to be

$$q_1 = e^{-125t}(a_1 \cos 161t + a_2 \sin 161t).$$

The arbitrary constants a_1 and a_2 are to be determined from the conditions that when $t = 0$, $q_1 = 8(10)^{-4}$ and $i_1 = \dfrac{dq_1}{dt} = 0$. The currents i and i_2 will then be obtained from equations (6) and (7). For the numerical results see Ex. 1 below.

EXERCISES

1. Complete the determination of the currents in the example above.

$$\text{ANS.} \quad i_1 = -0.21e^{-125t} \sin 161t,$$
$$i = 0.20(1 - e^{-125t} \cos 161t) - 0.05e^{-125t} \sin 161t,$$
$$i_2 = 0.20(1 - e^{-125t} \cos 161t) + 0.16e^{-125t} \sin 161t.$$

FIGURE 26

2. In Figure 26 let $E = 60$ volts, $R = 10$ ohms, $R_1 = 20$ ohms, and $C_2 = 5(10)^{-4}$ farad. Determine the currents if when the switch is closed the capacitor carries a charge of 0.03 coulomb.

$$\text{ANS.} \quad i = 2(1 - e^{-300t}), \ i_1 = 2 + e^{-300t},$$
$$i_2 = -3e^{-300t}.$$

3. In Ex. 2 let the initial charge on the capacitor be 0.01 coulomb, but leave the rest of the problem unchanged.

$$\text{ANS.} \quad i = 2(1 + e^{-300t}), \ i_1 = 2 - e^{-300t}, \ i_2 = 3e^{-300t}.$$

4. In Ex. 2 and Figure 26 replace the direct-current element $E = 60$ volts with an alternating-current element $e = 60 \sin 377t$ volts, and leave the rest of Ex. 2 unchanged.

$$\text{ANS.} \quad i = -7.95e^{-300t} + 4.45 \sin 377t + 1.95 \cos 377t,$$
$$i_1 = 3.97e^{-300t} + 0.78 \sin 377t - 0.97 \cos 377t,$$
$$i_2 = -11.92e^{-300t} + 3.67 \sin 377t + 2.92 \cos 377t.$$

5. In Figure 27 use $E = 30$ volts, $R = 20$ ohms, $R_1 = 30$ ohms, $R_2 = 10$ ohms, $C_1 = 4(10)^{-5}$ farad, $L_2 = 0.02$ henry, and assume that when the switch is closed $(t = 0)$, $q_1 = 0.002$ coulomb and $i = 0$. Find the currents for $t > 0$.

$$\text{ANS.} \quad i = 1.00 + e^{-800t}(-1.00 \cos 332t + 0.70 \sin 332t),$$
$$i_1 = e^{-800t}(-0.67 \cos 332t - 2.01 \sin 332t),$$
$$i_2 = 1.00 + e^{-800t}(-0.33 \cos 332t + 2.71 \sin 332t).$$

FIGURE 27

FIGURE 28

6. In Ex. 5 double the size of R_2 and leave the rest of the problem unchanged.   ANS. $i = 0.75 - 0.30e^{-730t} - 0.45e^{-1370t}$,
$$i_1 = -1.43e^{-730t} + 0.76e^{-1370t},$$
$$i_2 = 0.75 + 1.13e^{-730t} - 1.21e^{-1370t}.$$

7. For the network in Figure 28 assume that each capacitor has a zero charge when the switch is closed at $t = 0$. Show that for $t > 0$ the current i is given by $i = ER^{-1}e^{-t/[R(C_1+C_2+C_3)]}$. Hence show that so far as the current i alone is concerned, the network in Figure 28 can be replaced by an equivalent single RC circuit whose capacitor has a capacitance $C = C_1 + C_2 + C_3$.

FIGURE 29

FIGURE 30

8. In the sense of Ex. 7 show that the current i in Figure 29 may be obtained from an equivalent single RL circuit with resistance R given by

$$\frac{1}{R} = \frac{1}{R_1} + \frac{1}{R_2} + \frac{1}{R_3}.$$

9. For the network of Figure 30, find an equivalent RC circuit.

10. For Ex. 9 what initial charge on the capacitor is implied by assuming that the currents are zero at $t = 0$?   ANS. $q = EC$.

11. For the network of Figure 31 find an equivalent RL circuit.

12. In Figure 32 let $E = 40$ volts, $R = 8$ ohms, $R_1 = 10$ ohms, $R_2 = 20$ ohms, $L_1 = 0.10$ henry, $L_2 = 0.08$ henry, and assume that when the switch is closed each current is zero. Find the currents for $t > 0$. You may find it desirable to use the operator $D \equiv d/dt$ and the methods of Chapter 13.   ANS. $i = 2.73 - 0.65e^{-142t} - 2.08e^{-388t}$,
$i_1 = 1.82 - 1.25e^{-142t} - 0.57e^{-388t}$,
$i_2 = 0.91 + 0.60e^{-142t} - 1.51e^{-288t}$.

FIGURE 31

FIGURE 32

67. Change of conditions in a circuit. Consider the circuit shown schematically in Figure 33. Suppose that no current is flowing, the switch s_2 is closed, and the switch s_1 is open as shown.

Then at time zero the switch s_1 is to be closed and one one-hundredth of a second later the switch s_2 is to be opened. We wish to determine the currents flowing in the circuit. Let us use specific values for the parameters: $E = 16$ volts, $R = 4$ ohms, $L = 0.10$ henry, $R_1 = 16$ ohms.

FIGURE 33

Between the closing of s_1 and the opening of s_2, for $0 < t \leqq 0.01$, the current i must satisfy the equation

(1)
$$0.10 \frac{di}{dt} + 4i = 16,$$

and when $t = 0$, $i = 0$. Then it follows readily that

(2)
$$i = 4(1 - e^{-40t}), \ 0 \leqq t \leqq 0.01.$$

Of course, $i_1 = 0$, and $i = i_1 + i_2$ so that $i_2 = i$.

From equation (2) we can compute the current i at time $t = 0.01$ so that we know the initial current which must be used in the succeeding problem, which arises when the switch s_2 is opened. In fact, at $t = 0.01$, $i = 4(1 - 0.67) = 1.32$ (amp).

It is helpful to measure time from the beginning of each separate problem, and in order to avoid confusion we shall use T to stand for time after the opening of switch s_2.

The initial condition that when $T = 0$, $i = 1.32$, has already been determined by the terminal condition of the first part of our problem. Furthermore, with the switch s_2 open, the current i must satisfy, for $T > 0$, the equation

$$(3) \qquad\qquad 0.10 \frac{di}{dT} + 20i = 16.$$

The general solution of equation (3) is

$$i = 0.80 + ae^{-200T},$$

where a is an arbitrary constant. Since $i = 1.32$ at $T = 0$, it follows that $a = 0.52$. Hence the current i is given by the equation

$$(4) \qquad\qquad i = 0.80 + 0.52e^{-200T}, \; 0 \leqq T.$$

Note also that $i_1 = i$ and $i_2 = 0$.

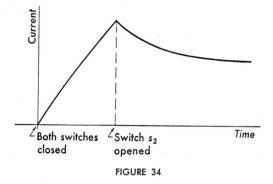

FIGURE 34

Using equations (2) and (4), each in its own time range, we can draw a graph of the current i as a function of time. The result is exhibited in Figure 34.

In the following exercises a few other simple problems in change of circuit conditions appear. A clear and extensive exposition of the subject will be found in E. B. Kurtz and G. F. Corcoran, *Introduction to Electric Transients*, New York, John Wiley & Sons, 1935.

EXERCISES

1. Alter the example of this section by leaving the switch s_2 closed until 0.02 sec after the switch s_1 was closed. Obtain the current i and draw its graph.   ANS. $i = 4(1 - e^{-40t}), \; 0 \leqq t \leqq 0.02;$
$i = 0.80 + 1.40e^{-200T}, \; 0 \leqq T.$

2. Show, for Ex. 1 and for the example above it, that the graph of i as a function of t has a discontinuous slope at the time the switch s_2 is opened.

3. Draw a circuit diagram like Figure 33, page 219, except that the switch s_2 is to be open. Use $R = 2$ ohms, $L = 0.10$ henry, $R_1 = 6$ ohms, and $E = 10$ volts. Let the switch s_1 be closed first. Then 0.01 second later let the switch s_2 be closed, thus cutting out the resistance R_1. Find the current i and draw its graph.

$$\text{ANS.}\quad i = 1.25(1 - e^{-80t}),\ 0 \le t \le 0.01;$$
$$i = 5 - 4.31e^{-20T},\ 0 \le T.$$

4. In Ex. 3 change R_1 to 8 ohms, leaving the remainder of the exercise unaltered. $\quad$ ANS. $\quad i = 1 - e^{-100t},\ 0 \le t \le 0.01;$
$$i = 5 - 4.37e^{-20T},\ 0 \le T.$$

5. In the circuit of Ex. 3 let the switch s_1 be closed first, but let s_2 remain open until the current i has reached the steady state. Then close the switch s_2 and determine the current. $\quad$ ANS. $\quad i = 5 - 3.75e^{-20T},\ 0 \le T.$

FIGURE 35

6. In Figure 35 take $E = 10$ volts, $R = 5$ ohms, $R_1 = 10$ ohms, $L = 0.05$ henry, $L_1 = 0.05$ henry. Let s_1 be closed and s_2 remain open until the current reaches the steady state. Then close s_2 at $t = 0$ and compute the currents present. Draw the graphs.

$$\text{ANS.}\quad i = 2 - \tfrac{4}{3}e^{-100t},\ i_1 = \tfrac{2}{3}e^{-200t},\ i_2 = i - i_1.$$

7. In the example of this section leave the parameters E, R, R_1, and L literal, use $t = t_0$ instead of $t = 0.01$ as the time for opening switch s_2. Obtain the current i both for $0 \le t \le t_0$ and for $0 \le T$. Your answer can be checked by comparison with the answers for the example and for Ex. 1.

8. For the circuit of Figure 36 suppose that, with the switch s in the position shown, the current i has reached its steady-state value, $i = E/R$. Then let the switch be thrown at time $t = 0$ to the position designated by a dotted line. Find the current i_1.

ANS. $i_1 = (E/R)e^{-Rt/L}$.

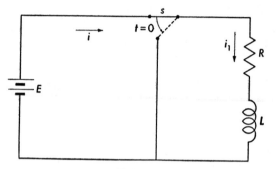

FIGURE 36

9. In the sense of Ex. 7, solve Ex. 3 literally and check your answer.
10. In the sense of Ex. 7, solve Ex. 6 literally and check your answer.

Chapter 15

The Existence of Solutions

68. Preliminary remarks. The methods of Chapter 2 are strictly dependent upon certain special properties (variables separable, exactness, etc.) which may, or may not, be possessed by an individual equation. It is intuitively plausible that no collection of methods can be found which would permit the explicit solution, in the sense of Chapter 2, of all differential equations. We may seek solutions in other forms, employing infinite series or other limiting processes; we may resort to numerical approximations.

Confronted with a situation such as that described in the preceding paragraph, the pure mathematician frequently reacts by searching for what is known as an existence theorem. He seeks to determine conditions which are sufficient to insure the existence of a solution with certain properties. It may happen that in discovering such a theorem and a proof of it the mathematician will hit upon a method, practical or not, for constructing a solution of the equation.

69. Nature of solutions of a particular equation. Before proceeding to a statement of an existence theorem, let us examine in some detail the solutions of a simple equation,

$$(1) \qquad\qquad 2y \, dx - x \, dy = 0.$$

Equation (1) has the general solution $y = cx^2$, including the solution $x = 0$ by our usual convention. This family of curves consists of the two axes and all parabolas which have the origin as vertex and have their foci on the y-axis, as shown in Figure 37, page 224.

Additional solutions of equation (1) may be formed by combining parts of different elements of the family of solutions given above. Since we need to retain continuity of y and dy/dx, we permit ourselves to pass from one element of the family to another only where the two intersect and have a common tangent. In this case the elements intersect only at the origin.

As an example, the curve defined by

$$y = x^2, \qquad 0 \leqq x,$$
$$y = -4x^2, \quad x < 0,$$

is a solution of equation (1). Note the continuity of its slope at the origin.

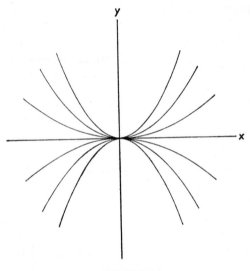

FIGURE 37

It is evident that, given any point in the xy-plane, we can find a solution which passes through that point. If the given point is not the origin, then the solution which passes through the given point is unique in the vicinity of that point. See Section 31.

Now write equation (1) in the form

(2) $$\frac{dy}{dx} = \frac{2y}{x}.$$

The right member of equation (2) is discontinuous at each point where $x = 0$ and is continuous elsewhere. Through each point where the right member of equation (2) is continuous there is a solution unique near that point. At the origin trouble is to be expected because of the clustering of solutions there as indicated earlier. In searching for solutions through a point $x = 0, y = y_0 \neq 0$, it is more natural to write the equation (2) in the form

$$(3) \qquad \frac{dx}{dy} = \frac{x}{2y},$$

and to consider x as the dependent variable. Then the slope is dx/dy and it is continuous at $(0, y_0)$, $y_0 \neq 0$. Again a solution passing through the point in question exists and is unique near that point.

70. An existence theorem. We now state without proof an existence theorem for certain first-order equations. A proof of this theorem can be found in Ince, *op. cit.*, 62–66.

Consider the equation of order one and degree one,

$$(1) \qquad \frac{dy}{dx} = f(x, y).$$

Let T denote the rectangular region defined by

$$|x - x_0| \leq a, \quad |y - y_0| \leq b,$$

a region with the point (x_0, y_0) at its center. Let the function $f(x, y)$ in equation (1) be single-valued and continuous in T and let $f(x, y)$ satisfy the "Lipschitz condition" that there exists a constant K such that

$$|f(x, y_1) - f(x, y_2)| < K|y_1 - y_2|$$

for every pair of points (x, y_1) and (x, y_2), of the same abscissa, in T.

Under the conditions imposed on $f(x, y)$ above, there exists an interval about x_0, $|x - x_0| \leq h$, and a function $y(x)$ which has the properties:

  (a) $y = y(x)$ is a solution of equation (1) on the interval $|x - x_0| \leq h$;

  (b) On the interval $|x - x_0| \leq h$, $y(x)$ satisfies the inequality $|y(x) - y_0| \leq b$;

  (c) At $x = x_0$, $y = y(x_0) = y_0$;

  (d) $y(x)$ is unique on the interval $|x - x_0| \leq h$ in the sense that it is the only function which has all of the properties (a), (b), and (c).

The interval $|x - x_0| \leq h$ may, or may not, need to be smaller than the interval $|x - x_0| \leq a$ over which conditions were imposed upon $f(x, y)$.

In rough language the theorem states that if $f(x, y)$ is sufficiently well behaved near the point (x_0, y_0), then the differential equation

$$(1) \qquad \frac{dy}{dx} = f(x, y)$$

has a solution which passes through the point (x_0, y_0) and that solution is unique near (x_0, y_0).

It is important that the solution under discussion can actually be exhibited. The function $y(x)$ is the limit of a sequence of functions $y_n(x)$; $n = 1, 2, \cdots$, defined as follows:

$$y = y(x) = \lim_{n \to \infty} y_n(x);$$

where

$$y_1(x) = y_0 + \int_{x_0}^{x} f(t, y_0)dt,$$

$$y_2(x) = y_0 + \int_{x_0}^{x} f[t, y_1(t)]dt,$$

$$y_3(x) = y_0 + \int_{x_0}^{x} f[t, y_2(t)]dt,$$

$$\cdots$$

$$y_n(x) = y_0 + \int_{x_0}^{x} f[t, y_{n-1}(t)]dt.$$

The student should use this process to construct a solution of the boundary value problem

$$(2) \qquad \frac{dy}{dx} = \frac{2y}{x}; \text{ when } x = 1, y = 1.$$

It will be found that

$$y_1(x) = 1 + 2 \ln x,$$
$$y_2(x) = 1 + 2 \ln x + 2 \ln^2 x,$$
$$y_3(x) = 1 + 2 \ln x + 2 \ln^2 x + \tfrac{4}{3} \ln^3 x,$$
$$\cdots$$

$$y_n(x) = 1 + \sum_{k=1}^{n} \frac{2^k \ln^k x}{k!},$$

and that

$$y = e^{2 \ln x} = x^2.$$

Chapter 16

Equations of Order One
and Higher Degree

71. Factoring the left member. If an equation

$$(1) \qquad f(x, y, y') = 0$$

is of degree higher than one, it may be possible to factor the left member into parts each of which is of degree one. The problem of solving (1) is then replaced by two or more problems of simpler type. The latter may be capable of solution by the methods of Chapters 2 and 4.

Since y' will appear to powers in the example and exercises, let us simplify the printing and writing by a common device, using p for y'; i. e.,

$$p = \frac{dy}{dx}.$$

EXAMPLE: Solve the differential equation

$$(2) \qquad xyp^2 + (x + y)p + 1 = 0.$$

The left member of equation (2) is readily factored. Thus (2) leads to

$$(xp + 1)(yp + 1) = 0,$$

from which it follows that either

$$(3) \qquad yp + 1 = 0$$

or

$$(4) \qquad xp + 1 = 0.$$

From equation (3) in the form

$$y \, dy + dx = 0$$

it follows that

(5) $$y^2 = -2(x - c_1).$$

Equation (4) may be written

$$x \, dy + dx = 0$$

from which, for $x \neq 0$,

$$dy + \frac{dx}{x} = 0$$

so that

(6) $$y = - \ln (c_2 x).$$

Equation (2) may be rewritten

$$xy(dy)^2 + (x + y)(dx)(dy) + (dx)^2 = 0$$

in which form $x = 0$ is seen to be a solution. But (6) may be written in the form $x = c_3 e^{-y}$ where $c_3 = 1/c_2$. Then $x = 0$ is a special case of this latter solution and need not be listed separately.

We say, and it is very rough language, that the general solution of (2) is (5) and (6). Particular solutions may be made up from this general solution; they may be drawn from (5) alone, from (6) alone, or conceivably pieced together by using (5) in some intervals and (6) in others. At a point where a solution from (5) is to be joined with a solution from (6) the slope must remain continuous, so by Ex. 21 below the piecing together must take place along the line $y = x$. Note (Ex. 23) that the second derivative, which does not enter the differential equation, need not be continuous.

The existence of these three sets of particular solutions of (2), solutions from (5), from (6), or from (5) and (6), leads to an interesting phenomenon in boundary value problems. Consider the problem of finding a solution of (2) such that the solution passes through the point $(-\frac{1}{2}, 2)$. If the result is to be valid for the interval $-1 < x < -\frac{1}{4}$, there are two answers (Ex. 24). If the result is to be valid for $-1 < x < \frac{1}{2}$, there is only one answer (Ex. 25), one of the two answers to Ex. 24. If the result is to be valid in $-1 < x < 2$, there is only one answer (Ex. 26) and it is different from either of the answers to Ex. 24.

EXERCISES

In Exs. 1–18 find the general solution in the sense of (5) and (6) above.

1. $y^2p^2 - x^2 = 0.$ ANS. $y^2 = c_1 + x^2,\ x^2 + y^2 = c_2^2.$

2. $x^2p^2 + xp - y^2 - y = 0.$ ANS. $y = c_1x,\ x(y+1) = c_2.$

3. $x^2p^2 - 7xyp + 12y^2 = 0.$ ANS. $y = c_1x^3,\ y = c_2x^4.$

4. $xp^2 - 2(y + 2x)p + 8y = 0.$ ANS. $y = 4x + c_1,\ y = c_2x^2.$

5. $p^2 - (x^2y + 3)p + 3x^2y = 0.$ ANS. $y = 3x + c_1,\ x^3 = 3\ln(c_2y).$

6. $xp^2 - (1 + xy)p + y = 0.$ ANS. $y = \ln(c_1x),\ x = \ln(c_2y).$

7. $p^2 - x^2y^2 = 0.$ ANS. $x^2 = 2\ln(c_1y),\ x^2 = -2\ln(c_2y).$

8. $(x + y)^2p^2 = y^2.$ ANS. $x = y\ln(c_1y),\ y(2x + y) = c_2.$

9. $xp^2 + (1 - x^2y)p - xy = 0.$ ANS. $y = c_1e^{x^2/2},\ x = c_2e^{-y}.$

10. $yp^2 + (x - y^2)p - xy = 0.$ ANS. $x^2 + y^2 = c_1^2,\ y = c_2e^x.$

11. $p^2 - xy(x + y)p + x^3y^3 = 0.$

       ANS. $y(x^2 + c_1) = -2,\ x^3 = 3\ln(c_2y).$

12. $(4x - y)p^2 + 6(x - y)p + 2x - 5y = 0.$

       ANS. $x + y = c_1,\ (2x + y)^2 = c_2(y - x).$

13. $(x - y)^2p^2 = y^2.$ ANS. $x = -y\ln(c_1y),\ y(2x - y) = c_2.$

14. $xyp^2 + (xy^2 - 1)p - y = 0.$ ANS. $y^2 = 2\ln(c_1x),\ x = -\ln(c_2y).$

15. $(x^2 + y^2)^2p^2 = 4x^2y^2.$ ANS. $y^2 - x^2 = c_1y,\ y(3x^2 + y^2) = c_2.$

16. $(y + x)^2p^2 + (2y^2 + xy - x^2)p + y(y - x) = 0.$

       ANS. $y^2 + 2xy = c_1,\ y^2 + 2xy - x^2 = c_2.$

17. $xy(x^2 + y^2)(p^2 - 1) = p(x^4 + x^2y^2 + y^4).$

       ANS. $y^2(y^2 + 2x^2) = c_1,\ y^2 = 2x^2\ln(c_2x).$

18. $xp^3 - (x^2 + x + y)p^2 + (x^2 + xy + y)p - xy = 0.$

       ANS. $y = c_1x,\ y = x + c_2,\ x^2 = 2(y - c_3).$

Exs. 19–26 refer to the example of this section. There the differential equation

$$(2) \qquad xyp^2 + (x + y)p + 1 = 0$$

was shown to have the general solution

$$(5) \qquad y^2 = -2(x - c_1)$$

and

$$(6) \qquad y = -\ln(c_2x).$$

19. Show that, of the family (5) above the only curve which passes through the point $(1, 1)$ is $y = (3 - 2x)^{1/2}$ and that this solution is valid for $x < 3/2.$

20. Show that, of the family (6) above the only curve which passes through the point $(1, 1)$ is $y = 1 - \ln x$ and that this solution is valid for $0 < x$.

21. Show that, if a solution of (2) is to be pieced together from (5) and (6), then where the pieces join the slopes of the curves must be equal. Hence, show that the pieces must be joined at a point on the line $y = x$.

22. Show that the curve determined by

$$y = (3 - 2x)^{1/2} \quad \text{for } x \leqq 1,$$
$$y = 1 - \ln x \quad \text{for } 1 \leqq x,$$

is a solution of equation (2) and is valid for all x. The interesting portion of this curve is shown in Figure 38.

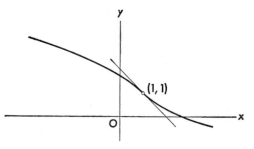

FIGURE 38

23. Show for the solution given in Ex. 22 that y'' is not continuous at $x = 1$. Show that as $x \to 1^-$, $y'' \to -1$ and as $x \to 1^+$, $y'' \to +1$.

24. Find those solutions of (2) which are valid in $-1 < x < -\frac{1}{4}$ and each of which has its graph passing through the point $(-\frac{1}{2}, 2)$.
    ANS. $y = (3 - 2x)^{1/2}$; and $y = 2 - \ln 2 - \ln (-x)$.

25. Find that solution of (2) which is valid for $-1 < x < \frac{1}{2}$ and has its graph passing through the point $(-\frac{1}{2}, 2)$.   ANS. $y = (3 - 2x)^{1/2}$.

26. Find that solution of (2) which is valid for $-1 < x < 2$ and has its graph passing through the point $(-\frac{1}{2}, 2)$.
    ANS. $y = (3 - 2x)^{1/2}$ for $x \leqq 1$,
           $y = 1 - \ln x$ for $1 \leqq x$.

72. Singular solutions.

Let us solve the differential equation

(1) $$y^2 p^2 - a^2 + y^2 = 0.$$

Here

$$yp = \pm \sqrt{a^2 - y^2},$$

so we may write

(2) $$\frac{y\, dy}{\sqrt{a^2 - y^2}} = dx,$$

or

$$(3) \qquad - \frac{y \, dy}{\sqrt{a^2 - y^2}} = dx,$$

or (if the division by $\sqrt{a^2 - y^2}$ cannot be effected)

$$(4) \qquad a^2 - y^2 = 0.$$

From (2) it follows that

$$(5) \qquad x = c_1 - \sqrt{a^2 - y^2},$$

while from (3) that

$$(6) \qquad x = c_2 + \sqrt{a^2 - y^2},$$

and from (4) that

$$(7) \qquad y = a \text{ or } y = -a.$$

Graphically, the solutions (5) are left-hand semicircles with radius a and centered on the x-axis; the solutions (6) are right-hand semicircles of radius a, centered on the x-axis. We may combine (5) and (6) into

$$(8) \qquad (x - c)^2 + y^2 = a^2,$$

which is called the general solution of (1).

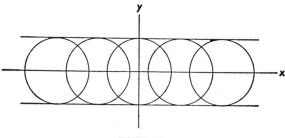

FIGURE 39

From either of the equations (7) we get $p = 0$ so that they, too, satisfy the differential equation (1). But neither of equations (7) is a special case of (8). Then $y = a$ and $y = -a$ are called singular solutions.

A *singular solution* of a nonlinear first-order differential equation is any solution which

(a) is not a special case of the general solution, and

(b) is, at each of its points, tangent to some element of the one-parameter family which is the general solution.

A linear equation cannot have a singular solution.

Figure 39 shows several elements of the family of circles given by equation (8) and also shows the two lines representing $y = a$ and $y = -a$. At each point of either line, the line is tangent to an element of the family of circles. A curve which at each of its points is tangent to an element of a one-parameter family of curves is called an *envelope* of that family.

73. The c-discriminant equation.   Consider the differential equation of the first order,

$$(1) \qquad\qquad f(x, y, p) = 0; \quad p = \frac{dy}{dx},$$

in which the left member is a polynomial in x, y, and p. It may not be possible to factor the left member into factors which are themselves polynomials in x, y, and p. Then the equation is said to be irreducible.

The general solution of (1) will be a one-parameter family of curves,

$$(2) \qquad\qquad \varphi(x, y, c) = 0.$$

A singular solution, if it exists, for equation (1) must be an envelope of the family (2). Each point on the envelope is a point of tangency of the envelope with some element of the family (2) and is determined by the value of c which identifies that element of the family. Then the envelope has parametric equations, $x = x(c)$ and $y = y(c)$, with the c of equation (2) as the parameter. The functions $x(c)$ and $y(c)$ are as yet unknown to us. But the x and y of the point of contact must also satisfy equation (2), from which we get, by differentiation with respect to c, the equation

(3) $$\frac{\partial \varphi}{\partial x}\frac{dx}{dc} + \frac{\partial \varphi}{\partial y}\frac{dy}{dc} + \frac{\partial \varphi}{\partial c} = 0.$$

The slope of the envelope and the slope of the family element concerned must be equal at the point of contact. That slope can be determined by differentiating equation (2) with respect to x, keeping c constant. Thus it follows that

(4) $$\frac{\partial \varphi}{\partial x} + \frac{\partial \varphi}{\partial y}\frac{dy}{dx} = 0.$$

Equations (3) and (4) both hold at the point of contact and from them it follows that

(5) $$\frac{\partial \varphi}{\partial c} = 0.$$

We now have two different equations, $\varphi = 0$ and $\dfrac{\partial \varphi}{\partial c} = 0$, which must be satisfied by x, y, and c. These two equations may be taken as the desired parametric equations. They contain any envelope which may exist for the original family of curves, $\varphi = 0$. Fortunately, there is no need for us to put these equations into the form $x = x(c)$, $y = y(c)$.

The equation which results from the elimination of c from the equations $\varphi = 0$ and $\dfrac{\partial \varphi}{\partial c} = 0$ is called the *c-discriminant equation** of the family $\varphi = 0$. It is a necessary and sufficient condition that the equation

(2) $$\varphi(x,\ y,\ c) = 0,$$

considered as an equation in c, have equal roots.

There is nothing in our work to guarantee that the c-discriminant equation, or any part of it, will be a solution of the differential equation. In order to get the c-discriminant equation we need to have the general solution. During the process of obtaining the general solution we find also the singular solution, if there is one.

---

* The c-discriminant equation may contain a locus of cusps of the elements of the general solution and a locus of nodes of those elements, as well as the envelope which aroused our interest in it.

74. The p-discriminant equation. Suppose that in the irreducible differential equation

$$(1) \qquad\qquad f(x, y, p) = 0$$

the polynomial f is of degree n in p. There will be n roots of equation (1), each yielding a result of the form

$$(2) \qquad\qquad p = g(x, y).$$

If at a point (x_0, y_0) the equation (1) has, as an equation in p, all its roots distinct, then near (x_0, y_0) there will be n distinct equations of the type of equation (2). Near (x_0, y_0) the right members of these n equations will be single-valued and may satisfy the conditions of the existence theorem described in Chapter 15. But if at (x_0, y_0) equation (1) has equal roots, then at least two of the n equations like (2) will have right members assuming the same value at (x_0, y_0). For such equations there is no region, no matter how small, surrounding (x_0, y_0) in which the right member is single-valued. Hence the existence theorem of Chapter 15 cannot be applied when equation (1) has equal roots as an equation in p. Therefore we must give separate consideration to the locus of points (x, y) for which (1) has equal roots.

The condition that equation (1) have equal roots as an equation in p is that both $f = 0$ and $\dfrac{\partial f}{\partial p} = 0$. These two equations in the three variables x, y, and p are parametric equations of a curve in the xy-plane with p playing the role of parameter. The equation which results when p is eliminated from the parametric equations $f = 0$ and $\dfrac{\partial f}{\partial p} = 0$ is called the *p-discriminant equation.*

If an envelope of the general solution of $f = 0$ exists, it will be contained in the p-discriminant equation. No proof is included here.* For us the p-discriminant equation is useful in two ways. When a singular solution is obtained in the natural course of solving the equation, as occurs in Sections 75–77, the p-discriminant equation

---

* For more detail on singular solutions and the discriminants see E. L. Ince, *Ordinary Differential Equations*, London, Longmans, Green and Co., 1927, pp. 82–92.

furnishes us with a check. If none of our methods of attack leads to a general solution, then the p-discriminant equation offers curves which may be particular (including singular) solutions of the differential equation. Then the p-discriminant equation should be tested for possible solutions of the differential equation. Such particular solutions make, of course, no contribution toward finding the general solution.

The p-discriminant equation may contain singular solutions, solutions which are not singular, and curves which are not solutions at all.

EXERCISES

1. For the quadratic equation

$$f = Ap^2 + Bp + C = 0,$$

with A, B, C functions of x and y, show that the p-discriminant obtained by eliminating p from $f = 0$ and $\dfrac{\partial f}{\partial p} = 0$ is the familiar equation

$$B^2 - 4AC = 0.$$

2. For the cubic $p^3 + Ap + B = 0$, show that the p-discriminant equation is $4A^3 + 27B^2 = 0$.
3. For the cubic $p^3 + Ap^2 + B = 0$, show that the p-discriminant equation is $B(4A^3 + 27B) = 0$.
4. Set up the condition that the equation $x^3p^2 + x^2yp + 4 = 0$ (Ex. 1, page 246) have equal roots as a quadratic in p. Compare with the singular solution $xy^2 = 16$.
5. Show that the condition that the equation $xyp^2 + (x + y)p + 1 = 0$ of the example of Section 71, have equal roots in p is $(x - y)^2 = 0$ and that it does not yield a solution of the differential equation. Was there a singular solution?
6. For the equation $y^2p^2 - a^2 + y^2 = 0$ of Section 72, find the condition for equal roots in p and compare with the singular solution.
7. For the differential equation of Ex. 6 show that the curve defined by

$$y = [a^2 - (x + 2a)^2]^{1/2} \quad \text{for} \quad -3a < x \leqq -2a,$$
$$y = a \qquad\qquad\qquad \text{for} \quad -2a \leqq x \leqq 2a,$$
$$y = [a^2 - (x - 2a)^2]^{1/2} \quad \text{for} \quad 2a \leqq x < 3a,$$

is a solution. Sketch the curve and show how it was pieced together from the general solution and the singular solution given in equations (5), (6), and (7) of Section 72.

In Ex. 8–16 obtain (a) the p-discriminant equation and (b) those solutions of the differential equation which are contained in the p-discriminant.

8. $xp^2 - 2yp + 4x = 0.$ ANS.   (a) $y^2 - 4x^2 = 0$; (b) $y = 2x, y = -2x.$

9. $3x^4p^2 - xp - y = 0.$ ANS.   (a) $x^2(1 + 12x^2y) = 0$; (b) $x = 0, 12x^2y = -1.$

10. $p^2 - xp - y = 0.$ ANS.   (a) $x^2 + 4y = 0$; (b) None.

11. $p^2 - xp + y = 0.$ ANS.   (a) $x^2 - 4y = 0$; (b) $x^2 - 4y = 0.$

12. $p^2 + 4x^5p - 12x^4y = 0.$ ANS.   (a) $x^4(x^6 + 3y) = 0$; (b) $3y = -x^6.$

13. $4y^3p^2 - 4xp + y = 0.$ ANS.   (a) $(y^2 - x)(y^2 + x) = 0$; (b) Same as (a).

14. $4y^3p^2 + 4xp + y = 0.$ See also Ex. 13.   ANS.   (a) $(y^2 - x)(y^2 + x) = 0$; (b) None.

15. $p^3 + xp^2 - y = 0.$ ANS.   (a) $y(4x^3 - 27y) = 0$; (b) $y = 0.$

16. $y^4p^3 - 6xp + 2y = 0.$ ANS.   (a) $y^3(y^2 - 2x)(y^4 + 2xy^2 + 4x^2) = 0$; (b) $y = 0, y^2 = 2x.$

17. For the differential equation of Ex. 4 above, the general solution is $cxy + 4x + c^2 = 0.$ Find the condition that this quadratic equation in c have equal roots. Compare with the singular solution.

18. For the general solution

$$(x^2 - 1)c^2 - 2xyc + y^2 - 1 = 0$$

of Example (b), Section 76, find the condition that the equation have equal roots when considered as a quadratic in c. Compare with the singular solution given in that example.

19. Consider the differential equation $xp^2 - 3yp + 9x^2 = 0$ of Example (a), Section 75. Verify that the singular solution $y^2 = 4x^3$ is the envelope of the family of curves given by the general solution $x^3 = c(y - c)$. That is, show that the last two equations have the common solution $x = c^{2/3}, y = 2c,$ counted twice. Then obtain the slopes of the two curves at the point of intersection. Each slope turns out to be $3c^{1/3}.$

75. Eliminating the dependent variable. Suppose the equation

$$(1) \qquad f(x, y, p) = 0; \; p = \frac{dy}{dx},$$

is of a form such that we can readily solve it for the dependent variable y and write

(2) $$y = g(x, p).$$

We can differentiate equation (2) with respect to x and, since $\frac{dy}{dx} = p$, get an equation

(3) $$h\left(x, p, \frac{dp}{dx}\right) = 0$$

involving only x and p. If we can solve equation (3), we will have two equations relating x, y, and p, namely, equation (2) and the solution of (3). These together form parametric equations of the solution of (1) with p now considered a parameter. Of, if p be eliminated between (2) and the solution of (3), then a solution in the nonparametric form is obtained.

EXAMPLE (a): Solve the differential equation

(4) $$xp^2 - 3yp + 9x^2 = 0.$$

Rewrite (4) as

(5) $$3y = xp + 9x^2/p.$$

Then differentiate both members of (5) with respect to x, using the fact that $\frac{dy}{dx} = p$, thus getting

$$3p = p + \frac{18x}{p} + \left(x - \frac{9x^2}{p^2}\right)\frac{dp}{dx},$$

or

(6) $$2p\left(1 - \frac{9x}{p^2}\right) = x\left(1 - \frac{9x}{p^2}\right)\frac{dp}{dx}.$$

From (6) it follows that either

(7) $$1 - \frac{9x}{p^2} = 0$$

or

(8) $$2p = x\frac{dp}{dx}.$$

First consider (8), which leads to

$$2\frac{dx}{x} = \frac{dp}{p}$$

so that

(9) $$p = cx^2.$$

Therefore equations (4) and (9), with p as a parameter, constitute a solution of (4) looked upon as a differential equation with $p = dy/dx$.

In this example it is easy to eliminate p from equations (4) and (9), so we perform that elimination. The result is

$$x \cdot c^2x^4 - 3y \cdot cx^2 + 9x^2 = 0.$$

Disregarding for the moment the possibility that $x = 0$, we can write our solution as

$$c^2x^3 - 3cy + 9 = 0,$$

or

$$3cy = c^2x^3 + 9.$$

Now put $c = 3k$ to get

(10) $$ky = k^2x^3 + 1.$$

Equation (10) with k as an arbitrary constant is called the general solution of the differential equation (4).

It can be seen, rewriting (4) in the form

$$x(dy)^2 - 3y(dy)(dx) + 9x^2(dx)^2 = 0,$$

that $x = 0$ is also a solution of the differential equation. This solution can be fitted into the general solution by a simple device. In equation (10) replace k by $1/c_1$, thus obtaining

(11) $$c_1y = x^3 + c_1{}^2.$$

Putting $c_1 = 0$ in (11) yields the solution $x = 0$.

We have yet to deal with equation (7). Note that (7) is an algebraic relation between x and p in contrast to the differential relation (8) which we have already used. We reason that the elimination of p from (7) and (4) may lead to a solution of the differential equation (4) and that that solution will not involve an arbitrary constant. From (7) it is seen that $p = 3x^{1/2}$ or $p = -3x^{1/2}$. Either of these expressions for p may be substituted into (4) and will lead to

$$(12) \qquad\qquad y^2 = 4x^3.$$

It is not difficult to show that equation (12) is a solution of the differential equation. This solution is not a special case of the general solution (10) or (11). It is a singular solution. Equation (12) has for its graph the envelope of the family of curves given by equation (11). The solution (12) is also easily obtained from the p-discriminant equation.

EXAMPLE (b): Solve the differential equation

$$(13) \qquad\qquad xp^2 - yp - x = 0.$$

The equation is readily solved for y, yielding

$$y = xp - \frac{x}{p}.$$

Then differentiation with respect to x gives

$$p = p - \frac{1}{p} + \left(x + \frac{x}{p^2}\right)\frac{dp}{dx},$$

or

$$\frac{1}{p} = x\left(1 + \frac{1}{p^2}\right)\frac{dp}{dx}.$$

Thus we are led to the differential equation

$$\frac{dx}{x} = \frac{p^2 + 1}{p}\, dp,$$

from which

$$\ln x = p^2/2 + \ln p + \ln c,$$

or

$$(14) \qquad\qquad x = cpe^{p^2/2}.$$

From equation (13) we get

$$y = x(p^2 - 1)/p.$$

Therefore, using (14), we find y in the form

(15) $$y = c(p^2 - 1)e^{p^2/2}.$$

Equations (14) and (15) are parametric equations of the general solution of the original differential equation. In sketching a curve of the family of solutions, for each value of p inserted in (14) and (15) a pair of values x and y is obtained. Thus for each p used we get a point on the desired curve.

The parameter p could have been eliminated by solving the quadratic (13) for p and substituting in (14). The result would be more difficult to sketch than the same curve in parametric form, (14) and (15).

The student should use the p-discriminant equation to show that equation (13) has no singular solution.

It frequently happens, as exhibited in answers to some of the exercises below, that it is inconvenient, even out of the question, to obtain y in terms of p and c alone. It may be best to leave the solution in the form

(16) $$\varphi(x, p) = 0$$

and

(17) $$y = g(x, p).$$

Then in computation we would choose p and determine x from equation (16), after which y would be found from equation (17) using the values of both x and p.

76. Clairaut's equation. Any differential equation of the form

(1) $$y = px + f(p),$$

where $f(p)$ contains neither x nor y explicitly, can be solved at once by the method of Section 75. Equation (1) is called *Clairaut's equation*.

Let us differentiate both members of (1) with respect to x, thus getting

$$p = p + [x + f'(p)]p'$$

or

$$(2) \qquad [x + f'(p)]\frac{dp}{dx} = 0.$$

Then either

$$(3) \qquad \frac{dp}{dx} = 0$$

or

$$(4) \qquad x + f'(p) = 0.$$

The solution of the differential equation (3) is, of course, $p = c$, where c is an arbitrary constant. Returning to the differential equation (1) we can now write its general solution as

$$(5) \qquad y = cx + f(c),$$

a result very easily verified by direct substitution into the differential equation (1). Note that (5) is the equation of a family of straight lines.

Now consider equation (4). Since $f(p)$ and $f'(p)$ are known functions of p, equations (4) and (1) together constitute a set of parametric equations giving x and y in terms of the parameter p. Indeed, from equation (4) it follows that

$$(6) \qquad x = -f'(p)$$

which, combined with equation (1), yields also

$$(7) \qquad y = f(p) - pf'(p).$$

If $f(p)$ is not a linear function of p and not a constant, it can be shown (Exs. 1 and 2 below) that (6) and (7) are parametric equations of a nonlinear solution of the differential equation (1). Since the general solution (5) represents a straight line for each value of c, the solution (6) and (7) cannot be a special case of (5); it is a singular solution.

EXAMPLE (a): Solve the differential equation

$$(8) \qquad y = px + p^3.$$

Since (8) is a Clairaut equation we can write its general solution

$$y = cx + c^3$$

at once.

Then using (6) and (7) we obtain the parametric equations

(9) $x = -3p^2, \; y = -2p^3,$

of the singular solution.   The parameter p may be eliminated from equations (9), thus yielding the form

(10) $27y^2 = -4x^3$

for the singular solution.   See Figure 40.

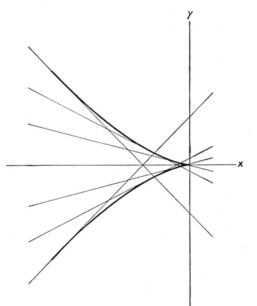

FIGURE 40

EXAMPLE (b): Solve the differential equation

(11) $(x^2 - 1)p^2 - 2xyp + y^2 - 1 = 0.$

Rewrite (11) as

$$x^2p^2 - 2xyp + y^2 - 1 - p^2 = 0.$$

Then it is clear that the equation is of the form

(12)
$$(y - xp)^2 - 1 - p^2 = 0$$

and so could be broken up into two equations each of Clairaut's form. Then the general solution of (11) is obtained by replacing p everywhere in it by an arbitrary constant c. That is,

(13)
$$(x^2 - 1)c^2 - 2xyc + y^2 - 1 = 0$$

is the general solution of (11). The solution (13) is composed of two families of straight lines

(14)
$$y = c_1 x + \sqrt{1 + c_1^2}$$
and

(15)
$$y = c_2 x - \sqrt{1 + c_2^2}.$$

From the p-discriminant equation for (11) we obtain at once the singular solution

(16)
$$x^2 + y^2 = 1.$$

EXERCISES

1. Let α be a parameter and prove that if $f''(\alpha)$ exists, then

(17)
$$x = -f'(\alpha),\ y = f(\alpha) - \alpha f'(\alpha)$$

is a solution of the differential equation $y = px + f(p)$. Hint: use dx and dy to get p in terms of α and then show that $y - px - f(p)$ vanishes identically.

2. Prove that if $f''(\alpha) \neq 0$, then (17) above is not a special case of the general solution $y = cx + f(c)$. Hint: show that the slope of the graph of one solution depends upon x while the slope of the graph of the other does not depend upon x.

In Exs. 3–30 find the general solution and also the singular solution, if it exists.

3. $p^2 + x^3 p - 2x^2 y = 0$.   ANS. $c^2 + cx^2 = 2y$; sing. sol. $8y = -x^4$.
4. $p^2 + 4x^5 p - 12x^4 y = 0$.

    ANS. $12y = c(c + 4x^3)$; sing. sol. $3y = -x^6$.
5. $2xp^3 - 6yp^2 + x^4 = 0$.   ANS. $2c^3 x^3 = 1 - 6c^2 y$; sing. sol. $2y = x^2$.
6. $p^2 - xp + y = 0$.   ANS. $y = cx - c^2$; sing. sol. $x^2 = 4y$.

7. $y = px + kp^2$.   ANS. $y = cx + kc^2$; sing. sol. $x^2 = -4ky$.

8. $x^8p^2 + 3xp + 9y = 0$.   ANS. $x^3(y + c^2) + c = 0$; sing. sol. $4x^6y = 1$.

9. $x^4p^2 + 2x^3yp - 4 = 0$.   ANS. $x^2(1 + cy) = c^2$.

10. $xp^2 - 2yp + 4x = 0$.

ANS. $x^2 = c(y - c)$; sing. sol. $y = 2x$ and $y = -2x$.

11. $3x^4p^2 - xp - y = 0$.   ANS. $xy = c(3cx - 1)$; sing. sol. $12x^2y = -1$.

12. $xp^2 + (x - y)p + 1 - y = 0$.

ANS. $xc^2 + (x - y)c + 1 - y = 0$; sing. sol. $(x + y)^2 = 4x$.

13. $p(xp - y + k) + a = 0$.

ANS. $c(xc - y + k) + a = 0$; sing. sol. $(y - k)^2 = 4ax$.

14. $x^6p^3 - 3xp - 3y = 0$.   ANS. $3xy = c(xc^2 - 3)$; sing. sol. $9x^3y^2 = 4$.

15. $y = x^6p^3 - xp$.   ANS. $xy = c(c^2x - 1)$; sing. sol. $27x^3y^2 = 4$.

16. $xp^4 - 2yp^3 + 12x^3 = 0$.

ANS. $2c^3y = c^4x^2 + 12$; sing. sol. $3y^2 = \pm 8x^3$.

17. $xp^3 - yp^2 + 1 = 0$.   ANS. $xc^3 - yc^2 + 1 = 0$; sing. sol. $4y^3 = 27x^2$.

18. $y = px + p^n$, for $n \neq 0$, $n \neq 1$.

ANS. $y = cx + c^n$; sing. sol. $\left(\dfrac{x}{n}\right)^n = -\left(\dfrac{y}{n-1}\right)^{n-1}$.

19. $p^2 - xp - y = 0$.   ANS. $3x = 2p + cp^{-1/2}$ and $3y = p^2 - cp^{1/2}$.

20. $2p^3 + xp - 2y = 0$.   ANS. $x = 2p(3p + c)$ and $y = p^2(4p + c)$.

21. $2p^2 + xp - 2y = 0$.   ANS. $x = 4p \ln (pc)$ and $y = p^2[1 + 2 \ln (pc)]$.

22. $p^3 + 2xp - y = 0$.   ANS. $4x = -3p^2 + cp^{-2}$ and $2y = -p^3 + cp^{-1}$.

23. $4xp^2 - 3yp + 3 = 0$.

ANS. $2x = 3p^{-2} + cp^{-4}$ and $3y = 9p^{-1} + 2cp^{-3}$.

24. $p^3 - xp + 2y = 0$.   ANS. $x = p(c - 3p)$ and $2y = p^2(c - 4p)$.

25. $5p^2 + 6xp - 2y = 0$.   ANS. $p^3(x + p)^2 = c$ and $2y = 6xp + 5p^2$.

26. $2xp^2 + (2x - y)p + 1 - y = 0$.

ANS. $p^2x = (1 + p)^{-1} + \ln [c(1 + p)]$ and
$py = 1 + (1 + p)^{-1} + 2 \ln [c(1 + p)]$.

27. $5p^2 + 3xp - y = 0$.   ANS. $p^3(x + 2p)^2 = c$ and $y = 3xp + 5p^2$.

28. $p^2 + 3xp - y = 0$.   ANS. $p^3(5x + 2p)^2 = c$ and $y = 3xp + p^2$.

29. $y = xp + x^3p^2$.   ANS. $x^2 = cp^{-4/3} - 2p^{-1}$ and $y = xp + x^3p^2$.

30. $8y = 3x^2 + p^2$.   ANS. $(p - 3x)^3 = c(p - x)$ and $8y = 3x^2 + p^2$.

77. Eliminating the independent variable.

Suppose that a differential equation

$$(1) \qquad\qquad f(x,\, y,\, p) = 0; \; p = \frac{dy}{dx},$$

can readily be solved for the independent variable x.   Then we can proceed very much as we did in Section 75, but this time differentiating with respect to y and using the fact that

$$\frac{dx}{dy} = \frac{1}{p}.$$

This is, of course, nothing new at all. Since (1) is a first-order equation the roles of independent and dependent variable can be interchanged at will using the relation

$$\frac{dy}{dx} = \left(\frac{dx}{dy}\right)^{-1}.$$

EXAMPLE: Solve the differential equation

(2) $$yp^2 - xp + 2y = 0.$$

First solve for x, obtaining

(3) $$x = yp + \frac{2y}{p},$$

and then differentiate both members of equation (3) with respect to y. The resulting relation is

$$\frac{1}{p} = p + \frac{2}{p} + \left(y - \frac{2y}{p^2}\right)\frac{dp}{dy}$$

or

$$\frac{1}{p} + p + y\left(1 - \frac{2}{p^2}\right)\frac{dp}{dy} = 0.$$

Therefore we are led to the equation

(4) $$\frac{dy}{y} + \frac{p^2 - 2}{p(1 + p^2)}\, dp = 0$$

from which

$$\frac{dy}{y} + \frac{3p\, dp}{1 + p^2} - \frac{2dp}{p} = 0.$$

Hence

$$\ln y = -\tfrac{3}{2}\ln (1 + p^2) + 2\ln p + \ln c,$$

so that

(5) $$y = cp^2(1 + p^2)^{-3/2}.$$

From equation (3) it follows that

$$x = p^{-1}y(p^2 + 2).$$

Therefore, using (5) we may write

(6) $$x = cp(p^2 + 2)(1 + p^2)^{-3/2}.$$

Equations (5) and (6) are a set of parametric equations for the general solution of (2). There is no singular solution of (2).

EXERCISES

In Exs. 1–10 find the general solution and the singular solution in non-parametric form. That is, eliminate the parameter after obtaining the solutions in parametric form.

1. $xp^2 + yp = 3y^4$.   ANS. $3y = c(1 + cxy)$; sing. sol. $12xy^2 = -1$.

2. $9xp^2 + 3yp + y^8 = 0$.   ANS. $c^2xy^3 + c + y^3 = 0$; sing. sol. $4xy^6 = 1$.

3. $p^2 + xy^2p + y^3 = 0$.   ANS. $cy(x - c) = 1$; sing. sol. $x^2y = 4$.

4. $4xp^2 + 4yp - y^4 = 0$.   ANS. $y(c^2x - 1) = 2c$; sing. sol. $xy^2 = -1$.

5. $4yp^2 - 2xp + y = 0$.   ANS. $cx = y^2 + c^2$; sing. sols. $x = \pm 2y$.

6. $9p^2 + 12xy^4p + 4y^5 = 0$.
     ANS. $c^2y^3 + 4cxy^3 + 4 = 0$; sing. sol. $x^2y^3 = 1$.

7. $2xy^2p^2 - y^3p - 1 = 0$.   ANS. $2c^2x = cy^2 + 1$; sing. sol. $y^4 = -8x$.

8. $p^2 + 2xy^3p + y^4 = 0$.   ANS. $4cy^2(x - c) = 1$; sing. sol. $xy = -1$.

9. $9y^2p^2 - 3xp + y = 0$.   ANS. $y^3 = c(x - c)$; sing. sol. $x^2 = 4y^3$.

10. $y^4p^3 - 6xp + 2y = 0$.   ANS. $y^3 = 18c(x - 6c^2)$; sing. sol. $y^2 = 2x$.

In Exs. 11–15 find the general solution in parametric form.

11. $xp^2 - yp - y = 0$.   ANS. $x = c(p + 1)e^p$ and $y = cp^2e^p$.

12. $y^2p^3 - xp + y = 0$.   ANS. $y = cp^{-1} - \frac{1}{4}p^{-3}$ and $px = y(yp^3 + 1)$.

13. $yp^2 - xp + y = 0$.
     ANS. $x = c(p^{-2} + 1)e^{-1/(2p^2)}$ and $y = cp^{-1}e^{-1/(2p^2)}$.

14. $yp^3 - 3xp + 3y = 0$.
     ANS. $\ln y = c - p^{-3} - 2\ln p$ and $3px = y(p^3 + 3)$.

15. $y^3p^3 - xp + y = 0$.
     ANS. $5y^2 = cp^{-4/3} - 2p^{-3}$ and $5px = y(3 + cp^{5/3})$.

MISCELLANEOUS EXERCISES

1. $x^3p^2 + x^2yp + 4 = 0$.   ANS. $cxy + 4x + c^2 = 0$; sing. sol. $xy^2 = 16$.

2. $6xp^2 - (3x + 2y)p + y = 0$.   ANS. $y^3 = c_1x$, $2y = x + c_2$.

3. $9p^2 + 3xy^4p + y^5 = 0$.   ANS. $cy^3(x - c) = 1$; sing. sol. $x^2y^3 = 4$.

4. $4y^3p^2 - 4xp + y = 0$.   ANS. $y^4 = 4c(x - c)$; sing. sol. $y^2 = x$.

5. $x^6p^2 - 2xp - 4y = 0$.   ANS. $x^2(y - c^2) = c$; sing. sol. $4x^4y = -1$.

6. $5p^2 + 6xp - 2y = 0$.   ANS. $x = cp^{-3/2} - p$ and $2y = 6cp^{-1/2} - p^2$.

7. Do Ex. 6 by another method.

8. $y^2p^2 - y(x + 1)p + x = 0$.   ANS. $x^2 - y^2 = c_1,\ y^2 = 2(x - c_2)$.

9. $4x^5p^2 + 12x^4yp + 9 = 0$.   ANS. $x^3(2cy - 1) = c^2$; sing. sol. $x^3y^2 = 1$.

10. $4y^2p^3 - 2xp + y = 0$.

ANS. $y^2 = 2c(x - 2c^2)$; sing. sol. $8x^3 = 27y^4$.

11. $p^4 + xp - 3y = 0$.   ANS. $5x = 4p^3 + cp^{1/2}$ and $15y = 9p^4 + cp^{3/2}$.

12. Do Ex. 11 by another method.

13. $xp^2 + (k - x - y)p + y = 0$, the equation of Ex. 5, p. 14.

ANS. $xc^2 + (k - x - y)c + y = 0$;
sing. sol. $(x - y)^2 - 2k(x + y) + k^2 = 0$.

14. $x^2p^3 - 2xyp^2 + y^2p + 1 = 0$.

ANS. $x^2c^3 - 2xyc^2 + y^2c + 1 = 0$; sing. sol. $27x = -4y^3$.

15. $16xp^2 + 8yp + y^6 = 0$.   ANS. $y^2(c^2x + 1) = 2c$; sing. sol. $xy^4 = 1$.

16. $xp^2 - (x^2 + 1)p + x = 0$.   ANS. $x^2 = 2(y - c_1),\ y = \ln(c_2x)$.

17. $p^3 - 2xp - y = 0$.   ANS. $8x = 3p^2 + cp^{-2/3}$ and $4y = p^3 - cp^{1/3}$.

18. Do Ex. 17 by another method.

19. $9xy^4p^2 - 3y^5p - 1 = 0$.   ANS. $cy^3 = c^2x - 1$; sing. sol. $y^6 = -4x$.

20. $x^2p^2 - (2xy + 1)p + y^2 + 1 = 0$.

ANS. $x^2c^2 - (2xy + 1)c + y^2 + 1 = 0$; sing. sol. $4x^2 - 4xy - 1 = 0$.

21. $x^2p^2 = (x - y)^2$.   ANS. $x(x - 2y) = c_1,\ y = -x\ln(c_2x)$.

22. $xp^3 - 2yp^2 + 4x^2 = 0$.   See Ex. 10 above.

ANS. $x^2 = 4c(y - 8c^2)$; sing. sol. $8y^3 = 27x^4$.

23. $(p + 1)^2(y - px) = 1$.

ANS. $(c + 1)^2(y - cx) = 1$; sing. sol. $4(x + y)^3 = 27x^2$.

24. $p^3 - p^2 + xp - y = 0$.

ANS. $y = cx + c^3 - c^2$; sing. sol. with parametric equations
$x = 2\alpha - 3\alpha^2$ and $y = \alpha^2 - 2\alpha^3$.

25. $xp^2 + y(1 - x)p - y^2 = 0$.   ANS. $xy = c_1,\ x = \ln(c_2y)$.

26. $yp^2 - (x + y)p + y = 0$.

ANS. $py = ce^{1/p}$ and $px = y(p^2 - p + 1)$; sing. sol. $y = x$.

27. $p^2 + yp - x - 1 = 0$.

ANS. $x = -1 - p(p^2 - 1)^{-1/2}\ln\{[p + (p^2 - 1)^{1/2}]c\}$
and $y = -p - (p^2 - 1)^{-1/2}\ln\{[p + (p^2 - 1)^{1/2}]c\}$.

Chapter 17

Special Equations of Order Two

78. Dependent variable missing. Consider a second-order equation,

(1) $$f(x, y', y'') = 0,$$

which does not contain the dependent variable y explicitly. Let us put

$$y' = p.$$

Then

$$y'' = \frac{dp}{dx}$$

and equation (1) may be replaced by

(2) $$f\left(x, p, \frac{dp}{dx}\right) = 0,$$

an equation of order one in p. If we can find p from equation (2), then y can be obtained from $y' = p$ by an integration.

EXAMPLE: Solve the equation

(3) $$xy'' - (y')^3 - y' = 0$$

of Example (b), page 13.

Since y does not appear explicitly in the differential equation (3), put $y' = p$. Then

$$y'' = \frac{dp}{dx}$$

so that equation (3) becomes

$$x \frac{dp}{dx} - p^3 - p = 0.$$

Separation of variables leads to

$$\frac{dp}{p(p^2 + 1)} = \frac{dx}{x}$$

or

$$\frac{dp}{p} - \frac{p\,dp}{p^2 + 1} = \frac{dx}{x}$$

from which

(4) $$\ln p - \tfrac{1}{2}\ln(p^2 + 1) + \ln c_1 = \ln x$$

follows.

Equation (4) yields

(5) $$c_1 p(p^2 + 1)^{-1/2} = x$$

which we wish to solve for p.   From (5) we conclude that

$$c_1^2 p^2 = x^2(1 + p^2),$$

or

$$p^2 = \frac{x^2}{c_1^2 - x^2}.$$

But $p = y'$, so we have

(6) $$dy = \pm\, \frac{x\,dx}{\sqrt{c_1^2 - x^2}}.$$

The solution of (6) is

$$y - c_2 = \mp(c_1^2 - x^2)^{1/2},$$

or

(7) $$x^2 + (y - c_2)^2 = c_1^2.$$

Equation (7) is the desired general solution of the differential equation (3).   Note that in dividing by p early in the work we might have discarded the solutions $y = k(p = 0)$, where k is constant. But (7) can be put in the form

(8) $$c_3(x^2 + y^2) + c_4 y + 1 = 0,$$

with new arbitrary constants c_3 and c_4. Then the choice $c_3 = 0$, $c_4 = -1/k$ yields the solution $y = k$.

79. Independent variable missing. A second-order equation

$$(1) \qquad f(y, y', y'') = 0$$

in which the independent variable x does not appear explicitly can be reduced to a first-order equation in y and y'. Put

$$y' = p,$$

then

$$y'' = \frac{dp}{dx} = \frac{dy}{dx}\frac{dp}{dy} = p\,\frac{dp}{dy},$$

so that equation (1) becomes

$$(2) \qquad f\left(y, p, p\,\frac{dp}{dy}\right) = 0.$$

We try to determine p in terms of y from equation (2) and then substitute the result into $y' = p$.

EXAMPLE: Solve the equation

$$(3) \qquad yy'' + (y')^2 + 1 = 0$$

of Ex. 8, page 14.

Since the independent variable does not appear explicitly in equation (3), we put $y' = p$ and obtain

$$y'' = p\,\frac{dp}{dy}$$

as above. Then equation (3) becomes

$$(4) \qquad yp\,\frac{dp}{dy} + p^2 + 1 = 0$$

in which the variables p and y are easily separated.

From (4) it follows that

$$\frac{p\,dp}{p^2 + 1} + \frac{dy}{y} = 0$$

from which

$$\tfrac{1}{2} \ln \, (p^2 + 1) + \ln y = \ln c_1$$

so that

(5) $$p^2 + 1 = c_1{}^2 y^{-2}.$$

We solve equation (5) for p and find that

$$p = \pm \, \frac{(c_1{}^2 - y^2)^{1/2}}{y}.$$

Therefore

$$\frac{dy}{dx} = \pm \, \frac{(c_1{}^2 - y^2)^{1/2}}{y}$$

or

$$\pm \, y(c_1{}^2 - y^2)^{-1/2} \, dy = dx.$$

Then

$$\mp \, (c_1{}^2 - y^2)^{1/2} = x - c_2,$$

from which we obtain the final result

$$(x - c_2)^2 + y^2 = c_1{}^2.$$

EXERCISES

1. $y'' = x(y')^3$.   ANS. $x = c_1 \sin \, (y + c_2)$.
2. $x^2 y'' + (y')^2 - 2xy' = 0$; when $x = 2$, $y = 5$ and $y' = -4$.
                  ANS. $y = \tfrac{1}{2} x^2 + 3x - 3 + 9 \ln \, (3 - x)$.
3. $x^2 y'' + (y')^2 - 2xy' = 0$; when $x = 2$, $y = 5$ and $y' = 2$.
                  ANS. $x^2 = 2(y - 3)$.

4. $yy'' + (y')^2 = 0$.   ANS. See Ex. 20, page 14.
5. $y^2 y'' + (y')^3 = 0$.   ANS. $x = c_1 y - \ln \, (c_2 y)$.
6. $(y + 1)y'' = (y')^2$.   ANS. $y + 1 = c_2 e^{c_1 x}$.
7. $2ay'' + (y')^3 = 0$.   ANS. $(y - c_2)^2 = 4a(x - c_1)$.
8. Do Ex. 7 by another method.
9. $xy'' = y' + x^5$; when $x = 1$, $y = \tfrac{1}{2}$ and $y' = 1$.
                  ANS. $24y = x^6 + 9x^2 + 2$.
10. $xy'' + y' + x = 0$; when $x = 2$, $y = -1$ and $y' = -\tfrac{1}{2}$.
                  ANS. $y = -\tfrac{1}{4} x^2 + \ln \, (\tfrac{1}{2} x)$.
11. $y'' = 2y(y')^3$.   ANS. $y^3 = 3(c_2 - x - c_1 y)$.
12. $yy'' + (y')^3 - (y')^2 = 0$.   ANS. $x = y - c_1 \ln \, (c_2 y)$.
13. $y'' + \beta^2 y = 0$.   Check your result by solving the equation in two ways.
14. $yy'' + (y')^3 = 0$.   ANS. $x = c_1 + y \ln \, (c_2 y)$.
15. $y'' \cos x = y'$.   ANS. $y = c_2 + c_1 \ln \, (1 - \sin x)$.
16. $y'' = x(y')^2$; when $x = 2$, $y = \tfrac{1}{4}\pi$ and $y' = -\tfrac{1}{4}$.   ANS. $x = 2 \cot y$.

17. $y'' = x(y')^2$; when $x = 0$, $y = 1$ and $y' = \frac{1}{2}$.

$$\text{ANS.} \quad y = 1 + \tfrac{1}{2} \ln \frac{2 + x}{2 - x}.$$

18. $y'' = -e^{-2y}$; when $x = 3$, $y = 0$ and $y' = 1$.   ANS. $y = \ln (x - 2)$.

19. $y'' = -e^{-2y}$; when $x = 3$, $y = 0$ and $y' = -1$.

$$\text{ANS.} \quad y = \ln (4 - x).$$

20. $2y'' = \sin 2y$; when $x = 0$, $y = \pi/2$ and $y' = 1$.

$$\text{ANS.} \quad x = - \ln (\csc y + \cot y).$$

21. $2y'' = \sin 2y$; when $x = 0$, $y = -\pi/2$ and $y' = 1$.

$$\text{ANS.} \quad x = \ln (- \csc y - \cot y).$$

22. Show that if you can perform the integrations encountered, then you can solve any equation of the form $y'' = f(y)$.

23. $x^3 y'' - x^2 y' = 3 - x^2$.   ANS. $y = x^{-1} + x + c_1 x^2 + c_2$.

24. $y'' = (y')^2$.   ANS. $y = - \ln [c_2(c_1 - x)]$; or $x = c_1 + c_3 e^{-y}$.

25. $y'' = e^x (y')^2$.   ANS. $c_1 y + c_2 = - \ln (c_1 e^{-x} - 1)$.

26. $2y'' = (y')^3 \sin 2x$; when $x = 0$, $y = 1$ and $y' = 1$.

$$\text{ANS.} \quad y = 1 + \ln (\sec x + \tan x).$$

27. $x^2 y'' + (y')^2 = 0$.   ANS. $c_1{}^2 y = c_1 x + \ln [c_2(c_1 x - 1)]$.

28. $y'' = 1 + (y')^2$.   ANS. $e^y \cos (x + c_1) = c_2$.

29. Do Ex. 28 by another method.

30. $y'' = [1 + (y')^2]^{3/2}$.   Solve in three ways, by considering the geometric significance of the equation, and by the methods of this chapter.

31. $yy'' = (y')^2[1 - y' \sin y - yy' \cos y]$.   ANS. $x = c_1 \ln (c_2 y) - \cos y$.

32. $(1 + y^2)y'' + (y')^3 + y' = 0$.

$$\text{ANS.} \quad x = c_2 + c_1 y - (1 + c_1{}^2) \ln (y + c_1).$$

33. $[yy'' + 1 + (y')^2]^2 = [1 + (y')^2]^3$.   ANS. $(y - c_1)^2 + (x - c_2)^2 = c_1{}^2$.

34. $x^2 y'' = y'(2x - y')$; when $x = -1$, $y = 5$ and $y' = 1$.

$$\text{ANS.} \quad 2y - 1 = (x - 2)^2 + 8 \ln (x + 2).$$

35. $x^2 y'' = y'(3x - 2y')$.   ANS. $2y = x^2 + c_2 - c_1 \ln (x^2 + c_1)$.

36. $xy'' = y'(2 - 3xy')$.   ANS. $3y = c_2 + \ln (x^3 + c_1)$.

37. $x^4 y'' = y'(y' + x^3)$; when $x = 1$, $y = 2$ and $y' = 1$.

$$\text{ANS.} \quad y = 1 + x^2 - \ln \left(\frac{1 + x^2}{2} \right).$$

38. $y'' = 2x + (x^2 - y')^2$.   ANS. $3y = x^3 + c_2 - 3 \ln (x + c_1)$.

39. $(y'')^2 - 2y'' + (y')^2 - 2xy' + x^2 = 0$; when $x = 0$, $y = \frac{1}{2}$ and $y' = 1$.

$$\text{ANS.} \quad 2y = 1 + x^2 + 2 \sin x.$$

40. $(y'')^2 - xy'' + y' = 0$.

$$\text{ANS.} \quad \text{General solution:} \ 2y = c_1 x^2 - 2c_1{}^2 x + c_2;$$
$$\text{family of singular solutions:} \ 12y = x^3 + k.$$

41. $(y'')^3 = 12y'(xy'' - 2y')$.

$$\text{ANS.} \quad \text{General solution:} \ y = c_1(x - c_1)^3 + c_2;$$
$$\text{family of singular solutions:} \ 9y = x^4 + k.$$

42. $3yy'y'' = (y')^3 - 1$.   ANS. $27c_1(y + c_1)^2 = 8(x + c_2)^3$.

43. $4y(y')^2 y'' = (y')^4 + 3$.   ANS. $256c_1(y - c_1)^3 = 243(x - c_2)^4$.

80. The catenary. Let a cable of uniformly distributed weight w (lb per ft) be suspended between two supports at points A and B as indicated in Figure 41. The cable will sag and there will be a lowest point V as indicated in the figure. We wish to determine the curve formed by the suspended cable. That curve is called the *catenary*.

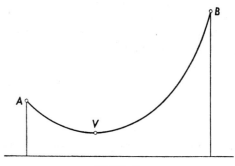

FIGURE 41

Choose coordinate axes as shown in Figure 42, the y-axis vertical through the point V and the x-axis horizontal and passing at a distance y_0 (to be chosen later) below V. Let s represent length (ft) of

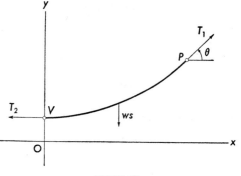

FIGURE 42

the cable measured from V to the variable point P with coordinates (x, y). Then the portion of the cable from V to P is subject to the three forces shown in Figure 42. Those forces are: (a) the gravitational force ws (lb) acting downward through the center of gravity of the portion of the cable from V to P, (b) the tension T_1 (lb) acting tangentially at P, and (c) the tension T_2 (lb) acting horizontally (again tangentially) at V. The tension T_1 is a variable; the tension T_2 is constant.

Since equilibrium is assumed, the algebraic sum of the vertical components of these forces is zero and the algebraic sum of the horizontal components of these forces is also zero. Therefore, if θ is the angle of inclination, from the horizontal, of the tangent to the curve at the point (x, y), we have

$$(1) \qquad\qquad T_1 \sin \theta - ws = 0$$

and

$$(2) \qquad\qquad T_1 \cos \theta - T_2 = 0.$$

But $\tan \theta$ is the slope of the curve of the cable, so that

$$(3) \qquad\qquad \tan \theta = \frac{dy}{dx}.$$

We may eliminate the variable tension T_1 from equations (1) and (2) and obtain

$$(4) \qquad\qquad \tan \theta = \frac{ws}{T_2}.$$

The constant T_2/w has the dimension of a length. Put $T_2/w = a$ (ft). Then equation (4) becomes

$$(5) \qquad\qquad \tan \theta = \frac{s}{a}.$$

From equations (3) and (5) we see that

$$(6) \qquad\qquad \frac{s}{a} = \frac{dy}{dx}.$$

Now we know from calculus that, since s is the length of arc of the curve, then

$$(7) \qquad\qquad \frac{ds}{dx} = \sqrt{1 + \left(\frac{dy}{dx}\right)^2}.$$

From (6) we get $\dfrac{1}{a}\dfrac{ds}{dx} = \dfrac{d^2y}{dx^2}$, so that the elimination of s yields the differential equation

(8)
$$\frac{d^2y}{dx^2} = \frac{1}{a}\sqrt{1 + \left(\frac{dy}{dx}\right)^2}.$$

The desired equation of the curve assumed by the suspended cable is that solution of the differential equation (8) which also satisfies the boundary conditions

(9)   when $x = 0$, $y = y_0$ and $\dfrac{dy}{dx} = 0$.

Equation (8) fits into either of the types studied in this chapter. It is left as an exercise for the student to solve the differential equation (8) with the conditions (9) and arrive at the result

(10) $$y = a \cosh \frac{x}{a} + y_0 - a.$$

Then, of course, the sensible choice $y_0 = a$ is made so that the equation of the desired curve (the catenary) is

$$y = a \cosh \frac{x}{a}.$$

Chapter 18

The Power Series Method

81. Introduction. The solution of linear equations with constant coefficients can be accomplished by the methods developed earlier in the book. The general linear equation of the first order yields to an integrating factor as was seen in Chapter 2. For linear ordinary differential equations with variable coefficients and of order greater than one, probably the most generally effective method of attack yet devised is that based upon the use of power series

In order to simplify the work and the statement of theorems, the equations treated here will be restricted to those with polynomial coefficients. The difficulties to be encountered, the methods of attack, and the results accomplished all remain essentially unchanged when the coefficients are permitted to be functions (called analytic) which have power series expansions valid about some point.

Consider the homogeneous linear equation of the second order,

$$(1) \qquad b_0(x)y'' + b_1(x)y' + b_2(x)y = 0,$$

with polynomial coefficients. If $b_0(x)$ does not vanish at $x = 0$, then in some interval about $x = 0$, staying away from the nearest point where $b_0(x)$ does vanish, it is safe to divide throughout by $b_0(x)$. Thus we replace equation (1) by

$$(2) \qquad y'' + p(x)y' + q(x)y = 0,$$

in which the coefficients $p(x)$, $q(x)$, are rational functions of x with denominators which do not vanish at $x = 0$.

We shall now show that it is reasonable to expect* a solution of

---

* This is no proof. For proof see, for instance, E. D. Rainville, *Intermediate Differential Equations*, New York, John Wiley & Sons, 1943, pp. 80–83

(2) which is a power series in x and which contains two arbitrary constants. Let $y = y(x)$ be a solution of equation (2). We assign arbitrarily the values of y and y' at $x = 0$; $y(0) = A$, $y'(0) = B$.

Equation (2) yields

$$(3) \qquad y''(x) = -p(x)y'(x) - q(x)y(x),$$

so that $y''(0)$ may be computed directly because $p(x)$ and $q(x)$ are well behaved at $x = 0$. From equation (3) we get

$$(4) \quad y'''(x) = -p(x)y''(x) - p'(x)y'(x) - q(x)y'(x) - q'(x)y(x),$$

and thus $y'''(0)$ can be computed once $y''(0)$ is known.

The above process can be continued as long as we wish, and therefore we can determine successively $y^{(n)}(0)$ for as many integral values of n as may be desired. Now, by Maclaurin's formula in calculus,

$$(5) \qquad y(x) = y(0) + \sum_{n=1}^{\infty} y^{(n)}(0) \frac{x^n}{n!};$$

that is, the right member of (5) will converge to the value $y(x)$ throughout some interval about $x = 0$ if $y(x)$ is sufficiently well behaved at and near $x = 0$. Thus we can determine the function $y(x)$ and are led to a solution in power series form.

In actually obtaining the solution for specific equations we shall use a method illustrated in the examples, a technique far superior to the brute force method above. What we have gained from the present discussion is the knowledge that it is reasonable to seek a power series solution. Once we know that, it remains only to develop good methods for finding the solution and theorems regarding the validity of the results so found.

82. Equations of higher order and degree. Careful examination of the procedure used in Section 81 shows that the method was dependent only upon our being able to solve the original equation for y'' and upon the existence of the various derivatives of the right member of equation (3) of that section. Hence, if we have at hand an equation of the form

$$(1) \qquad y^{(k)} = f(x, y, y', \cdots, y^{(k-1)})$$

of order k and of any degree, then we can anticipate the existence of a power series solution under the following conditions. Suppose the right member f in equation (1) is such that it, and its various derivatives with respect to x, exist at $x = 0$. Then we may expect to assign arbitrarily the values of y and its first $(k - 1)$ derivatives at $x = 0$, (thus having k arbitrary constants) and proceed to determine $y^{(n)}(0)$ for $n \geq k$ from equation (1).

83. Convergence of power series. From calculus we know that the power series

$$\sum_{n=0}^{\infty} a_n x^n$$

converges either at $x = 0$ alone, or for all finite x, or the series converges in an interval $-R < x < R$, and diverges outside that interval. Unless the series converges at only one point, it represents, where it does converge, a function $f(x)$ in the sense that the series has at each value x the sum $f(x)$.

If

$$f(x) = \sum_{n=0}^{\infty} a_n x^n, \quad -R < x < R,$$

then also

$$f'(x) = \sum_{n=0}^{\infty} n a_n x^{n-1}, \quad -R < x < R,$$

and

$$\int_0^x f(y)dy = \sum_{n=0}^{\infty} \frac{a_n x^{n+1}}{n+1}, \quad -R < x < R.$$

That is, the series is termwise differentiable and integrable in the sense that the series of the derivatives of the separate terms converges to the derivative of the sum of the original series and similarly for integration. It is important that the interval of convergence remains unchanged. We are not concerned here with convergence behavior at the endpoints of that interval.

Let us look more closely into the reason that a series has a particular interval of convergence rather than some other one.   An elementary example from calculus is

$$(1) \qquad \frac{1}{1 - x} = \sum_{n=0}^{\infty} x^n, \quad -1 < x < 1.$$

It is reasonable to suspect that the misbehavior of the function $1/(1 - x)$ at $x = 1$ is what lies behind the fact that the interval of convergence terminates at $x = 1$.   That it must extend that far is not so evident.   The point $x = -1$ has no bearing in this instance; the interval is terminated at that end by the requirement that it be symmetric about $x = 0$.

Now let us replace x in (1) by $(-x^2)$ to get

$$(2) \qquad \frac{1}{1 + x^2} = \sum_{n=0}^{\infty} (-1)^n x^{2n}, \quad -1 < x < 1.$$

Again the interval of convergence is $-1 < x < 1$ but the function $f(x) = 1/(1 + x^2)$ is well behaved for all real x.   What stopped the interval of convergence at $x = 1$ is not so clear.   The fact is that we need to consider x as a complex variable in order to understand what is going on here.

We use the ordinary Argand diagram for complex numbers.   Let $x = a + ib$, a and b real, with $i = \sqrt{-1}$, and associate with the point (a, b) in the plane the number $a + ib$.   Now mark on the diagram those points (values of x) for which the function $1/(1 + x^2)$ does not exist.   The points are $x = i$, $x = -i$, where the denominator $(1 + x^2)$ vanishes.   In books on functions of a complex variable it is shown that the series in (2) converges for all values of x inside the circle shown in Figure 43. The interval of convergence

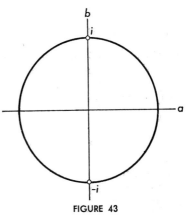

FIGURE 43

given in (2) is merely a cross section of the region of convergence in the complex plane.

A power series in a complex variable x always has as its region of convergence the interior of a circle, if we are willing to admit the extreme cases in which the circle degenerates into a single point or expands, extending over the whole complex plane.

Points at which the denominator of a rational function vanishes, are the most elementary examples of singularities of an analytic function. The circle of convergence of a power series cannot have inside it a singularity of the function represented by the series. The circle of convergence has its center at the origin and passes through the singularity nearest the origin.

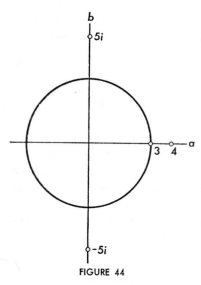

FIGURE 44

The function

$$\frac{x - 2}{(x - 3)(x - 4)(x^2 + 25)}$$

has a denominator which vanishes at $x = 3, 4, 5i, -5i$. The function then has a power series expansion valid inside a circle (Figure 44) with center at $x = 0$ and extending as far as the nearest ($x = 3$) of the points where the function misbehaves. For real x the interval of convergence is $-3 < x < 3$.

84. Ordinary points and singular points. For a linear differential equation

$$(1) \qquad b_0(x)y^{(n)} + b_1(x)y^{(n-1)} + \cdots + b_n(x)y = R(x)$$

with polynomial coefficients, the point $x = x_0$ is called an *ordinary point* of the equation if $b_0(x_0) \neq 0$. A *singular point* of the linear equation (1) is any point $x = x_1$ for which $b_0(x_1) = 0$. In this chapter we shall obtain power series solutions valid near an ordinary point of a linear equation. In the next chapter we shall get power series solutions valid near a certain kind of singular point of the equation.

A knowledge of the location of the singular points of a differential equation will be useful to us later. Any point which is not a singular point is an ordinary point, so we list only the former.

We have left undiscussed the matter of a "point at infinity" in the complex plane, a concept of great utility. It is not necessary for this elementary discussion. As a result of this omission, however, it is necessary for us to attach the words "in the finite plane" to any statement purporting to list all singular points of a differential equation. The concept of a point at infinity will be introduced in Section 109.

The differential equation

$$(2) \qquad (1 - x^2)y'' - 6xy' - 4y = 0$$

has $x = 1$ and $x = -1$ as its only singular points in the finite complex plane. The equation

$$y'' + 2xy' + y = 0$$

has no singular points in the finite plane. The equation

$$xy'' + y' + xy = 0$$

has the origin, $x = 0$, as the only singular point in the finite plane.

EXERCISES

For each equation list all its singular points in the finite plane.

1. $(x^2 + 1)y'' - 3xy' + 4y = 0.$ ANS. $x = i, -i.$
2. $x(1 - x)y'' - (1 + x)y' - 4xy = 0.$ ANS. $x = 0, 1.$
3. $5y'' - 2xy' + (1 + 4x^2)y = 0.$ ANS. None.
4. $x(x + 2)^2y'' - 3xy' + (x + 2)y = 0.$ ANS. $x = 0, -2.$
5. $x^3y'' - xy' + 7y = 0.$
6. $x^2(x - 4)y'' + (x - 5)y = 0.$
7. $y'' + 9y = 0.$
8. $x(x^2 + 4)y'' + (x^2 + 4)y' - xy = 0.$
9. $x(x^2 - 5x + 6)y'' - y' + (x - 2)y = 0.$
10. $x(1 + 4x^2)y'' + y' + xy = 0.$

85. Validity of the solutions near an ordinary point. Suppose $x = 0$ is an ordinary point of the linear equation

$$(1) \qquad b_0(x)y'' + b_1(x)y' + b_2(x)y = 0.$$

It is proved in more advanced books that there is a solution

$$(2) \qquad y = \sum_{n=0}^{\infty} a_n x^n$$

which contains two arbitrary constants, namely, a_0 and a_1, and which converges inside a circle with center at $x = 0$ and extending out to the singular point (or points) nearest $x = 0$. If the differential equation has no singular points in the finite plane, then the solution (2) is valid for all finite x. There remains, of course, the job of finding a_n for $n \geq 2$. That is a major part of our work in solving a particular equation.

It is necessary to realize that the theorem quoted states that the series involved converges inside a certain circle. It does not state that the series diverges outside that circle. In a particular instance it may be that the circle of convergence happens to extend farther than the minimum given by the theorem. In any case the circle of convergence passes through a singular point of the equation—it may not be the nearest singular point.

86. Solutions near an ordinary point. In solving numerical equations, the technique employed in the following examples will be found useful.

EXAMPLE (a): Solve the equation

$$(1) \qquad (1 - x^2)y'' - 6xy' - 4y = 0$$

near the ordinary point $x = 0$.

The only singular points which this equation has in the finite plane are $x = 1$ and $x = -1$. Hence we know in advance that there is a solution

$$(2) \qquad y = \sum_{n=0}^{\infty} a_n x^n$$

valid in $|x| < 1$ and with a_0 and a_1 arbitrary.

In order to determine the a_n, $n > 1$, we substitute the y of equation (2) into the left member of (1).   We get

$$\sum_{n=0}^{\infty} n(n-1)a_n x^{n-2} - \sum_{n=0}^{\infty} n(n-1)a_n x^n - \sum_{n=0}^{\infty} 6na_n x^n - \sum_{n=0}^{\infty} 4a_n x^n = 0,$$

or

$$(3) \qquad \sum_{n=0}^{\infty} n(n-1)a_n x^{n-2} - \sum_{n=0}^{\infty} (n^2 + 5n + 4)a_n x^n = 0,$$

in which we have combined series which contained the same powers of x.

Next let us factor the coefficient in the second series in equation (3), writing

$$(4) \qquad \sum_{n=0}^{\infty} n(n-1)a_n x^{n-2} - \sum_{n=0}^{\infty} (n+1)(n+4)a_n x^n = 0.$$

Relations for the determination of the a_n will be obtained by using the fact that for a power series to vanish identically over any interval each coefficient in the series must be zero.   Therefore we wish next to write the two series in equation (4) in a form in which the exponents on x will be the same, so that we can easily pick off the coefficient of each power of x.

Let us shift the index in the second series, replacing n everywhere by $(n-2)$.   Then the summation which started with the old $n = 0$ will start with $n - 2 = 0$, or the new $n = 2$.   Thus we obtain

$$(5) \qquad \sum_{n=0}^{\infty} n(n-1)a_n x^{n-2} - \sum_{n=2}^{\infty} (n-1)(n+2)a_{n-2} x^{n-2} = 0.$$

In equation (5) the coefficient of each separate power of x must be zero.   For $n = 0$ and $n = 1$, the second series has not yet started, so we get contributions only from the first series.   In detail we have

$$n = 0: \quad 0 \cdot a_0 = 0,$$
$$n = 1: \quad 0 \cdot a_1 = 0,$$
$$n \geqq 2: \quad n(n-1)a_n - (n-1)(n+2)a_{n-2} = 0.$$

As was expected, a_0 and a_1 are arbitrary. The relation for $n \geq 2$ can be used to determine the other a's in terms of a_0 and a_1. Since $n(n-1) \neq 0$ for $n \geq 2$, we can write

$$(6) \qquad n \geq 2: \quad a_n = \frac{n+2}{n}\, a_{n-2}.$$

Equation (6) is called a *recurrence relation*. It gives a_n in terms of preceding a's. In this particular case each a is determined by the a with subscript two lower than its own and so, eventually, by either a_0 or a_1 according to whether the original a had an even or an odd subscript.

A recurrence relation is a special kind of *difference equation*. In difference equations the arguments of the unknown function (the subscripts in our relations) need not differ by integers. There are books and courses on difference equations and the calculus of finite differences paralleling the books and courses on differential equations and calculus.

It is convenient to arrange the iterated instances of the relation (6) in two vertical columns (two columns because the subscripts in (6) differ by two), thus using successively $n = 2, 4, 6, \cdots$, and $n = 3, 5, 7, \cdots$, to obtain

$$a_2 = \frac{4}{2}\, a_0 \qquad\qquad a_3 = \frac{5}{3}\, a_1$$

$$a_4 = \frac{6}{4}\, a_2 \qquad\qquad a_5 = \frac{7}{5}\, a_3$$

$$a_6 = \frac{8}{6}\, a_4 \qquad\qquad a_7 = \frac{9}{7}\, a_5$$

$$\cdot \qquad\qquad\qquad\qquad \cdot$$
$$\cdot \qquad\qquad\qquad\qquad \cdot$$
$$\cdot \qquad\qquad\qquad\qquad \cdot$$

$$a_{2k} = \frac{2k+2}{2k}\, a_{2k-2} \qquad a_{2k+1} = \frac{2k+3}{2k+1}\, a_{2k-1}.$$

Next obtain the product of corresponding members of the equations in the first column. The result,

$$k \geq 1: \quad a_2 a_4 a_6 \cdots a_{2k} = \frac{4 \cdot 6 \cdot 8 \cdots (2k+2)}{2 \cdot 4 \cdot 6 \cdots (2k)}\, a_0 a_2 a_4 \cdots a_{2k-2},$$

simplifies at once to

$$k \geq 1: \quad a_{2k} = (k+1)a_0,$$

thus giving us each a with an even subscript in terms of a_0.

Similarly, from the right column in the array above we get

$$k \geq 1: \quad a_{2k+1} = \frac{5 \cdot 7 \cdot 9 \cdots (2k+3)}{3 \cdot 5 \cdot 7 \cdots (2k+1)} a_1,$$

or

$$k \geq 1: \quad a_{2k+1} = \frac{2k+3}{3} a_1,$$

thus giving us each a with an odd subscript in terms of a_1.

We need next to substitute the expressions we have obtained for the a's into the assumed series for y,

$$(2) \qquad y = \sum_{n=0}^{\infty} a_n x^n.$$

The nature of our expressions for the a's, depending on whether the subscript is odd or even, dictates that we should first split the series in (2) into two series, one containing all the terms with even subscripts, and the other containing all the terms with odd subscripts. We write

$$y = \left[a_0 + \sum_{k=1}^{\infty} a_{2k} x^{2k} \right] + \left[a_1 x + \sum_{k=1}^{\infty} a_{2k+1} x^{2k+1} \right],$$

and then use our known results for a_{2k} and a_{2k+1} to obtain the general solution in the form

$$(7) \quad y = a_0 \left[1 + \sum_{k=1}^{\infty} (k+1) x^{2k} \right] + a_1 \left[x + \sum_{k=1}^{\infty} \frac{2k+3}{3} x^{2k+1} \right].$$

These series converge at least for $|x| < 1$ as we know from the theory. That they converge there and only there can be verified by applying elementary convergence tests.

It happens in this example that the solution (7) may be written more simply as

$$(8) \qquad y = a_0 \sum_{k=0}^{\infty} (k + 1)x^{2k} + a_1 \sum_{k=0}^{\infty} \frac{2k + 3}{3} x^{2k+1}.$$

Indeed, the series can be summed in terms of elementary functions,

$$y = \frac{a_0}{(1 - x^2)^2} + \frac{a_1(3x - x^3)}{3(1 - x^2)^2}.$$

Such simplifications may be important, when they can be accomplished in a particular problem, but it must be realized that our goal was to obtain equation (7) and to know where it is a valid solution. Additional steps taken after that goal is reached are frequently irrelevant to the essential desire to find a computable solution of the differential equation.

The length of the work in solving this particular equation is largely due to detailed steps, many of which will be taken mentally as we acquire more experience.

EXAMPLE (b): Solve the equation

$$(9) \qquad y'' + (x - 1)^2 y' - 4(x - 1)y = 0$$

about the ordinary point $x = 1$.

To solve an equation "about the point $x = x_0$" means to obtain solutions valid in a region surrounding the point, solutions expressed in powers of $(x - x_0)$.

We first translate the axes, putting $x - 1 = v$. Then equation (9) becomes

$$(10) \qquad \frac{d^2y}{dv^2} + v^2 \frac{dy}{dv} - 4vy = 0.$$

Always in a pure translation, $x - x_0 = v$, we have $\frac{dy}{dx} = \frac{dy}{dv}$, etc.

As usual we put

$$(11) \qquad y = \sum_{n=0}^{\infty} a_n v^n$$

and from (10) obtain

$$(12) \quad \sum_{n=0}^{\infty} n(n-1)a_n v^{n-2} + \sum_{n=0}^{\infty} na_n v^{n+1} - \sum_{n=0}^{\infty} 4a_n v^{n+1} = 0.$$

Collecting like terms in (12) yields

$$\sum_{n=0}^{\infty} n(n-1)a_n v^{n-2} + \sum_{n=0}^{\infty} (n-4)a_n v^{n+1} = 0,$$

which, with a shift of index from n to $(n-3)$ in the second series, gives us

$$(13) \quad \sum_{n=0}^{\infty} n(n-1)a_n v^{n-2} + \sum_{n=3}^{\infty} (n-7)a_{n-3} v^{n-2} = 0.$$

Therefore a_0 and a_1 are arbitrary and for the remainder we have

$$n = 2: \quad 2a_2 = 0,$$
$$n \geqq 3: \quad n(n-1)a_n + (n-7)a_{n-3} = 0,$$
$$\text{or } a_n = -\frac{n-7}{n(n-1)} a_{n-3}.$$

This time the a's fall into three groups, those which come from a_0, from a_1, and from a_2. We use three columns:

a_0 arb.	a_1 arb.	$a_2 = 0$
$a_3 = -\dfrac{-4}{3\cdot 2}a_0$	$a_4 = -\dfrac{-3}{4\cdot 3}a_1$	$a_5 = -\dfrac{-2}{5\cdot 4}a_2 = 0$
$a_6 = -\dfrac{-1}{6\cdot 5}a_3$	$a_7 = -\dfrac{0}{7\cdot 6}a_4 = 0$	$a_8 = (\ )a_5 = 0$
$a_9 = -\dfrac{2}{9\cdot 8}a_6$	$a_{10} = -\dfrac{3}{10\cdot 9}a_7 = 0$	$a_{11} = 0$
.	.	.
.	.	.
.	.	.
$a_{3k} = -\dfrac{3k-7}{3k(3k-1)}a_{3k-3}$	$a_{3k+1} = 0, \, k \geqq 2$	$a_{3k+2} = 0, \, k \geqq 1.$

With the usual multiplication scheme, the first column yields

$$k \geq 1: \quad a_{3k} = \frac{(-1)^k[(-4)(-1) \cdot 2 \cdots (3k-7)]a_0}{[3 \cdot 6 \cdot 9 \cdots (3k)][2 \cdot 5 \cdot 8 \cdots (3k-1)]}.$$

For the a's which are determined by a_1, we see that $a_4 = \frac{1}{4}a_1$, but that each of the others is zero. Since $a_2 = 0$, all the a's proportional to it, a_5, a_8, etc., are also zero.

For y we now have

$$y = a_0 \left[1 + \sum_{k=1}^{\infty} \frac{(-1)^k[(-4)(-1) \cdot 2 \cdots (3k-7)]v^{3k}}{[3 \cdot 6 \cdot 9 \cdots (3k)][2 \cdot 5 \cdot 8 \cdots (3k-1)]} \right]$$
$$+ a_1(v + \tfrac{1}{4}v^4).$$

Since $v = x - 1$, the solution appears as

$$(14) \quad y = a_0 \left[1 + \sum_{k=1}^{\infty} \frac{(-1)^k[(-4)(-1) \cdot 2 \cdots (3k-7)](x-1)^{3k}}{[3 \cdot 6 \cdot 9 \cdots (3k)][2 \cdot 5 \cdot 8 \cdots (3k-1)]} \right]$$
$$+ a_1[(x-1) + \tfrac{1}{4}(x-1)^4].$$

The original differential equation has no singular point in the finite plane, so the series in (14) is convergent for all finite x. In computations, of course, it is most useful in the neighborhood of the point $x = 1$.

The coefficient of $(x-1)^{3k}$ is sufficiently complicated to warrant attempts to simplify it. In the product $3 \cdot 6 \cdot 9 \cdots (3k)$ there are k factors, each a multiple of 3. Thus we arrive at

$$3 \cdot 6 \cdot 9 \cdots (3k) = 3^k(1 \cdot 2 \cdot 3 \cdots k) = 3^k k!.$$

Furthermore, all but the first two factors inside the square bracket in the numerator also appear in the denominator. With a little more argument, testing the terms $k = 0, 1, 2$, since the factors to be cancelled do not appear until $k > 2$, it can be shown that

$$(15) \quad y = a_0 \sum_{k=0}^{\infty} \frac{4(-1)^k(x-1)^{3k}}{3^k(3k-1)(3k-4)k!} + a_1[(x-1) + \tfrac{1}{4}(x-1)^4].$$

In the exercises below, the equations are mostly homogeneous and of second order. Raising the order of the equation introduces nothing except additional labor, as can be seen by doing Ex. 13. A non-homogeneous equation with right member having a power series expansion is theoretically no worse to handle than a homogeneous one; it is merely a matter of equating coefficients in two power series.

The treatment of equations leading to recurrence relations involving more than two different a's is left for Chapter 21.

EXERCISES

Unless it is otherwise requested, find the general solution valid near the origin. Always state the region of validity of the solution.

1. $y'' + 2xy' + 2y = 0.$

ANS. $y = a_0 \sum_{k=0}^{\infty} \frac{(-1)^k x^{2k}}{k!} + a_1 \sum_{k=0}^{\infty} \frac{(-1)^k 2^k x^{2k+1}}{1 \cdot 3 \cdot 5 \cdots (2k+1)}$;
valid for all finite x.

2. $(1 + 4x^2)y'' - 8y = 0.$

ANS. $y = a_0(1 + 4x^2) + a_1 \sum_{k=0}^{\infty} \frac{(-1)^{k+1} 2^{2k} x^{2k+1}}{4k^2 - 1}$;
valid for $|x| < \tfrac{1}{2}$.

3. $(1 + x^2)y'' - 4xy' + 6y = 0.$

ANS. $y = a_0(1 - 3x^2) + a_1(x - \tfrac{1}{3}x^3)$;
valid for all finite x.

4. $(1 + x^2)y'' + 10xy' + 20y = 0.$

ANS. $y = \frac{a_0}{3} \sum_{k=0}^{\infty} (-1)^k (k+1)(2k+1)(2k+3)x^{2k}$

$+ \frac{a_1}{6} \sum_{k=0}^{\infty} (-1)^k (k+1)(k+2)(2k+3)x^{2k+1}$;
valid for $|x| < 1$.

5. $2y'' + xy' - 4y = 0.$

ANS. $y = a_0(1 + x^2 + \tfrac{1}{12}x^4).$

$+ a_1 \sum_{k=0}^{\infty} \frac{3(-1)^k x^{2k+1}}{2^{2k}k!(2k-3)(2k-1)(2k+1)}$;
valid for all finite x.

6. $y'' + 3xy' + 7y = 0.$

$$\text{ANS.} \quad y = a_0\left[1 + \sum_{k=1}^{\infty} \frac{(-1)^k 7 \cdot 13 \cdot 19 \cdots (6k+1)x^{2k}}{(2k)!}\right]$$

$$+ a_1\left[x + \sum_{k=1}^{\infty} \frac{(-1)^k 2^k[5 \cdot 8 \cdot 11 \cdots (3k+2)]x^{2k+1}}{(2k+1)!}\right];$$

valid for all finite x.

7. $(1 + 2x^2)y'' - 5xy' + 3y = 0.$

$$\text{ANS.} \quad y = a_0\left[1 + \sum_{k=1}^{\infty} \frac{3(-1)^k[(-1)\cdot 3 \cdot 7 \cdots (4k-5)]x^{2k}}{2^k k!(2k-3)(2k-1)}\right]$$

$$+ a_1(x + \tfrac{1}{3}x^3); \text{ valid for } |x| < 1/\sqrt{2}.$$

8. $y'' + x^2y = 0.$

$$\text{ANS.} \quad y = a_0\left[1 + \sum_{k=1}^{\infty} \frac{(-1)^k x^{4k}}{2^{2k}k! \cdot 3 \cdot 7 \cdot 11 \cdots (4k-1)}\right]$$

$$+ a_1\left[x + \sum_{k=1}^{\infty} \frac{(-1)^k x^{4k+1}}{2^{2k}k! \cdot 5 \cdot 9 \cdot 13 \cdots (4k+1)}\right];$$

valid for all finite x.

9. $y'' - 2(x+3)y' - 3y = 0.$ Solve about $x = -3.$

$$\text{ANS.} \quad y = a_0\left[1 + \sum_{k=1}^{\infty} \frac{3 \cdot 7 \cdot 11 \cdots (4k-1)(x+3)^{2k}}{(2k)!}\right]$$

$$+ a_1\left[(x+3) + \sum_{k=1}^{\infty} \frac{5 \cdot 9 \cdot 13 \cdots (4k+1)(x+3)^{2k+1}}{(2k+1)!}\right];$$

valid for all finite x.

10. $y'' + (x-2)y = 0.$ Solve about $x = 2.$

$$\text{ANS.} \quad y = a_0\left[1 + \sum_{k=1}^{\infty} \frac{(-1)^k(x-2)^{3k}}{3^k k![2 \cdot 5 \cdot 8 \cdots (3k-1)]}\right]$$

$$+ a_1\left[(x-2) + \sum_{k=1}^{\infty} \frac{(-1)^k(x-2)^{3k+1}}{3^k k![4 \cdot 7 \cdot 10 \cdots (3k+1)]}\right];$$

valid for all finite x.

11. $(1 - 4x^2)y'' + 6xy' - 4y = 0.$

ANS. $y = a_0(1 + 2x^2) + a_1 \left[x - \sum_{k=1}^{\infty} \frac{1 \cdot 5 \cdot 9 \cdots (4k - 3)x^{2k+1}}{k!(4k^2 - 1)} \right];$

valid for $|x| < \frac{1}{2}$.

12. $(1 + 2x^2)y'' + 3xy' - 3y = 0.$

ANS. $y = a_1x + a_0 \left[1 + \sum_{k=1}^{\infty} \frac{(-1)^{k+1} 3 \cdot 7 \cdot 11 \cdots (4k - 1)x^{2k}}{2^k(2k - 1)k!} \right];$

valid for $|x| < 1/\sqrt{2}$.

13. $y''' + x^2y'' + 5xy' + 3y = 0.$

ANS. $y = a_0 \left[1 + \sum_{k=1}^{\infty} \frac{(-1)^k x^{3k}}{2 \cdot 5 \cdot 8 \cdots (3k - 1)} \right]$

$+ a_1 \left[x + \sum_{k=1}^{\infty} \frac{(-1)^k x^{3k+1}}{3^k k!} \right]$

$+ a_2 \left[x^2 + \sum_{k=1}^{\infty} \frac{(-1)^k x^{3k+2}}{4 \cdot 7 \cdot 10 \cdots (3k + 1)} \right];$

valid for all finite x.

14. $y'' + xy' + 3y = x^2.$

ANS. $y = -\frac{2}{15} + \frac{1}{5}x^2 + a_0 \sum_{k=0}^{\infty} \frac{(-1)^k(2k + 1)x^{2k}}{2^k k!}$

$+ a_1 \sum_{k=0}^{\infty} \frac{(-1)^k(k + 1)x^{2k+1}}{1 \cdot 3 \cdot 5 \cdots (2k + 1)};$

valid for all finite x.

15. Solve the equation $y'' + 4y = 0$ both by series and by elementary methods and compare your answers.

16. Solve the equation $y'' - y = 0$ by series and by elementary methods.

Chapter 19

Solutions Near Regular
Singular Points

87. Regular singular points. Suppose that the point $x = x_0$ is a singular point of the equation

$$(1) \qquad b_0(x)y'' + b_1(x)y' + b_2(x)y = 0$$

with polynomial coefficients. Then $b_0(x_0) = 0$, so that $b_0(x)$ has a factor $(x - x_0)$ to some power.

Let us put equation (1) into the form

$$(2) \qquad y'' + p(x)y' + q(x)y = 0.$$

Since $x = x_0$ is a singular point, and since $p(x)$ and $q(x)$ are rational functions of x, at least one (maybe both) of $p(x)$ and $q(x)$ has a denominator which contains the factor $(x - x_0)$.

If $x = x_0$ is a singular point of equation (2), and if the denominator of $p(x)$ does not contain the factor $(x - x_0)$ to a power higher than one, and if the denominator of $q(x)$ does not contain the factor $(x - x_0)$ to a power higher than two, then $x = x_0$ is called a *regular singular point* of equation (2).

If $x = x_0$ is a singular point but is not a regular singular point, then it is called an *irregular singular point*.

EXAMPLE (a): Classify the singular points, in the finite plane, of the equation

$$(3) \qquad x(x - 1)^2(x + 2)y'' + x^2y' - (x^3 + 2x - 1)y = 0.$$

For this equation

$$p(x) = \frac{x}{(x-1)^2(x+2)}$$

and

$$q(x) = \frac{-(x^3 + 2x - 1)}{x(x-1)^2(x+2)}.$$

The singular points in the finite plane are $x = 0, 1, -2$. Consider $x = 0$. The factor x is absent from the denominator of $p(x)$ and it appears to the first power in the denominator of $q(x)$. Hence $x = 0$ is a regular singular point of equation (3).

Now consider $x = 1$. The factor $(x - 1)$ appears to the second power in the denominator of $p(x)$. That is a higher power than is permitted in the definition of a regular singular point. Hence it does not matter how $(x - 1)$ appears in $q(x)$; the point $x = 1$ is an irregular singular point.

The factor $(x + 2)$ appears to the first power in the denominator of $p(x)$, just as high as is permitted, and to the first power also in the denominator of $q(x)$, so $x = -2$ is a regular singular point.

In summary, equation (3) has in the finite plane the following singular points: regular singular points at $x = 0$, $x = -2$; irregular singular point at $x = 1$. The methods of Section 109 will show that (3) has also an irregular singular point "at infinity."

EXAMPLE (b): Classify the singular points in the finite plane of the equation

$$x^4(x^2 + 1)(x - 1)^2 y'' + 4x^3(x - 1)y' + (x + 1)y = 0.$$

Here

$$p(x) = \frac{4}{x(x^2 + 1)(x - 1)} = \frac{4}{x(x - i)(x + i)(x - 1)}$$

and

$$q(x) = \frac{x + 1}{x^4(x + i)(x - i)(x - 1)^2}.$$

Therefore the desired classification is:

R.S.P. at $x = i, -i, 1$; I.S.P. at $x = 0$.

Singular points of a linear equation of higher order are classified in much the same way. For instance, the singular point $x = x_0$ of the equation

$$y''' + p_1(x)y'' + p_2(x)y' + p_3(x)y = 0$$

is called regular if the factor $(x - x_0)$ does not appear in the denominator of $p_1(x)$ to a power higher than one, of $p_2(x)$ to a power higher than two, of $p_3(x)$ to a power higher than three. If it is not regular, a singular point is irregular.

This chapter is devoted to the solution of linear equations near regular singular points. Solutions near irregular singular points present a great deal more difficulty and are barely touched upon in Chapter 21.

EXERCISES

For each equation locate and classify all its singular points in the finite plane. See Section 109 for the concept of a singular point "at infinity." As additional exercises the student may perform the same classification for any of the differential equations appearing in this or the preceding chapter.

1. $x^2(x - 4)^2 y'' + 2x(x + 1)y' + y = 0$.

ANS.   R.S.P. at $x = 0$; I.S.P. at $x = 4$.

2. $x^2(x^2 - 1)y'' + 2x^3 y' + y = 0$.

ANS.   R.S.P. at $x = 0, 1, -1$; No I.S.P.

3. $y'' + x^2 y = 0$.   ANS.   No S.P. (in the finite plane).

4. $xy'' + y = 0$.   ANS.   R.S.P. at $x = 0$; No I.S.P.

5. $(x^2 + 4)(x - 1)^3 y'' - (x - 1)^2 y' + (x^2 + 4)^4 y = 0$.

ANS.   R.S.P. at $x = 2i, -2i$; I.S.P. at $x = 1$.

6. $x(x - 2)^3 y'' + y = 0$.   ANS.   R.S.P. at $x = 0$; I.S.P. at $x = 2$.

7. $x(x + 3)^2 y'' + 7y' + (x + 3)y = 0$.

ANS.   R.S.P. at $x = 0$; I.S.P. at $x = -3$.

8. $(x - 1)^4 y'' + 2(x - 1)^3 y' + y = 0$.

ANS.   No R.S.P.; I.S.P. at $x = 1$.

88. The indicial equation. As in Chapter 18, whenever we wish to obtain solutions about a point other than $x = 0$, we first translate the origin to that point and then proceed with the usual technique. Hence we concentrate our attention on solutions valid about $x = 0$.

Let $x = 0$ be a regular singular point of the equation

(1) $$y'' + p(x)y' + q(x)y = 0$$

where p and q are rational functions of x. Then $p(x)$ cannot have in its denominator the factor x to a power higher than one. Therefore

$$p(x) = \frac{r(x)}{x}$$

where $r(x)$ is a rational function of x and $r(x)$ exists at $x = 0$. We know that such a rational function, this $r(x)$, has a power series expansion about $x = 0$. Then there exists the expansion

(2) $$p(x) = \frac{p_0}{x} + p_1 + p_2 x + p_3 x^2 + \cdots,$$

valid in some region surrounding $x = 0$.

By a similar argument we find that there exists an expansion

(3) $$q(x) = \frac{q_0}{x^2} + \frac{q_1}{x} + q_2 + q_3 x + q_4 x^2 + \cdots$$

about $x = 0$.

We shall see in a formal manner that it is reasonable to expect equation (1) to have a solution of the form

(4) $$y = \sum_{n=0}^{\infty} a_n x^{n+c} = a_0 x^c + a_1 x^{1+c} + a_2 x^{2+c} + \cdots$$

for properly chosen c and a_n's. The facts will be stated in the next section.

If we put the series for y, $p(x)$, and $q(x)$ into equation (1) and consider only the first few terms, we get

$$c(c - 1)a_0 x^{c-2} + (1 + c)ca_1 x^{c-1} + (2 + c)(1 + c)a_2 x^c + \cdots$$

$$+ \left[\frac{p_0}{x} + p_1 + p_2 x + \cdots \right] \left[ca_0 x^{c-1} + (1+c)a_1 x^c + (2+c)a_2 x^{1+c} + \cdots \right]$$

$$+ \left[\frac{q_0}{x^2} + \frac{q_1}{x} + q_2 + \cdots \right] \left[a_0 x^c + a_1 x^{1+c} + a_2 x^{2+c} + \cdots \right] = 0.$$

Performing the indicated multiplications, we find that we have

$$c(c - 1)a_0x^{c-2} + (1 + c)ca_1x^{c-1} + (2 + c)(1 + c)a_2x^c + \cdots$$
$$+ p_0ca_0x^{c-2} + [p_0(1 + c)a_1 + p_1ca_0]x^{c-1} + \cdots + q_0a_0x^{c-2} +$$
$$[q_0a_1 + q_1a_0]x^{c-1} + \cdots = 0.$$

From the fact that the coefficient of x^{c-2} must vanish we obtain

$$(5) \qquad\qquad [c(c - 1) + p_0c + q_0]a_0 = 0.$$

We may insist that $a_0 \neq 0$ because a_0 is the coefficient of the lowest power of x appearing in the solution (4), no matter what that lowest power is. So from (5) it follows that

$$(6) \qquad\qquad c^2 + (p_0 - 1)c + q_0 = 0,$$

which is called the *indicial equation* (at $x = 0$). The p_0 and q_0 are known constants; equation (6) is a quadratic equation giving us two roots $c = c_1$ and $c = c_2$.

Superficially, it appears that there should be two solutions of the form (4), one from each of these values of c. In each solution the a_0 should be arbitrary and the succeeding a's should be determined by equating to zero the coefficients of the higher powers of $x(x^{c-1}, x^c, x^{1+c}$, etc.) in the identity just above equation (5).

This superficial conclusion is correct if the difference of the roots c_1 and c_2 is not integral. If that difference is integral, however, a logarithmic term may enter the solution. The reasons for this strange behavior will be made clear when we develop a method for obtaining the solutions.

89. Form and validity of the solutions near a regular singular point.

Let $x = 0$ be a regular singular point of the equation

$$(1) \qquad\qquad y'' + p(x)y' + q(x)y = 0.$$

It can be proved that equation (1) always has a general solution either of the form

$$(2) \qquad\qquad y = A \sum_{n=0}^{\infty} a_nx^{n+c_1} + B \sum_{n=0}^{\infty} b_nx^{n+c_2}$$

or of the form

$$(3) \qquad y = (A + B \ln x) \sum_{n=0}^{\infty} a_n x^{n+c_1} + B \sum_{n=0}^{\infty} b_n x^{n+c_2}$$

in which A and B are arbitrary constants. Furthermore, it is proved that the infinite series which occur in the above forms of solution converge in at least the annular region bounded by two circles centered at $x = 0$, one of arbitrarily small radius, the other extending to the singular point (of the equation) nearest $x = 0$.

90. Indicial equation with difference of roots nonintegral. The equation

$$(1) \qquad 2xy'' + (1 + x)y' - 2y = 0,$$

has a regular singular point at $x = 0$ and no other singular points for finite x. Let us assume that there is a solution of the form

$$(2) \qquad y = \sum_{n=0}^{\infty} a_n x^{n+c}.$$

Direct substitution of this y into equation (1) yields

$$\sum_{n=0}^{\infty} 2(n + c)(n + c - 1)a_n x^{n+c-1} + \sum_{n=0}^{\infty} (n + c)a_n x^{n+c-1}$$

$$+ \sum_{n=0}^{\infty} (n + c)a_n x^{n+c} - 2 \sum_{n=0}^{\infty} a_n x^{n+c} = 0,$$

or

$$(3) \qquad \sum_{n=0}^{\infty} (n + c)(2n + 2c - 1)a_n x^{n+c-1}$$

$$+ \sum_{n=0}^{\infty} (n + c - 2)a_n x^{n+c} = 0.$$

Having collected like terms, we next shift index in order to bring all the exponents of x down to the smallest one present. This choice is used in order to get a recurrence relation for a_n rather than one for a_{n+1} or some other a. In equation (3) we replace the index n in the second summation by $(n-1)$, thus getting

$$(4) \quad \sum_{n=0}^{\infty} (n+c)(2n+2c-1)a_n x^{n+c-1}$$

$$+ \sum_{n=1}^{\infty} (n+c-3)a_{n-1} x^{n+c-1} = 0.$$

Once more we reason that the total coefficient of each power of x in the left member of (4) must vanish. The second summation does not start its contribution until $n=1$. Hence the equations for the determination of c and the a's are

$$n=0: \quad c(2c-1)a_0 = 0,$$
$$n \geq 1: \quad (n+c)(2n+2c-1)a_n + (n+c-3)a_{n-1} = 0.$$

Since we may without loss of generality assume $a_0 \neq 0$, the indicial equation, that which determines c, is

$$(5) \qquad\qquad c(2c-1) = 0.$$

The indicial equation always comes from the $n=0$ term when the technique being presented in this book is employed.

From (5) we see that $c_1 = \frac{1}{2}$ and $c_2 = 0$. The difference of the roots is $s = c_1 - c_2 = \frac{1}{2}$, which is nonintegral. When s is not an integer, the method we are using always gives two linearly independent solutions of the form (2), one with each choice of c.

Let us return to the recurrence relation using the value $c = c_1 = \frac{1}{2}$. We have

$$n \geq 1: \quad (n+\tfrac{1}{2})(2n+1-1)a_n + (n+\tfrac{1}{2}-3)a_{n-1} = 0,$$

or

$$n \geq 1: \quad a_n = -\frac{(2n-5)a_{n-1}}{2n(2n+1)}.$$

As usual we use a vertical array and then form the product in order to get a formula for a_n. We have

$$a_0 \text{ arb.}$$

$$a_1 = -\frac{(-3)a_0}{2 \cdot 3}$$

$$a_2 = -\frac{(-1)a_1}{4 \cdot 5}$$

$$a_3 = -\frac{(1)a_2}{6 \cdot 7}$$

.
.
.

$$a_n = -\frac{(2n-5)a_{n-1}}{2n(2n+1)},$$

so that the product yields, for $n \geq 1$,

$$(6) \qquad a_n = \frac{(-1)^n[(-3)(-1)(1) \cdots (2n-5)]a_0}{[2 \cdot 4 \cdot 6 \cdots (2n)][3 \cdot 5 \cdot 7 \cdots (2n+1)]}.$$

The formula (6) may be simplified to the form

$$(7) \qquad a_n = \frac{(-1)^n \cdot 3a_0}{2^n n!(2n-3)(2n-1)(2n+1)}.$$

Using $a_0 = 1$, the a_n from (7), and the pertinent value of c, $c_1 = \frac{1}{2}$, a particular solution may now be written. It is

$$(8) \qquad y_1 = x^{1/2} + \sum_{n=1}^{\infty} \frac{(-1)^n 3x^{n+1/2}}{2^n n!(2n-3)(2n-1)(2n+1)}.$$

The notation y_1 is to emphasize that this particular solution corresponds to the root c_1 of the indicial equation. Our next task will be to get a particular solution y_2 corresponding to the smaller root c_2. Then the general solution, if it is desired, may be written at once as

$$y = Ay_1 + By_2$$

with A and B arbitrary constants.

In returning to the recurrence relation just above the indicial equation (5) with the intention of using $c = c_2 = 0$, it is evident that the a's will be different from those with $c = c_1$. Hence it is wise to change notation. Let us use b's instead of a's. With $c = 0$, the recurrence relation becomes $n \geq 1 : n(2n-1)b_n + (n-3)b_{n-1} = 0$. The corresponding vertical array is:

$$b_0 \ arb.$$

$$b_1 = -\frac{(-2)b_0}{1 \cdot 1}$$

$$b_2 = -\frac{(-1)b_1}{2 \cdot 3}$$

$$b_3 = -\frac{(0)b_2}{3 \cdot 5}$$

.
.
.

$$b_n = -\frac{(n-3)b_{n-1}}{n(2n-1)}.$$

Then $b_n = 0$ for $n \geqq 3$ and, using $b_0 = 1$, b_1 and b_2 may be computed and found to have the values $b_1 = 2$ and $b_2 = \frac{1}{6}b_1 = \frac{1}{3}$. Therefore a second solution is

$$(9) \qquad\qquad y_2 = 1 + 2x + \tfrac{1}{3}x^2.$$

Since the differential equation has no singular point, other than $x = 0$, in the finite plane, we conclude that the linearly independent solutions y_1 of (8) and y_2 of (9) are valid at least for $|x| > 0$. The validity of (9) is evident in this particular example because the series terminates.

The student should associate with each solution the region of validity guaranteed by the general theorem quoted in Section 89, though from now on the printed answers to exercises will omit statement of the region of validity.

EXERCISES

For each equation obtain two linearly independent solutions valid near the origin. Always state the region of validity of each solution which you obtain.

1. $4xy'' + 3y' - 3y = 0.$

$$\text{ANS.} \quad y_1 = x^{1/4} + \sum_{n=1}^{\infty} \frac{(-3)^n x^{n+1/4}}{n!5 \cdot 9 \cdot 13 \cdots (4n+1)};$$

$$y_2 = 1 + \sum_{n=1}^{\infty} \frac{(-3)^n x^n}{n!3 \cdot 7 \cdot 11 \cdots (4n-1)}.$$

2. $2xy'' + 5(1 + 2x)y' + 5y = 0.$

$$\text{ANS.} \quad y_1 = 1 + \sum_{n=1}^{\infty} \frac{3(-5)^n x^n}{n!(2n+1)(2n+3)};$$

$$y_2 = x^{-3/2} - 10x^{-1/2}.$$

3. $8x^2y'' + 10xy' - (1 + x)y = 0.$

$$\text{ANS.} \quad y_1 = x^{1/4} + \sum_{n=1}^{\infty} \frac{x^{n+1/4}}{2^n n! 7 \cdot 11 \cdot 15 \cdots (4n+3)};$$

$$y_2 = x^{-1/2} + \sum_{n=1}^{\infty} \frac{x^{n-1/2}}{2^n n! 1 \cdot 5 \cdot 9 \cdots (4n-3)}.$$

4. $3xy'' + (2 - x)y' - 2y = 0.$

$$\text{ANS.} \quad y_1 = \sum_{n=0}^{\infty} \frac{(3n+4)x^{n+1/3}}{4 \cdot 3^n n!};$$

$$y_2 = 1 + \sum_{n=1}^{\infty} \frac{(n+1)x^n}{2 \cdot 5 \cdot 8 \cdots (3n-1)}.$$

5. $9x^2y'' + 3x(x + 3)y' - (1 + 4x)y = 0.$

$$\text{ANS.} \quad y_1 = x^{1/3} + \tfrac{1}{5}x^{4/3};$$

$$y_2 = x^{-1/3} + \sum_{n=1}^{\infty} \frac{10(-1)^n x^{n-1/3}}{3^n n!(3n-5)(3n-2)}.$$

6. $2xy'' + (1 - 2x^2)y' - 4xy = 0.$

$$\text{ANS.} \quad y_1 = \sum_{k=0}^{\infty} \frac{x^{2k+1/2}}{2^k k!} = x^{1/2}e^{x^2/2}.$$

$$y_2 = 1 + \sum_{k=1}^{\infty} \frac{2^k x^{2k}}{3 \cdot 7 \cdot 11 \cdots (4k-1)}.$$

7. $x(4 - x)y'' + (2 - x)y' + 4y = 0.$

$$\text{ANS.} \quad y_1 = x^{1/2} + \sum_{n=1}^{\infty} \frac{(2n+3)[(-3)(-1) \cdot 1 \cdots (2n-5)]x^{n+1/2}}{3 \cdot 2^{3n} n!};$$

$$y_2 = 1 - 2x + \tfrac{1}{2}x^2.$$

8. $3x^2y'' + xy' - (1 + x)y = 0.$

$$\text{ANS.} \quad y_1 = x + \sum_{n=1}^{\infty} \frac{x^{n+1}}{n!\,7 \cdot 10 \cdot 13 \cdots (3n + 4)};$$

$$y_2 = x^{-1/3} + \sum_{n=1}^{\infty} \frac{x^{n-1/3}}{n!(-1) \cdot 2 \cdot 5 \cdots (3n - 4)}.$$

9. $2xy'' + (1 + 2x)y' + 4y = 0.$

$$\text{ANS.} \quad y_1 = \sum_{n=0}^{\infty} \frac{(-1)^n(2n + 3)x^{n+1/2}}{3 \cdot n!};$$

$$y_2 = 1 + \sum_{n=1}^{\infty} \frac{(-1)^n 2^n(n + 1)x^n}{1 \cdot 3 \cdot 5 \cdots (2n - 1)}.$$

10. $2xy'' + (1 + 2x)y' - 5y = 0.$

$$\text{ANS.} \quad y_1 = x^{1/2} + \tfrac{4}{3}x^{3/2} + \tfrac{4}{15}x^{5/2};$$

$$y_2 = \sum_{n=0}^{\infty} \frac{15(-1)^{n+1}x^n}{n!(2n - 5)(2n - 3)(2n - 1)}.$$

11. $2x^2y'' - 3x(1 - x)y' + 2y = 0.$

$$\text{ANS.} \quad y_1 = x^2 + \sum_{n=1}^{\infty} \frac{(-1)^n 3^n(n + 1)x^{n+2}}{5 \cdot 7 \cdot 9 \cdots (2n + 3)};$$

$$y_2 = x^{1/2} + \sum_{n=1}^{\infty} \frac{(-1)^{n+1} 3^n(2n - 1)x^{n+1/2}}{2^n n!}.$$

12. $2x^2y'' + x(4x - 1)y' + 2(3x - 1)y = 0.$

$$\text{ANS.} \quad y_1 = \sum_{n=0}^{\infty} \frac{(-1)^n 2^n x^{n+2}}{n!} = x^2 e^{-2x};$$

$$y_2 = x^{-1/2} + \sum_{n=1}^{\infty} \frac{(-1)^n 4^n x^{n-1/2}}{(-3)(-1) \cdot 1 \cdots (2n - 5)}.$$

13. $2xy'' - (1 + 2x^2)y' - xy = 0$.

$$\text{ANS.} \quad y_1 = x^{3/2} + \sum_{k=1}^{\infty} \frac{2^k x^{2k+3/2}}{7 \cdot 11 \cdot 15 \cdots (4k+3)};$$

$$y_2 = 1 + \sum_{k=1}^{\infty} \frac{x^{2k}}{2^k k!} = e^{x^2/2}.$$

14. The equation of Ex. 13 above has a particular solution $y_2 = e^{x^2/2}$ obtained by the series method. Make a change of dependent variable in the differential equation, using $y = ve^{x^2/2}$ (the device of Section 56) and thus obtain the general solution in "closed form."

$$\text{ANS.} \quad y = c_1 e^{x^2/2} + c_2 e^{x^2/2} \int_0^x \beta^{1/2} e^{-\beta^2/2} d\beta.$$

15. $2x^2 y'' + 3xy' - y = 0$.   ANS. $y_1 = x^{1/2}; y_2 = x^{-1}$.
16. $3x^2 y'' - xy' - 4y = 0$.   ANS. $y_1 = x^2; y_2 = x^{-2/3}$.

17. Obtain $\dfrac{dy}{dx}$ and $\dfrac{d^2y}{dx^2}$ in terms of derivatives of y with respect to a new independent variable t related to x by $t = \ln x$.

$$\text{ANS.} \quad \frac{dy}{dx} = e^{-t} \frac{dy}{dt}, \qquad \frac{d^2y}{dx^2} = e^{-2t}\left[\frac{d^2y}{dt^2} - \frac{dy}{dt}\right].$$

18. Use the result of Ex. 17 above to show that the change of independent variable from x to t, where $t = \ln x$, transforms the equation*

$$ax^2 \frac{d^2y}{dx^2} + bx \frac{dy}{dx} + cy = 0;\ a, b, c,\ \text{constants, into a linear equation}$$

with constant coefficients.

Solve Exs. 19–26 by the method implied by Ex. 18 above; that is, by changing independent variable to $t = \ln x$.

19. Ex. 15.
20. Ex. 16.
21. $x^2 y'' + 2xy' - 6y = 0$.   ANS. $y = c_1 x^2 + c_2 x^{-3}$.
22. $(4x^2 D^2 - 8xD + 5)y = 0$.   ANS. $y = c_1 x^{1/2} + c_2 x^{5/2}$.
23. $x^2 y'' - 7xy' + 16y = 0$.   ANS. $y = x^4(c_1 + c_2 \ln x)$.
24. $(x^2 D^2 + 3xD + 1)y = 0$.   ANS. $y = x^{-1}(c_1 + c_2 \ln x)$.
25. $(x^2 D^2 + 5xD + 13)y = 0$.

$$\text{ANS.} \quad y = x^{-2}\left[c_1 \cos\left(3 \ln x\right) + c_2 \sin\left(3 \ln x\right)\right].$$

---

* An equation, such as the one of this exercise, which contains only terms of the kind $cx^k D^k y$ with c constant and $k = 0, 1, 2, 3, \cdots$, is called an equation of *Cauchy type*, or of *Euler type*.

26. $(x^3D^3 + 4x^2D^2 - 8xD + 8)y = 0$. You will need to extend the result of Ex. 17 to the third derivative, obtaining

$$x^3 \frac{d^3y}{dx^3} = \frac{d^3y}{dt^3} - 3\frac{d^2y}{dt^2} + 2\frac{dy}{dt}.$$ ANS. $y = c_1x + c_2x^2 + c_3x^{-4}$.

91. Differentiation of a product of functions.

It will soon prove necessary for us to differentiate efficiently a product of a number of functions. Suppose that

(1) $u = u_1u_2u_3 \cdots u_n$,

each of the u's being a function of the parameter c. Let differentiation with respect to c be indicated by primes. Then from

$$\ln u = \ln u_1 + \ln u_2 + \ln u_3 + \cdots + \ln u_n$$

it follows that

$$\frac{u'}{u} = \frac{u_1'}{u_1} + \frac{u_2'}{u_2} + \frac{u_3'}{u_3} + \cdots + \frac{u_n'}{u_n}.$$

Hence

(2) $u' = u \left\{ \dfrac{u_1'}{u_1} + \dfrac{u_2'}{u_2} + \dfrac{u_3'}{u_3} + \cdots + \dfrac{u_n'}{u_n} \right\}.$

Thus to differentiate a product we may multiply the original product by a conversion factor (which converts the product into its derivative) consisting of the sum of the derivatives of the logarithms of the separate factors.

When the factors involved are themselves powers of polynomials, there is a convenient way of forming mentally the conversion factor. That factor is the sum of the conversion factors for the individual parts.

The way most of us learned to differentiate a power of a quantity is to multiply the exponent, the derivative of the original quantity, and the quantity with its exponent lowered by one. Thus, if

$$y = (ac + b)^k,$$

then

$$\frac{dy}{dc} = y \left\{ \frac{ka}{ac + b} \right\},$$

the division by $(ac + b)$ converting $(ac + b)^k$ into $(ac + b)^{k-1}$.

EXAMPLE (a): If

$$u = \frac{c^2(c+1)}{(4c-1)^3(7c+2)^6},$$

then

$$\frac{du}{dc} = u\left\{\frac{2}{c} + \frac{1}{c+1} - \frac{12}{4c-1} - \frac{42}{7c+2}\right\}.$$

Note that the denominator factors in the function u are thought of as numerator factors with negative exponents.

EXAMPLE (b): If

$$y = \frac{c+n}{c(c+1)(c+2) \cdots (c+n-1)},$$

then

$$\frac{dy}{dc} = y\left\{\frac{1}{c+n} - \frac{1}{c} - \frac{1}{c+1} - \frac{1}{c+2} - \cdots - \frac{1}{c+n-1}\right\}.$$

EXAMPLE (c): If

$$w = \frac{2^n c^3}{[(c+2)(c+3) \cdots (c+n+1)]^2},$$

then

$$\frac{dw}{dc} = w\left\{\frac{3}{c} - 2\left(\frac{1}{c+2} + \frac{1}{c+3} + \cdots + \frac{1}{c+n+1}\right)\right\}.$$

92. Indicial equation with equal roots.

When the indicial equation has equal roots it is evident that the method of Section 90 cannot yield two linearly independent solutions. The work with one value of c would be a pure repetition of that with the other value of c. A new attack is needed.

Consider the problem of solving the equation

$$(1) \qquad x^2y'' + 3xy' + (1 - 2x)y = 0$$

about the regular singular point $x = 0$. It will turn out that the roots of the indicial equation are equal, a fact which can be determined ahead of time by setting up the indicial equation as developed in the theory, page 276. Here

$$p(x) = \frac{3}{x}, \quad q(x) = \frac{1 - 2x}{x^2},$$

so $p_0 = 3$ and $q_0 = 1$. The indicial equation is

$$c^2 + 2c + 1 = 0,$$

with roots $c_1 = c_2 = -1$.

Any attempt to obtain solutions by putting

$$(2) \qquad\qquad y = \sum_{n=0}^{\infty} a_n x^{n+c}$$

into equation (1) is certain to force us to choose $c = -1$ and thus get only one solution. We know that we must not choose c yet if we are to get two solutions. Hence let us put the y of equation (2) into the left member of equation (1) and try to come as close as we can to making that left member zero without choosing c.

It is convenient to have a notation for the left member of equation (1); let us use

$$(3) \qquad\qquad L(y) = x^2 y'' + 3xy' + (1 - 2x)y.$$

For the y of equation (2) we find that

$$L(y) = \sum_{n=0}^{\infty} (n+c)(n+c-1)a_n x^{n+c} + \sum_{n=0}^{\infty} 3(n+c)a_n x^{n+c}$$
$$+ \sum_{n=0}^{\infty} a_n x^{n+c} - \sum_{n=0}^{\infty} 2a_n x^{n+c+1},$$

from which

$$L(y) = \sum_{n=0}^{\infty} [(n+c)^2 + 2(n+c) + 1]a_n x^{n+c} - \sum_{n=0}^{\infty} 2a_n x^{n+c+1}.$$

The usual simplifications lead to

$$(4) \qquad L(y) = \sum_{n=0}^{\infty} (n+c+1)^2 a_n x^{n+c} - \sum_{n=1}^{\infty} 2a_{n-1} x^{n+c}.$$

Recalling that the indicial equation comes from setting the coefficient in the $n = 0$ term equal to zero, we purposely avoid trying to make that term vanish yet. But by choosing the a's and leaving c as a parameter we can make every term but that first one in $L(y)$ vanish. Therefore we set equal to zero each coefficient, except for the $n = 0$ term, of the various powers of x on the right in equation (4); thus

(5) $\qquad n \geqq 1: \quad (n + c + 1)^2 a_n - 2a_{n-1} = 0.$

The successive application of the recurrence relation (5) will determine each a_n, $n \geqq 1$, in terms of a_0 and c. Indeed, from the array

$$a_1 = \frac{2a_0}{(c + 2)^2}$$

$$a_2 = \frac{2a_1}{(c + 3)^2}$$

$$\cdot$$
$$\cdot$$
$$\cdot$$

$$a_n = \frac{2a_{n-1}}{(c + n + 1)^2},$$

it follows by the usual multiplication device that

$$n \geqq 1: \quad a_n = \frac{2^n a_0}{[(c + 2)(c + 3) \cdots (c + n + 1)]^2}.$$

In order to arrive at a specific solution, let us choose $a_0 = 1$.

Using the a's determined above, we write a y which is dependent upon both x and c, namely,

(6) $\qquad\qquad y(x, c) = x^c + \sum_{n=1}^{\infty} a_n(c) x^{n+c},$

in which

(7) $\qquad n \geqq 1: \quad a_n(c) = \frac{2^n}{[(c + 2)(c + 3) \cdots (c + n + 1)]^2}.$

The y of equation (6) has been determined so that for that y the right member of equation (4) must reduce to a single term, the $n = 0$ term. That is, for the $y(x, c)$ of equation (6), we have

$$(8) \qquad L[y(x, c)] = (c + 1)^2 x^c.$$

A solution of the original differential equation is a function y for which $L(y) = 0$. Now we see why the choice $c = -1$ yields a solution; it makes the right member of equation (8) zero.

But the factor $(c + 1)$ occurs squared in equation (8), an automatic consequence of the equality of the roots of the indicial equation. We know from elementary calculus that if a function contains a power of a certain factor, dependent upon c, then the derivative with respect to c of that function contains the same factor to a power one lower than in the original.

For equation (8), in particular, differentiation of each member with respect to c yields

$$(9) \qquad \frac{\partial}{\partial c} L[y(x, c)] = L\left[\frac{\partial y(x, c)}{\partial c}\right] = 2(c + 1)x^c + (c + 1)^2 x^c \ln x,$$

the right member containing the factor $(c + 1)$ to the first power, as we knew it must from the theorem quoted.

In (9) the order of differentiations, with respect to x and c, was interchanged. It is best to avoid the need for justifying such steps by verifying the solutions, (13) and (14) below, directly. The verification in this instance is straightforward but a bit lengthy and is omitted here.

From equations (8) and (9) it can be seen that two solutions of the equation $L(y) = 0$ are

$$y_1 = [y(x, c)]_{c=-1} = y(x, -1)$$

and

$$y_2 = \left[\frac{\partial y(x, c)}{\partial c}\right]_{c=-1},$$

because $c = -1$ makes the right member of each of equations (8) and (9) vanish. That y_1 and y_2 are linearly independent will be evident later.

We have

$$(6) \qquad y(x,\,c) = x^c + \sum_{n=1}^{\infty} a_n(c)x^{n+c}$$

and we need $\partial y(x,\,c)/\partial c$. From (6) it follows that

$$\frac{\partial y(x,\,c)}{\partial c} = x^c \ln x + \sum_{n=1}^{\infty} a_n(c)x^{n+c} \ln x + \sum_{n=1}^{\infty} a_n'(c)x^{n+c},$$

which simplifies at once to the form

$$(10) \qquad \frac{\partial y(x,\,c)}{\partial c} = y(x,\,c) \ln x + \sum_{n=1}^{\infty} a_n'(c)x^{n+c}.$$

The solutions y_1 and y_2 will be obtained by putting $c = -1$ in equations (6) and (10); that is,

$$(11) \qquad y_1 = x^{-1} + \sum_{n=1}^{\infty} a_n(-1)x^{n-1}$$

and

$$(12) \qquad y_2 = y_1 \ln x + \sum_{n=1}^{\infty} a_n'(-1)x^{n-1}.$$

Therefore we need to evaluate $a_n(c)$ and $a_n'(c)$ at $c = -1$. We know that

$$a_n(c) = \frac{2^n}{[(c+2)(c+3) \cdots (c+n+1)]^2},$$

from which by the method of Section 91 we obtain immediately

$$a_n'(c) = -2a_n(c) \left\{ \frac{1}{c+2} + \frac{1}{c+3} + \cdots + \frac{1}{c+n+1} \right\}.$$

We now use $c = -1$ to obtain

$$a_n(-1) = \frac{2^n}{(n!)^2}$$

and

$$a_n'(-1) = -2 \cdot \frac{2^n}{(n!)^2} \left\{ 1 + \tfrac{1}{2} + \tfrac{1}{3} + \cdots + \tfrac{1}{n} \right\}.$$

A frequently used notation for a partial sum of the harmonic series is useful here. It is

$$H_n = 1 + \frac{1}{2} + \frac{1}{3} + \cdots + \frac{1}{n} = \sum_{k=1}^{n} \frac{1}{k}.$$

We can now write $a_n'(-1)$ more simply as

$$a_n'(-1) = -\frac{2^{n+1} H_n}{(n!)^2}.$$

Finally the desired solutions can be written in the form

$$(13) \qquad y_1 = x^{-1} + \sum_{n=1}^{\infty} \frac{2^n x^{n-1}}{(n!)^2},$$

and

$$(14) \qquad y_2 = y_1 \ln x - \sum_{n=1}^{\infty} \frac{2^{n+1} H_n x^{n-1}}{(n!)^2}.$$

The general solution, valid for all finite $x \neq 0$, is

$$y = A y_1 + B y_2,$$

with A and B arbitrary constants. The linear independence of y_1 and y_2 should be evident because of the presence of $\ln x$ in y_2. In detail, xy_1 has a power series expansion about $x = 0$, but xy_2 does not, so they cannot be proportional.

Examination of the procedure used in solving this differential equation shows that the method is in no way dependent upon the specific coefficients except in that the indicial equation has equal roots. That is, the success of the method is due to the fact that the $n = 0$ term in $L(y)$ contains a square factor.

When the indicial equation has equal roots, $c_2 = c_1$, then two linearly independent solutions will always appear in the form

$$y_1 = x^{c_1} + \sum_{n=1}^{\infty} a_n x^{n+c_1},$$

$$y_2 = y_1 \ln x + \sum_{n=1}^{\infty} b_n x^{n+c_1},$$

where c_1, a_n, b_n are dependent upon the coefficients in the particular equation being solved.

EXERCISES

Obtain two linearly independent solutions valid about $x = 0$ unless otherwise instructed.

1. $x^2 y'' - x(1 + x)y' + y = 0$.

ANS. $y_1 = \sum_{n=0}^{\infty} \dfrac{x^{n+1}}{n!} = xe^x; \; y_2 = y_1 \ln x - \sum_{n=1}^{\infty} \dfrac{H_n x^{n+1}}{n!}.$

2. $4x^2 y'' + (1 - 2x)y = 0$.

ANS. $y_1 = \sum_{n=0}^{\infty} \dfrac{x^{n+1/2}}{2^n (n!)^2}; \; y_2 = y_1 \ln x - \sum_{n=1}^{\infty} \dfrac{H_n x^{n+1/2}}{2^{n-1}(n!)^2}.$

3. $x^2 y'' + x(x - 3)y' + 4y = 0$.

ANS. $y_1 = \sum_{n=0}^{\infty} \dfrac{(-1)^n (n+1)x^{n+2}}{n!};$

$$y_2 = y_1 \ln x + \sum_{n=1}^{\infty} \dfrac{(-1)^{n+1}[n + (n+1)H_n]x^{n+2}}{n!}.$$

4. $xy'' + (1 - x^2)y' - xy = 0$.

ANS. $y_1 = 1 + \sum_{k=1}^{\infty} \dfrac{1 \cdot 3 \cdot 5 \cdots (2k-1)x^{2k}}{2^{2k}(k!)^2};$

$y_2 = y_1 \ln x$

$$+ \sum_{k=1}^{\infty} \frac{1 \cdot 3 \cdot 5 \cdots (2k-1) \left\{ 1 + \frac{1}{3} + \cdots + \frac{1}{2k-1} - H_k \right\} x^{2k}}{2^{2k}(k!)^2}.$$

5. Show that

$$1 + \frac{1}{3} + \frac{1}{5} + \cdots + \frac{1}{2k-1} = H_{2k} - \frac{1}{2}H_k$$

and apply the result to simplification of the formula for y_2 in the answer to Ex. 4.

6. $x(1+x)y'' + (1+5x)y' + 3y = 0$.

ANS. $y_1 = 1 + \frac{1}{2} \sum_{n=1}^{\infty} (-1)^n (n+1)(n+2)x^n$;

$$y_2 = y_1 \ln x - \frac{3}{2}(y_1 - 1) + \frac{1}{2} \sum_{n=1}^{\infty} (-1)^n (2n+3)x^n.$$

7. $xy'' + y' + xy = 0$.   This is known as Bessel's equation of index zero. It is widely encountered in both pure and applied mathematics. See also Sections 101 and 102.

ANS. $y_1 = \sum_{k=0}^{\infty} \frac{(-1)^k x^{2k}}{2^{2k}(k!)^2}$; $y_2 = y_1 \ln x - \sum_{k=1}^{\infty} \frac{(-1)^k H_k x^{2k}}{2^{2k}(k!)^2}$.

8. $x^2 y'' - x(1+3x)y' + (1-6x)y = 0$.

ANS. $y_1 = \sum_{n=0}^{\infty} \frac{3^n (n+1)(n+2)x^{n+1}}{2 \cdot n!}$;

$$y_2 = y_1 \ln x + \sum_{n=1}^{\infty} \frac{3^n (n+1)(n+2)(H_{n+2} - 2H_n - \frac{3}{2})x^{n+1}}{2 \cdot n!}.$$

9. $x^2 y'' + x(3+2x)y' + (1+3x)y = 0$.   In simplifying y_2 use the formula given in Ex. 5 above.

ANS. $y_1 = x^{-1} + \sum_{n=1}^{\infty} \frac{(-1)^n 1 \cdot 3 \cdot 5 \cdots (2n-1)x^{n-1}}{(n!)^2}$;

$$y_2 = y_1 \ln x + \sum_{n=1}^{\infty} \frac{(-1)^n 1 \cdot 3 \cdot 5 \cdots (2n-1)(2H_{2n} - 3H_n)x^{n-1}}{(n!)^2}.$$

10. $x^2y'' + x(x - 1)y' + (1 - x)y = 0$.

$$\text{ANS.} \quad y_1 = x; \; y_2 = y_1 \ln x + \sum_{n=1}^{\infty} \frac{(-1)^n x^{n+1}}{n \cdot n!}.$$

11. $x(x - 2)y'' + 2(x - 1)y' - 2y = 0$.

$$\text{ANS.} \quad y_1 = 1 - x; \; y_2 = y_1 \ln x + \tfrac{5}{2}x - \sum_{n=2}^{\infty} \frac{(n + 1)x^n}{2^n n(n - 1)}.$$

12. Solve the equation of Ex. 11 about the point $x = 2$.

$$\text{ANS.} \quad y_1 = 1 + (x - 2);$$

$$y_2 = y_1 \ln (x - 2) - \tfrac{5}{2}(x - 2) - \sum_{n=2}^{\infty} \frac{(-1)^n (n + 1)(x - 2)^n}{2^n n(n - 1)}.$$

13. Solve about $x = 4$: $\quad 4(x - 4)^2 y'' + (x - 4)(x - 8)y' + xy = 0$.

$$\text{ANS.} \quad y_1 = \sum_{n=0}^{\infty} \frac{(-1)^n (n + 1)(x - 4)^{n+1}}{2^{2n} n!};$$

$$y_2 = y_1 \ln (x - 4) + \sum_{n=1}^{\infty} \frac{(-1)^n (n + 1)(H_{n+1} - 2H_n - 1)(x - 4)^{n+1}}{2^{2n} n!}.$$

14. $x^2 y'' + 3x(1 + x)y' + (1 - 3x)y = 0$.

$$\text{ANS.} \quad y_1 = x^{-1} + 6 + \tfrac{9}{2}x;$$

$$y_2 = y_1 \ln x - 15 - \tfrac{81}{4}x + \sum_{n=3}^{\infty} \frac{2(-3)^n x^{n-1}}{n! n(n - 1)(n - 2)}.$$

15. $xy'' + (1 - x)y' - y = 0$.

$$\text{ANS.} \quad y_1 = 1 + \sum_{n=1}^{\infty} \frac{x^n}{n!} = e^x; \qquad y_2 = y_1 \ln x - \sum_{n=1}^{\infty} \frac{H_n x^n}{n!}.$$

16. Refer to Ex. 15 above. There one solution was found to be $y_1 = e^x$. Use the change of dependent variable, $y = ve^x$, to obtain the general solution of the differential equation in the form

$$y = k_1 e^x \int_{k_2}^{x} \beta^{-1} e^{-\beta} \, d\beta.$$

93. Indicial equation with difference of roots a positive integer, nonlogarithmic case.   Consider the equation

(1) $$xy'' - (4 + x)y' + 2y = 0.$$

As usual let $L(y)$ stand for the left member of (1) and put

(2) $$y = \sum_{n=0}^{\infty} a_n x^{n+c}.$$

At once we find that for the y of equation (2), the left member of equation (1) takes the form

$$L(y) = \sum_{n=0}^{\infty} [(n + c)(n + c - 1) - 4(n + c)]a_n x^{n+c-1}$$

$$- \sum_{n=0}^{\infty} (n + c - 2)a_n x^{n+c},$$

or

$$L(y) = \sum_{n=0}^{\infty} (n + c)(n + c - 5)a_n x^{n+c-1} - \sum_{n=1}^{\infty} (n + c - 3)a_{n-1} x^{n+c-1}.$$

The indicial equation is $c(c - 5) = 0$, so that

$$c_1 = 5, \quad c_2 = 0, \quad s = c_1 - c_2 = 5.$$

We reason that we may hope for two power series solutions, one starting with an x^0 term, one with an x^5 term.   If we use the large root $c = 5$ and try a series

$$\sum_{n=0}^{\infty} a_n x^{n+5},$$

it is evident that we can get at most one solution; the x^0 term would never enter.

On the other hand, if we use the smaller root $c = 0$, then a trial solution of the form has a chance of picking up both solutions because the $n = 5$ ($n = s$) term does contain x^5.

If s is a positive integer, we try a series of the form (2) using the smaller root c_2. If a_0 and a_s both turn out to be arbitrary, we obtain the general solution by this method. Otherwise the relation which should determine a_s will be impossible (with our usual assumption that $a_0 \neq 0$) and the general solution will involve a logarithm as it did in the case of equal roots. That logarithmic case will be treated in the next section.

Let us return to the numerical problem. Using the smaller root $c = 0$, we now know that for

$$(3) \qquad y = \sum_{n=0}^{\infty} a_n x^n$$

we get

$$L(y) = \sum_{n=0}^{\infty} n(n-5)a_n x^{n-1} - \sum_{n=1}^{\infty} (n-3)a_{n-1}x^{n-1}.$$

Therefore, to make $L(y) = 0$, we must have

$$n = 0: \quad 0 \cdot a_0 = 0, \; (a_0 \text{ arbitrary})$$
$$n \geq 1: \quad n(n-5)a_n - (n-3)a_{n-1} = 0.$$

Since division by $(n - 5)$ cannot be accomplished until $n > 5$, it is best to write out the separate relations through the critical one for a_5. We thus obtain

$$n = 1: \quad -4a_1 + 2a_0 = 0,$$
$$n = 2: \quad -6a_2 + a_1 = 0,$$
$$n = 3: \quad -6a_3 + 0 \cdot a_2 = 0,$$
$$n = 4: \quad -4a_4 - a_3 = 0,$$
$$n = 5: \quad 0 \cdot a_5 - 2a_4 = 0,$$
$$n \geq 6: \quad a_n = \frac{(n-3)a_{n-1}}{n(n-5)}.$$

It follows from these relations that

$$
\begin{aligned}
a_1 &= \tfrac{1}{2}a_0, \\
a_2 &= \tfrac{1}{6}a_1 = \tfrac{1}{12}a_0 \\
a_3 &= 0, \\
a_4 &= 0, \\
0 \cdot a_5 &= 0,
\end{aligned}
$$

so that a_5 is arbitrary. Each a_n, $n > 5$, will be obtained from a_5. In the usual way it is found that

$$
a_6 = \frac{3a_5}{6 \cdot 1},
$$

$$
a_7 = \frac{4a_6}{7 \cdot 2},
$$

$$
\cdot
$$
$$
\cdot
$$
$$
\cdot
$$

$$
a_n = \frac{(n-3)a_{n-1}}{n(n-5)},
$$

from which

$$
a_n = \frac{3 \cdot 4 \cdot 5 \cdots (n-3)a_5}{[6 \cdot 7 \cdot 8 \cdots n](n-5)!} = \frac{3 \cdot 4 \cdot 5a_5}{(n-2)(n-1)n(n-5)!}.
$$

Therefore, with a_0 and a_5 arbitrary, the general solution appears as

$$
y = a_0(1 + \tfrac{1}{2}x + \tfrac{1}{12}x^2) + a_5\left[x^5 + \sum_{n=6}^{\infty} \frac{60x^n}{(n-5)!n(n-1)(n-2)} \right].
$$

The coefficient of a_5 may also be written, with a shift of index, in the form

$$
\sum_{n=0}^{\infty} \frac{60x^{n+5}}{n!(n+5)(n+4)(n+3)}.
$$

Before proceeding to the exercises let us examine an equation for which the fortunate circumstance a_0 and a_s both arbitrary does not occur. For the equation

(4) $$x^2y'' + x(1 - x)y' - (1 + 3x)y = 0$$

the trial

$$y = \sum_{n=0}^{\infty} a_n x^{n+c}$$

leads to

$$L(y) = \sum_{n=0}^{\infty} (n + c + 1)(n + c - 1)a_n x^{n+c}$$

$$- \sum_{n=1}^{\infty} (n + c + 2)a_{n-1} x^{n+c}.$$

Since $c_1 = 1$ and $c_2 = -1$, we use $c = -1$ and find the relations

$$n \geqq 1: \quad n(n - 2)a_n - (n + 1)a_{n-1} = 0,$$

with a_0 arbitrary. Let us write down the separate relations out to the critical one,

$$n = 1: \quad -a_1 - 2a_0 = 0,$$
$$n = 2: \quad 0 \cdot a_2 - 3a_1 = 0,$$
$$n \geqq 3: \quad a_n = \frac{(n + 1)a_{n-1}}{n(n - 2)}.$$

It follows that

$$a_1 = -2a_0,$$
$$0 \cdot a_2 = 3a_1 = -6a_0.$$

These relations cannot be satisfied except by choosing $a_0 = 0$. But if that is done, a_2 will be the only arbitrary constant and the only solution coming out of the work will be that corresponding to the large value of c, $c = 1$. This is an instance where a logarithmic solution is indicated and the equation will be solved in the next section.

A good way to waste time is to use $a_0 = 0$, $a_1 = 0$, a_2 arbitrary, and to determine a_n, $n \geqq 3$, from the above recurrence relation. In that way extra work can be done to get a solution which will be reobtained automatically when solving the equation by the method of the next section.

EXERCISES

Obtain the general solution near $x = 0$ except when instructed otherwise.

1. $xy'' - (3 + x)y' + 2y = 0.$

$$\text{ANS.} \quad y = a_0(1 + \tfrac{2}{3}x + \tfrac{1}{6}x^2) + a_4 \sum_{n=4}^{\infty} \frac{24(n-3)x^n}{n!}.$$

2. $x(1 + x)y'' + (x + 5)y' - 4y = 0.$

$$\text{ANS.} \quad y = a_0(x^{-4} + 4x^{-3} + 5x^{-2}) + a_4(1 + \tfrac{4}{5}x + \tfrac{1}{5}x^2).$$

3. Solve the equation of Ex. 2 about the point $x = -1$.

$$\text{ANS.} \quad y = a_0[1 + (x + 1) + \tfrac{1}{2}(x + 1)^2]$$
$$+ \frac{a_5}{12} \sum_{n=5}^{\infty} (n-4)(n-3)(n+1)(x+1)^n.$$

4. $x^2 y'' + x^2 y' - 2y = 0.$

$$\text{ANS.} \quad y = a_0(x^{-1} - \tfrac{1}{2}) + 6a_3 \sum_{n=3}^{\infty} \frac{(-1)^{n+1}(n-2)x^{n-1}}{n!}.$$

5. $x(1 - x)y'' - 3y' + 2y = 0.$

$$\text{ANS.} \quad y = a_0(1 + \tfrac{2}{3}x + \tfrac{1}{3}x^2) + a_4 \sum_{n=4}^{\infty} (n-3)x^n.$$

6. Solve the equation of Ex. 5 about the point $x = 1$.

$$\text{ANS.} \quad y = a_0[(x-1)^{-2} + 4(x-1)^{-1}] + a_2[1 + \tfrac{2}{3}(x-1) + \tfrac{1}{6}(x-1)^2].$$

7. $xy'' + (4 + 3x)y' + 3y = 0.$

$$\text{ANS.} \quad y = a_0(x^{-3} - 3x^{-2} + \tfrac{9}{2}x^{-1}) + 6a_3 \sum_{n=3}^{\infty} \frac{(-3)^{n-3}x^{n-3}}{n!}.$$

8. $xy'' - 2(x + 2)y' + 4y = 0.$

$$\text{ANS.} \quad y = a_0(1 + x + \tfrac{1}{3}x^2) + a_5 \sum_{n=5}^{\infty} \frac{60 \cdot 2^{n-5}x^n}{(n-5)!n(n-1)(n-2)}.$$

9. $xy'' + (3 + 2x)y' + 4y = 0.$

$$\text{ANS.} \quad y = a_0 x^{-2} + a_2 \sum_{n=2}^{\infty} \frac{(-1)^n 2^{n-1} x^{n-2}}{n \cdot (n-2)!}.$$

10. $xy'' + (x^3 - 1)y' + x^2y = 0.$

ANS. $y = a_0 \sum_{k=0}^{\infty} \frac{(-1)^k x^{3k}}{3^k k!} + a_2\left[x^2 + \sum_{k=1}^{\infty} \frac{(-1)^k x^{3k+2}}{5 \cdot 8 \cdot 11 \cdots (3k+2)}\right].$

11. $x^2(4x - 1)y'' + x(5x + 1)y' + 3y = 0.$

ANS. $y = a_0(x^{-1} - 1) + a_4\left[x^3 + 12 \sum_{n=5}^{\infty} \frac{13 \cdot 17 \cdot 21 \cdots (4n-7)x^{n-1}}{(n-4)! \cdot n(n-1)}\right].$

94. Indicial equation with difference of roots a positive integer, logarithmic case. In the preceding section we examined the equation

(1) $$x^2y'' + x(1 - x)y' - (1 + 3x)y = 0$$

and found that its indicial equation has roots $c_1 = 1$, $c_2 = -1$. Since there is no power series solution starting with x^{c_2}, we suspect the presence of a logarithmic term and start to treat the equation in the manner of the previous logarithmic case, that of equal roots.

From the assumed form

$$y = \sum_{n=0}^{\infty} a_n x^{n+c}$$

we easily determine the left member of equation (1) to be

$$L(y) = \sum_{n=0}^{\infty} (n+c+1)(n+c-1)a_n x^{n+c} - \sum_{n=0}^{\infty} (n+c+3)a_n x^{n+c+1}$$

$$= \sum_{n=0}^{\infty} (n+c+1)(n+c-1)a_n x^{n+c} - \sum_{n=1}^{\infty} (n+c+2)a_{n-1} x^{n+c}.$$

As usual each term after the first one in the series for $L(y)$ can be made zero by choosing the a_n, $n \geq 1$, without choosing c. Let us put

$$n \geq 1: \quad a_n = \frac{(n+c+2)a_{n-1}}{(n+c+1)(n+c-1)},$$

from which it follows at once that

$$n \geq 1 : a_n = \frac{(c+3)(c+4) \cdots (c+n+2)a_0}{[(c+2)(c+3) \cdots (c+n+1)][c(c+1) \cdots (c+n-1)]},$$

or

$$n \geq 1 : \quad a_n = \frac{(c+n+2)a_0}{(c+2)[c(c+1) \cdots (c+n-1)]}.$$

For the a_n obtained above all terms after the first one in the power series for $L(y)$ have been made to vanish, so with

$$(2) \qquad y = a_0 x^c + \sum_{n=1}^{\infty} \frac{(c+n+2)a_0 x^{n+c}}{(c+2)[c(c+1) \cdots (c+n-1)]}$$

it must follow that

$$(3) \qquad\qquad L(y) = (c+1)(c-1)a_0 x^c.$$

From the larger root, $c = 1$, only one solution can be obtained. From the smaller root, $c = -1$, two solutions would be available following the technique of using $y(x, c)$ and $\partial y(x, c)/\partial c$ as in the case of equal roots if only the right member of (3) contained the factor $(c+1)^2$ instead of just $(c+1)$ to the first power. But a_0 is still arbitrary so we take $a_0 = (c+1)$ in order to get the desired square factor on the right in equation (3).

Another way of seeing that it is desirable to choose $a_0 = (c+1)$ is as follows. We know that eventually it is going to be necessary to use $c = -1$ in equation (2). But within the series, the denominator contains the factor $(c+1)$ for all terms after the $n = 1$ term. As equation (2) stands now the terms $n \geq 2$ would not exist with $c = -1$. Therefore we remove the troublesome factor $(c+1)$ from the denominator by choosing $a_0 = (c+1)$.

With $a_0 = (c+1)$ we have

$$(4) \quad y(x, c) = (c+1)x^c + \sum_{n=1}^{\infty} \frac{(c+1)(c+n+2)x^{n+c}}{(c+2)[c(c+1) \cdots (c+n-1)]}$$

for which

$$(5) \qquad\qquad L[y(x, c)] = (c+1)^2(c-1)x^c.$$

The same argument as was used when the indicial equation had equal roots shows that the two linearly independent solutions being sought may be obtained as

$$(6) \qquad y_1 = y(x, -1),$$

and

$$(7) \qquad y_2 = \left(\frac{\partial y(x, c)}{\partial c}\right)_{c=-1}.$$

Naturally, it is wise to perform the cancellation of the factor $(c + 1)$ from the numerator and denominator in the terms of the series in (4). But the factor $(c + 1)$ does not enter the denominator until the term $n = 2$. Therefore it seems best to write out the terms that far separately. We rewrite equation (4) as

$$(8) \quad y(x, c) = (c + 1)x^c + \frac{(c + 1)(c + 3)x^{1+c}}{(c + 2)c} + \frac{(c + 4)x^{2+c}}{(c + 2)c}$$

$$+ \sum_{n=3}^{\infty} \frac{(c + n + 2)x^{n+c}}{(c + 2)c[(c + 2)(c + 3) \cdots (c + n - 1)]}.$$

Differentiation with respect to c of the members of equation (8) yields

$$(9) \quad \frac{\partial y(x, c)}{\partial c} = y(x, c) \ln x + x^c$$

$$+ \frac{(c + 1)(c + 3)x^{1+c}}{(c + 2)c} \left\{\frac{1}{c + 1} + \frac{1}{c + 3} - \frac{1}{c + 2} - \frac{1}{c}\right\}$$

$$+ \frac{(c + 4)x^{2+c}}{(c + 2)c} \left\{\frac{1}{c + 4} - \frac{1}{c + 2} - \frac{1}{c}\right\}$$

$$+ \sum_{n=3}^{\infty} \frac{(c+n+2)x^{n+c}\left\{\frac{1}{c+n+2} - \frac{1}{c+2} - \frac{1}{c} - \left(\frac{1}{c+2} + \frac{1}{c+3} + \cdots + \frac{1}{c+n-1}\right)\right\}}{(c + 2)c[(c + 2)(c + 3) \cdots (c + n - 1)]}.$$

All that remains to be done is to get y_1 and y_2 by using $c = -1$ in the expressions above for $y(x, c)$ and $\partial y(x, c)/\partial c$. In the third term on the right in equation (9) we first (mentally) insert the factor $(c + 1)$ throughout the quantity in the curly brackets.

The desired solutions are thus found to be

$$y_1 = 0 \cdot x^{-1} + 0 \cdot x^0 - 3x + \sum_{n=3}^{\infty} \frac{(n+1)x^{n-1}}{(-1)[1 \cdot 2 \cdots (n-2)]}$$

and

$$y_2 = y_1 \ln x + x^{-1} - 2x^0 - 3x\{\tfrac{1}{3} - 1 + 1\}$$
$$+ \sum_{n=3}^{\infty} \frac{(n+1)x^{n-1}\left\{\dfrac{1}{n+1} - 1 + 1 - \left(1 + \tfrac{1}{2} + \cdots + \dfrac{1}{n-2}\right)\right\}}{(-1)[1 \cdot 2 \cdots (n-2)]}.$$

These results can be written more compactly as

$$(10) \qquad y_1 = -3x - \sum_{n=3}^{\infty} \frac{(n+1)x^{n-1}}{(n-2)!}$$

and

$$(11) \quad y_2 = y_1 \ln x + x^{-1} - 2 - x - \sum_{n=3}^{\infty} \frac{[1 - (n+1)H_{n-2}]x^{n-1}}{(n-2)!}.$$

It is also possible to absorb one more term into the summation and to improve the appearance of these results. The student can show that

$$y_1 = -\sum_{n=0}^{\infty} \frac{(n+3)x^{n+1}}{n!}$$

and

$$y_2 = y_1 \ln x + x^{-1} - 2 - \sum_{n=0}^{\infty} \frac{[1 - (n+3)H_n]x^{n+1}}{n!},$$

so long as the common conventions (definitions) $H_0 = 0$ and $0! = 1$ are used.

The general solution of the original differential equation is

$$y = Ay_1 + By_2$$

and it is valid for all finite $x \neq 0$, since the differential equation has no other singular points in the finite plane.

The step taken in passing from equation (4) to equation (8) should be used regularly in this type of solution. Without its use indeterminate forms which may cause confusion will be encountered.

An essential point in this method is the choice $a_0 = (c - c_2)$ where c_2 is the smaller root of the indicial equation.

EXERCISES

Find two linearly independent solutions valid about $x = 0$, unless otherwise instructed.

1. $xy'' + y = 0$.

$$\text{ANS.} \quad y_1 = \sum_{n=1}^{\infty} \frac{(-1)^n x^n}{n!(n-1)!};$$

$$y_2 = y_1 \ln x + 1 + x - \sum_{n=2}^{\infty} \frac{(-1)^n (H_n + H_{n-1}) x^n}{n!(n-1)!}.$$

2. $x^2 y'' - 3xy' + (3 + 4x)y = 0$.

$$\text{ANS.} \quad y_1 = \sum_{n=2}^{\infty} \frac{(-1)^{n+1} 4^n x^{n+1}}{n!(n-2)!};$$

$$y_2 = y_1 \ln x + y_1 + x + 4x^2 + \sum_{n=2}^{\infty} \frac{(-4)^n (H_n + H_{n-2}) x^{n+1}}{n!(n-2)!}.$$

3. $2xy'' + 6y' + y = 0$.

$$\text{ANS.} \quad y_1 = \sum_{n=2}^{\infty} \frac{(-1)^{n+1} x^{n-2}}{2^n n!(n-2)!};$$

$$y_2 = y_1 \ln x + y_1 + x^{-2} + \tfrac{1}{2} x^{-1} + \sum_{n=2}^{\infty} \frac{(-1)^n (H_n + H_{n-2}) x^{n-2}}{2^n n!(n-2)!}.$$

4. $4x^2 y'' + 2x(2 - x)y' - (1 + 3x)y = 0$.

$$\text{ANS.} \quad y_1 = \sum_{n=1}^{\infty} \frac{x^{n-1/2}}{2^{n-1}(n-1)!};$$

$$y_2 = y_1 \ln x + 2x^{-1/2} - \sum_{n=2}^{\infty} \frac{H_{n-1}x^{n-1/2}}{2^{n-1}(n-1)!}.$$

5. $x^2y'' - x(6+x)y' + 10y = 0.$

$$\text{ANS.} \quad y_1 = \sum_{n=3}^{\infty} \frac{(n+1)x^{n+2}}{2(n-3)!};$$

$$y_2 = y_1 \ln x + \tfrac{1}{2}y_1 + x^2 - x^3 + \tfrac{3}{2}x^4 + \sum_{n=3}^{\infty} \frac{[1-(n+1)H_{n-3}]x^{n+2}}{2(n-3)!}.$$

6. $x^2y'' + xy' + (x^2-1)y = 0.$ This is Bessel's equation of index one. See also Sections 101 and 102.

$$\text{ANS.} \quad y_1 = \sum_{k=1}^{\infty} \frac{(-1)^k x^{2k-1}}{2^{2k-1}k!(k-1)!};$$

$$y_2 = y_1 \ln x + x^{-1} - \sum_{k=1}^{\infty} \frac{(-1)^k (H_k + H_{k-1})x^{2k-1}}{2^{2k}k!(k-1)!}.$$

7. $xy'' + (3+2x)y' + 8y = 0.$

$$\text{ANS.} \quad y_1 = \sum_{n=2}^{\infty} \frac{(-1)^{n+1}2^n(n+1)x^{n-2}}{(n-2)!};$$

$$y_2 = y_1 \ln x + x^{-2} + 4x^{-1} + \sum_{n=2}^{\infty} \frac{(-2)^n[(n+1)H_{n-2}-1]x^{n-2}}{(n-2)!}.$$

8. $x(1-x)y'' + 2(1-x)y' + 2y = 0.$

$$\text{ANS.} \quad y_1 = -2 + 2x;$$

$$y_2 = y_1 \ln x + x^{-1} + 1 - 5x + \sum_{n=3}^{\infty} \frac{2x^{n-1}}{(n-1)(n-2)}.$$

9. Show that the answers to Ex. 8 may be replaced by

$$y_3 = 1 - x; \quad y_4 = y_3 \ln x - \tfrac{1}{2}x^{-1} + 2x - \sum_{n=3}^{\infty} \frac{x^{n-1}}{(n-1)(n-2)}.$$

10. Solve the equation of Ex. 8 near the point $x = 1$.

ANS. $y_1 = 2(x - 1)$;

$$y_2 = y_1 \ln (x - 1) + 1 - 3(x - 1) + \sum_{n=2}^{\infty} \frac{(-1)^{n+1}(n + 1)(x - 1)^n}{n - 1}.$$

11. $x^2 y'' - 5xy' + (8 + 5x)y = 0.$

ANS. $y_1 = \sum_{n=2}^{\infty} \frac{(-1)^{n+1} 5^n x^{n+2}}{n!(n - 2)!}$;

$$y_2 = y_1 \ln x + y_1 + x^2 + 5x^3 + \sum_{n=2}^{\infty} \frac{(-5)^n (H_n + H_{n-2}) x^{n+2}}{n!(n - 2)!}.$$

12. $xy'' + (3 - x)y' - 5y = 0.$

ANS. $y_1 = -\sum_{n=2}^{\infty} \frac{(n + 1)(n + 2) x^{n-2}}{2(n - 2)!}$;

$$y_2 = y_1 \ln x - \tfrac{1}{2} y_1 + x^{-2} - 3x^{-1}$$

$$- \sum_{n=2}^{\infty} \frac{(n + 1)(n + 2)(H_{n+2} - H_n - H_{n-2}) x^{n-2}}{2(n - 2)!}.$$

13. $x^2 y'' + x(1 - 2x)y' - (x + 1)y = 0.$

ANS. $y_1 = \sum_{n=2}^{\infty} \frac{1 \cdot 3 \cdot 5 \cdots (2n - 3) x^{n-1}}{n!(n - 2)!}$;

$$y_2 = y_1 \ln x + x^{-1} + 1 - y_1 +$$

$$\sum_{n=2}^{\infty} \frac{1 \cdot 3 \cdot 5 \cdots (2n - 3) \left\{ 2 \left(1 + \tfrac{1}{3} + \cdots + \dfrac{1}{2n - 3} \right) - H_n - H_{n-2} \right\} x^{n-1}}{n!(n - 2)!}.$$

95. Summary.

Confronted by a linear equation

(1) $$L(y) = 0,$$

we first determine the location and nature of the singular points of the equation. In practice the use to which the results will be put will dictate that solutions are desired near a certain point or points. In seeking solutions valid about the point $x = x_0$, always first translate the origin, putting $x - x_0 = v$.

Solutions valid near an ordinary point $x = 0$ of equation (1) take the form

$$(2) \qquad y = \sum_{n=0}^{\infty} a_n x^n$$

with a_0 and a_1 arbitrary, if equation (1) is of second order.

If $x = 0$ is a regular singular point of equation (1) we wish to get solutions valid near $x = 0$, then we first put

$$(3) \qquad y = \sum_{n=0}^{\infty} a_n x^{n+c}.$$

For the y of (3) we obtain by substitution the series for $L(y)$. From the $n = 0$ term of that series the indicial equation may be written down. When the difference of the roots of the indicial equation is not an integer, or if the roots are equal, the technique is straightforward following the method of Section 90 or of Section 92.

When the roots differ by a nonzero integer, then the solution may, or may not, involve $\ln x$. The recurrence relation for $n = s$, where s is the difference of the roots, is the critical one. We must then determine whether the relations for $n = 1, 2, \cdots, s$ leave a_0 and a_s both arbitrary. If they do so, then two power series of the form (3) will be solutions of the differential equation. If a_0 and a_s are not both arbitrary a logarithmic case is present. Then the device of Section 94 may be used.

The technique may be varied, if desired, by always choosing the a_n in terms of c so that the series for $L(y)$ reduces to a single term. Thus a series of the form

$$(4) \qquad y(x, c) = a_0 \left[x^c + \sum_{n=1}^{\infty} f_n(c) x^{n+c} \right]$$

will be determined for which

$$(5) \qquad L[y(x, c)] = a_0(c - c_1)(c - c_2) x^{c-k},$$

where k is zero or one for the equations being treated here and c_1 and

c_2 are the roots of the indicial equation. Then it can be determined from the actual coefficients in (4) whether the use of $c = c_1$ and $c = c_2$ will result in two solutions of the differential equation. If $c_1 = c_2$ the results would be identical and the use of $\partial y(x, c)/\partial c$ is indicated. The other logarithmic case will be identified by the fact that some one or more of the coefficients $f_n(c)$ will not exist when $c = c_2$, the smaller root. Then again the differentiation process is needed, after the introduction of $a_0 = c - c_2$.

The method sketched above has a disadvantage in that it seems to tempt the user into automatic application of rules, always a dangerous procedure in mathematics. When a student thoroughly understands what is happening in each of the four possible cases, this method may safely be used and it saves some labor.

Extension of the methods of this and the preceding chapter to linear equations of higher order is direct. As an example, a fourth order equation whose indicial equation has roots $c = 2, 2, 2, \frac{1}{2}$ would be treated as follows. A series would be determined for $y(x, c)$,

$$y(x, c) = a_0 \left[x^c + \sum_{n=1}^{\infty} f_n(c)x^{n+c} \right]$$

for which the left member of the original equation reduces to one term, such as

$$L[y(x, c)] = (c - 2)^3(2c - 1)a_0 x^c.$$

Then four linearly independent solutions could be obtained as

$$y_1 = y(x, 2), \ y_2 = \left[\frac{\partial y(x, c)}{\partial c} \right]_{c=2}, \ y_3 = \left[\frac{\partial^2 y(x, c)}{\partial c^2} \right]_{c=2}, \ y_4 = y(x, \tfrac{1}{2}).$$

MISCELLANEOUS EXERCISES

In each exercise obtain solutions valid near $x = 0$.

1. $2xy'' + (1 + 2x)y' - 3y = 0.$
2. $x(1 - x^2)y'' - (7 + x^2)y' + 4xy = 0.$
3. $4x^2y'' - 2x(2 + x)y' + (3 + x)y = 0.$
4. $xy'' + 3y' - y = 0.$
5. $4x^2y'' + (3x + 1)y = 0.$
6. $x^2y'' + x(3x - 1)y' + (3x + 1)y = 0.$

7. $2xy'' + y' + y = 0.$

8. $4x^2y'' - x^2y' + y = 0.$

9. $2x^2y'' - x(1 + 2x)y' + (1 + 3x)y = 0.$

10. $4x^2y'' + 3x^2y' + (1 + 3x)y = 0.$

11. $4x^2y'' + 2x^2y' - (x + 3)y = 0.$

12. $x^2y'' + x(3 + x)y' + (1 + 2x)y = 0.$

13. $x(1 - 2x)y'' - 2(2 + x)y' + 8y = 0.$

14. $x^2y'' - 3xy' + 4(1 + x)y = 0.$

15. $4x^2y'' + 2x(x - 4)y' + (5 - 3x)y = 0.$

16. $x(1 - x)y'' - (4 + x)y' + 4y = 0.$

$$\text{ANS.} \quad y = a_0(1 + x + \tfrac{1}{2}x^2) + \frac{a_5}{12} \sum_{n=5}^{\infty} (n - 4)(n - 3)(n + 1)x^n.$$

17. Solve the equation of Ex. 16 about the point $x = 1$.

$$\text{ANS.} \quad y = a_0[(x - 1)^{-4} + 4(x - 1)^{-3} + 5(x - 1)^{-2}] \\ + a_4[1 + \tfrac{4}{5}(x - 1) + \tfrac{1}{5}(x - 1)^2].$$

18. $x(1 - x)y'' + (1 - 4x)y' - 2y = 0.$

19. Show that the solutions of Ex. 18 may be written in the form

$$y_1 = (1 - x)^{-2},$$
$$y_2 = (1 - x)^{-2}(\ln x - x).$$

20. $xy'' + (1 - x)y' + 3y = 0.$

$$\text{ANS.} \quad y_1 = 1 - 3x + \tfrac{3}{2}x^2 - \tfrac{1}{6}x^3;$$

$$y_2 = y_1 \ln x + 7x - \tfrac{23}{4}x^2 + \tfrac{11}{12}x^3 - 6 \sum_{n=4}^{\infty} \frac{x^n}{n!n(n - 1)(n - 2)(n - 3)}.$$

21. $xy'' - (2 + x)y' - 2y = 0.$

22. $2x^2y'' - x(2x + 7)y' + 2(x + 5)y = 0.$

23. $(1 - x^2)y'' - 10xy' - 18y = 0.$

24. $y'' + 2xy' - 8y = 0.$

25. $2x(1 - x)y'' + (1 - 2x)y' + 8y = 0.$

26. $2x^2y'' - x(1 + 2x)y' + (1 + 4x)y = 0.$

27. $x^2y'' - x(1 + x^2)y' + (1 - x^2)y = 0.$

28. $x^2y'' + x(x^2 - 3)y' + 4y = 0.$

29. $(1 + x^2)y'' - 2y = 0.$

30. $x^2y'' - 3x(1 + x)y' + 4(1 - x)y = 0.$

31. $y''' + xy = 0.$

32. $xy'' + (1 - x^2)y' + 2xy = 0.$

33. $x(1 - x^2)y'' + 5(1 - x^2)y' - 4xy = 0.$

34. $x^2y'' + xy' - (x^2 + 4)y = 0.$

35. $2xy'' + (3 - x)y' - 3y = 0.$

36. $xy'' + (2 - x)y' - y = 0.$

37. $y'' - 2xy' + 6y = 0.$

38. $2(1 + x^2)y'' + 7xy' + 2y = 0.$
39. $3xy'' + 2(1 - x)y' - 2y = 0.$
40. $xy'' - (1 + 3x)y' - 4y = 0.$
41. $x^2y'' - x(3 + 2x)y' + (4 - x)y = 0.$
42. $2x(1 - x)y'' + y' + 4y = 0.$
43. $x(1 + 4x)y'' + (1 + 8x)y' + y = 0.$
44. $xy'' + (3 - 2x)y' - 4y = 0.$
45. $(1 - x^2)y'' - 2xy' + 12y = 0.$
46. $x^2(1 + x)y'' + x(3 + 5x)y' + (1 + 4x)y = 0.$
47. $x^2y'' + x^2y' + (3x - 2)y = 0.$
48. $2x^2y'' + 3xy' - (1 + x)y = 0.$

Chapter 20

Equations of Hypergeometric Type

96. Equations to be treated in this chapter. With the methods studied in Chapters 18 and 19 we are able to solve many equations which appear frequently in modern physics and engineering as well as in pure mathematics. We shall consider briefly the hypergeometric equation, Bessel's equation, and the equations which lead to the study of Laguerre, Legendre, and Hermite polynomials. There are, in mathematical literature, thousands of research papers devoted entirely or in part to the study of the functions which are solutions of the equations to be studied in this chapter. Here we do no more than call to the attention of the student the existence of these special functions which are of such great value to the theoretical physicist, engineer, and to many mathematicians.

97. The factorial function. It will be convenient for us to employ a notation which is widely encountered in advanced mathematics. We define the factorial function $(a)_n$, for n zero or a positive integer, by

$$(1) \qquad (a)_n = a(a + 1)(a + 2) \cdots (a + n - 1), \text{ for } n \geqq 1,$$
$$(a)_0 = 1 \text{ for } a \neq 0.$$

Thus the symbol $(a)_n$ denotes a product of n factors starting with the factor a, each factor being one larger than the factor before it. For instance,

$$(7)_4 = 7 \cdot 8 \cdot 9 \cdot 10,$$
$$(-5)_3 = (-5)(-4)(-3),$$
$$(-\tfrac{1}{2})_3 = (-\tfrac{1}{2})(\tfrac{1}{2})(\tfrac{3}{2}).$$

The factorial function is a generalization of the ordinary factorial $n!$; indeed, $(1)_n = 1 \cdot 2 \cdot 3 \cdots n = n!$.

98. The hypergeometric equation. It is shown in various places* that any second-order linear differential equation with only three singular points, each of them regular, can be transformed by change of variables into the hypergeometric equation

$$(1) \qquad x(1 - x)y'' + [c - (a + b + 1)x]y' - aby = 0,$$

in which a, b, c are fixed parameters.

Let us solve equation (1) about the regular singular point $x = 0$. For the moment let c be not an integer. For (1) the indicial equation has roots zero and $(1 - c)$. We put

$$y = \sum_{n=0}^{\infty} e_n x^n$$

in equation (1) and thus arrive, after the usual simplifications, at

$$(2) \qquad \sum_{n=0}^{\infty} n(n + c - 1)e_n x^{n-1} - \sum_{n=0}^{\infty} (n + a)(n + b)e_n x^n = 0.$$

Shift index in (2) to get

$$(3) \qquad \sum_{n=0}^{\infty} n(n + c - 1)e_n x^{n-1}$$

$$- \sum_{n=1}^{\infty} (n + a - 1)(n + b - 1)e_{n-1} x^{n-1} = 0.$$

We thus find that e_0 is arbitrary and, for $n \geqq 1$,

$$(4) \qquad e_n = \frac{(n + a - 1)(n + b - 1)}{n(n + c - 1)} e_{n-1}.$$

The recurrence relation (4) may be solved by our customary device. The result is, for $n \geqq 1$,

---

* See, for instance, E. D. Rainville, *Intermediate Differential Equations*, New York, John Wiley & Sons, 1943, Chapters 5–6.

$$(5) \quad e_n = \frac{a(a+1)(a+2)\cdots(a+n-1)\cdot b(b+1)(b+2)\cdots(b+n-1)e_0}{n!c(c+1)(c+2)\cdots(c+n-1)}.$$

But (5) is greatly simplified by use of the factorial function. We rewrite (5) as

$$(6) \qquad\qquad e_n = \frac{(a)_n(b)_n}{n!(c)_n}\cdot e_0.$$

Let us choose $e_0 = 1$ and write our first solution of the hypergeometric equation as

$$(7) \qquad\qquad y_1 = 1 + \sum_{n=1}^{\infty} \frac{(a)_n(b)_n x^n}{(c)_n n!}.$$

The particular solution y_1 in (7) is called the hypergeometric function and for it a common symbol is $F(a, b; c; x)$. That is,

$$F(a, b; c; x) = 1 + \sum_{n=1}^{\infty} \frac{(a)_n(b)_n x^n}{(c)_n n!},$$

and $y_1 = F(a, b; c; x)$ is a solution of equation (1).

The other root of the indicial equation is $(1 - c)$. We may put

$$y = \sum_{n=0}^{\infty} f_n x^{n+1-c}$$

into equation (1), determine f_n in the usual manner, and arrive at a second solution

$$(8) \qquad y_2 = x^{1-c} + \sum_{n=1}^{\infty} \frac{(a+1-c)_n(b+1-c)_n x^{n+1-c}}{(2-c)_n n!}.$$

In the hypergeometric notation this second solution (8) may be written

$$y_2 = x^{1-c}F(a+1-c, b+1-c; 2-c; x),$$

which means exactly the same as (8). The solutions (7) and (8) are valid in $0 < |x| < 1$, a region extending to the nearest other singular point of the differential equation (1).

If c is an integer, one of the solutions (7) or (8) is correct, but the other involves a zero denominator. For example, if $c = 5$, then in (8), $(2 - c)_n = (-3)_n$ and as soon as $n \geqq 4$, $(-3)_n = 0$. For,

$$(-3)_4 = (-3)(-2)(-1)(0) = 0.$$

If c is an integer, but a and b are nonintegral, one of the solutions about $x = 0$ of the hypergeometric equation is of logarithmic type. If c and one or both of a and b are integers, the solution may or may not involve a logarithm. To save space we omit logarithmic solutions of the hypergeometric equation.

99. Laguerre polynomials.

The equation

$$(1) \qquad xy'' + (1 - x)y' + ny = 0$$

is called Laguerre's equation. If n is a nonnegative integer, one solution of equation (1) is a polynomial.

Consider the solution of (1) about the regular singular point $x = 0$. The indicial equation has equal roots $c = 0, 0$. Hence one solution will involve a logarithm. We seek the nonlogarithmic solution.

Let us put

$$y = \sum_{k=0}^{\infty} a_k x^k$$

into (1) and obtain, in the usual way,

$$(2) \qquad \sum_{k=0}^{\infty} k^2 a_k x^{k-1} - \sum_{k=1}^{\infty} (k - 1 - n)a_{k-1}x^{k-1} = 0.$$

From (2) we find that

$$k \geqq 1: \quad a_k = \frac{(k - 1 - n)a_{k-1}}{k^2}$$

$$= \frac{(-n)(-n + 1) \cdots (-n + k - 1)a_0}{(k!)^2} = \frac{(-n)_k}{(k!)^2} a_0.$$

If n is a nonnegative integer, $(-n)_k = 0$ for $k > n$. Therefore, with a_0 chosen equal to unity, one solution of equation (1) is

$$(3) \qquad y_1 = \sum_{k=0}^{n} \frac{(-n)_k x^k}{(k!)^2}.$$

The right member of (3) is called the Laguerre polynomial and is usually denoted by $L_n(x)$:

$$(4) \qquad L_n(x) = \sum_{k=0}^{n} \frac{(-n)_k x^k}{(k!)^2} = \sum_{k=0}^{n} \frac{(-1)^k n! x^k}{(k!)^2 (n-k)!}.$$

The student should prove the equivalence of the two summations in (4) by showing that $(-n)_k = \dfrac{(-1)^k n!}{(n-k)!}$.

One solution of (1) is $y_1 = L_n(x)$. The associated logarithmic solution may, after considerable simplification, be put in the form

$$(5) \quad y_2 = L_n(x) \ln x + \sum_{k=1}^{n} \frac{(-n)_k (H_{n-k} - H_n - 2H_k) x^k}{(k!)^2}$$

$$+ \sum_{k=1}^{\infty} \frac{(-1)^n n! (k-1)! \, x^{k+n}}{[(k+n)!]^2}.$$

The solution (3) is valid for all finite x; the solution (5) is valid for $0 < |x| < \infty$.

100. The Gamma function. In Section 101 we shall need to employ a nonelementary function called the Gamma function. We define the function $\Gamma(x)$ by

$$(1) \qquad \Gamma(x) = \int_0^\infty e^{-t} t^{x-1} \, dt, \; x > 0.$$

If x is to be complex, the definition (1) is valid for the real part of x greater than zero.

Consider

$$(2) \qquad \Gamma(x+1) = \int_0^\infty e^{-t} t^x \, dt$$

and integrate by parts on the right to obtain

$$\Gamma(x+1) = \left[-e^{-t}t^x\right]_0^\infty + x \int_0^\infty e^{-t}t^{x-1}\, dt$$
$$= 0 + 0 + x\Gamma(x).$$

We have derived the functional relation

(3) $\Gamma(x+1) = x\Gamma(x).$

By repeated use of the relation (3) we find that, if n is an integer,

$$\Gamma(a+n) = (a+n-1)\Gamma(a+n-1)$$
$$= (a+n-1)(a+n-2)\Gamma(a+n-2)$$
$$= \cdots$$
$$= (a+n-1)(a+n-2) \cdots (a)\Gamma(a)$$
$$= (a)_n\Gamma(a).$$

Therefore the factorial function of Section 97 and the Gamma function are related by

(4) $(a)_n = \dfrac{\Gamma(a+n)}{\Gamma(a)}, \quad n \text{ integer}, \ n > 0.$

Actually (4), but not the proof given here, is valid for any complex a except zero or a negative integer.

Since

$$\Gamma(1) = \int_0^\infty e^{-t}t^0\, dt = \left[-e^{-t}\right]_0^\infty = 0 + 1 = 1,$$

we see that (4) yields

$$n! = (1)_n = \frac{\Gamma(1+n)}{\Gamma(1)} = \Gamma(1+n);$$

that is,

(5) $\Gamma(1+n) = n!$, n a positive integer.

Equation (5) is also valid for $n = 0$ with the customary definition $0! = 1$.

The function $\Gamma(x)$ has many other interesting properties but (3), (4), and (5) above are all we need to employ in this book.

101. Bessel's equation with index not an integer. The equation

$$(1) \qquad x^2y'' + xy' + (x^2 - n^2)y = 0$$

is called Bessel's equation of index n. Equation (1) has a regular singular point at $x = 0$, but no other singular points in the finite plane. At $x = 0$ the roots of the indicial equation are $c_1 = n$, $c_2 = -n$. In this section we assume that n is not an integer.

It is a simple exercise in the methods of Chapter 19 to show that if $n \neq$ an integer, then two linearly independent solutions of (1) are

$$(2) \qquad y_1 = \sum_{k=0}^{\infty} \frac{(-1)^k x^{2k+n}}{2^{2k} k! (1 + n)_k},$$

$$(3) \qquad y_2 = \sum_{k=0}^{\infty} \frac{(-1)^k x^{2k-n}}{2^{2k} k! (1 - n)_k},$$

valid in $0 < |x| < \infty$.
The function

$$y_3 = \frac{1}{2^n \Gamma(1 + n)} y_1 = \sum_{k=0}^{\infty} \frac{(-1)^k x^{2k+n}}{2^{2k+n} k! \Gamma(k + n + 1)},$$

also a solution of equation (1), is called $J_n(x)$, the Bessel function of the first kind and of index n. Thus

$$(4) \qquad y_3 = J_n(x) = \sum_{k=0}^{\infty} \frac{(-1)^k x^{2k+n}}{2^{2k+n} k! \Gamma(k + n + 1)}$$

is a solution of (1) and the general solution of (1) may be written

$$(5) \qquad y = AJ_n(x) + BJ_{-n}(x), \quad n \neq \text{an integer.}$$

That $J_{-n}(x)$ is a solution of the differential equation (1) should be evident from the fact that the parameter n enters (1) only in the term n^2. It is also true that

$$J_{-n}(x) = \frac{1}{2^{-n} \Gamma(1 - n)} y_2.$$

102. Bessel's equation with index an integer. In Bessel's equation

(1) $$x^2 y'' + xy' + (x^2 - n^2)y = 0,$$

let n now be zero or a positive integer. Then

(2) $$y_1 = J_n(x) = \sum_{k=0}^{\infty} \frac{(-1)^k x^{2k+n}}{2^{2k+n} k! \Gamma(k + n + 1)}$$

is one solution of equation (1). Any solution linearly independent of (2) must contain $\ln x$. We have already solved (1) for $n = 0$ in Ex. 7, page 292, and for $n = 1$ in Ex. 6, page 304.

For n an integer $\geqq 2$, put

$$y = \sum_{j=0}^{\infty} a_j x^{j+c},$$

proceed with the technique of Section 94, determine $y(x, c)$ and $\frac{\partial}{\partial c} y(x, c)$, and then use $c = -n$ to obtain two solutions

(3) $$y_2 = \sum_{k=n}^{\infty} \frac{(-1)^k x^{2k-n}}{2^{2k-1}(1 - n)_{n-1}(k - n)! k!}$$

and

(4) $$y_3 = y_2 \ln x + x^{-n} + \sum_{k=1}^{n-1} \frac{(-1)^k x^{2k-n}}{2^{2k}(1 - n)_k k!}$$

$$+ \sum_{k=n}^{\infty} \frac{(-1)^{k+1}(H_{k-n} + H_k - H_{n-1}) x^{2k-n}}{2^{2k-1}(1 - n)_{n-1}(k - n)! k!}.$$

A shift of index in (3) from k to $(k + n)$ yields

$$y_2 = \sum_{k=0}^{\infty} \frac{(-1)^{k+n} x^{2k+n}}{2^{2k+2n-1}(1 - n)_{n-1} k! (k + n)!}.$$

But for $n \geqq 2$, $(1 - n)_{n-1} = (-1)^{n-1}(n - 1)!$, so that

$$y_2 = \frac{-1}{2^{n-1}(n-1)!} \, J_n(x).$$

We can therefore replace the solution (3) with

$$(5) \qquad\qquad y_1 = J_n(x).$$

By similar manipulations we replace the solution (4) with

$$(6) \quad y_4 = J_n(x) \ln x + \sum_{k=0}^{n-1} \frac{(-1)^{k+1}(n-1)!x^{2k-n}}{2^{2k+1-n}k!(1-n)_k}$$

$$+ \tfrac{1}{2} \sum_{k=0}^{\infty} \frac{(-1)^{k+1}(H_k + H_{k+n})x^{2k+n}}{2^{2k+n}k!(k+n)!}.$$

For n an integer > 1, equations (5) and (6) may be used as the fundamental pair of linearly independent solutions of Bessel's equation (1).

103. Hermite polynomials.   The equation

$$(1) \qquad\qquad y'' - 2xy' + 2ny = 0$$

is called Hermite's equation.   Since equation (1) has no singular points in the finite plane, $x = 0$ is an ordinary point of the equation. We put

$$y = \sum_{j=0}^{\infty} a_j x^j$$

and employ the methods of Chapter 18 to obtain the general solution

$$(2) \quad y = a_0 \left[1 + \sum_{k=1}^{\infty} \frac{2^k(-n)(-n+2)\, \cdots\, (-n+2k-2)x^{2k}}{(2k)!} \right]$$

$$+ a_1 \left[x + \sum_{k=1}^{\infty} \frac{2^k(1-n)(1-n+2)\, \cdots\, (1-n+2k-2)x^{2k+1}}{(2k+1)!} \right],$$

valid for all finite x and with a_0 and a_1 arbitrary.

Interest in equation (1) is greatest when n is a positive integer or zero.   If n is an even integer, the coefficient of a_0 in (2) terminates, each term for $k \geq \frac{1}{2}(n + 2)$ being zero.   If n is an odd integer, the coefficient of a_1 in (2) terminates, each term for $k \geq \frac{1}{2}(n + 1)$ being zero.   Thus Hermite's equation always has a polynomial solution, of degree n, for n zero or a positive integer.   It is elementary but tedious to obtain from (2) a single expression for this polynomial solution.   The result is

$$(3) \qquad H_n(x) = \sum_{k=0}^{[\frac{1}{2}n]} \frac{(-1)^k n!(2x)^{n-2k}}{k!(n - 2k)!},$$

in which $[\frac{1}{2}n]$ stands for the greatest integer $\leq \frac{1}{2}n$.

The polynomial $H_n(x)$ of (3) is the Hermite polynomial; $y = H_n(x)$ is a solution of equation (1).

104. Legendre polynomials.   The equation

$$(1) \qquad (1 - x^2)y'' - 2xy' + n(n + 1)y = 0$$

is called Legendre's equation.   Let us solve (1) about the regular singular point $x = 1$.   We put $x - 1 = v$ and obtain the transformed equation

$$(2) \qquad v(v + 2)\frac{d^2y}{dv^2} + 2(v + 1)\frac{dy}{dv} - n(n + 1)y = 0.$$

At $v = 0$ equation (2) has, as roots of its indicial equation, $c = 0, 0$.   Hence one solution is logarithmic.   We are interested here only in the nonlogarithmic solution.

Following the methods of Chapter 19, put

$$y = \sum_{k=0}^{\infty} a_k v^k$$

into equation (2) and thus arrive at the results: a_0 is arbitrary and

$$(3) \qquad k \geq 1: \quad a_k = \frac{-(k - n - 1)(k + n)a_{k-1}}{2k^2}.$$

Solve the recurrence relation (3) and thus obtain

$$a_k = \frac{(-1)^k(-n)_k(1 + n)_k a_0}{2^k(k!)^2},$$

with the factorial notation of Section 97.

We may now write one solution of equation (1) in the form

$$(4) \qquad y_1 = 1 + \sum_{k=1}^{\infty} \frac{(-1)^k (-n)_k (n+1)_k (x-1)^k}{2^k (k!)^2}.$$

Since $k! = (1)_k$, we may put (4) into the form

$$(5) \qquad y_1 = 1 + \sum_{k=1}^{\infty} \frac{(-n)_k (n+1)_k}{(1)_k k!} \left(\frac{1-x}{2}\right)^k.$$

The right member of equation (5) is an example of the hypergeometric function which we met in Section 98. In fact

$$(6) \qquad y_1 = F\left(-n, n+1; 1; \frac{1-x}{2}\right).$$

If n is a positive integer or zero, the series in (4), (5), or (6) terminates. It is then called the Legendre polynomial and designated $P_n(x)$. We write our nonlogarithmic solution of Legendre's equation as

$$(7) \qquad y_1 = P_n(x) = F\left(-n, n+1; 1; \frac{1-x}{2}\right).$$

It is possible, but a bit laborious, to solve Legendre's equation about the ordinary point $x = 0$ and by elementary devices to put the polynomial solution in the form

$$(8) \qquad y_1 = P_n(x) = \sum_{k=0}^{[\frac{1}{2}n]} \frac{(-1)^k (2n-2k)! x^{n-2k}}{2^n k! (n-k)! (n-2k)!},$$

somewhat similar to the form (3) of the Hermite polynomial in Section 103.

105. The confluent* hypergeometric equation. The equation

$$(1) \qquad xy'' + (c-x)y' - ay = 0$$

---

* The concept of confluence of singularities is treated in Chapter 7 of E. D. Rainville's *Intermediate Differential Equations*, New York, John Wiley & Sons, 1943.

has a regular singular point at $x = 0$ with zero and $(1 - c)$ as roots of the indicial equation there. Equation (1) is called the confluent hypergeometric equation. If c is not an integer, there is no logarithmic solution of (1) about $x = 0$, so we restrict ourselves here to that simple situation.

In the usual manner we put

$$y = \sum_{n=0}^{\infty} b_n x^n$$

into (1) and thus find that b_0 is arbitrary and

$$n \geq 1: \quad b_n = \frac{(n - 1 + a)b_{n-1}}{n(n - 1 + c)}.$$

The recurrence relation yields

$$n \geq 1: \quad b_n = \frac{(a)_n b_0}{n!(c)_n}$$

in the notation of the factorial function of Section 97.

Therefore equation (1) has a solution

$$(2) \qquad y_1 = 1 + \sum_{n=1}^{\infty} \frac{(a)_n x^n}{(c)_n n!},$$

valid for all finite x. Note how much the right member of (2) resembles the hypergeometric function

$$(3) \qquad F(a, b; c; x) = 1 + \sum_{n=1}^{\infty} \frac{(a)_n (b)_n x^n}{(c)_n n!}$$

of Section 98. In (2) the series has only one numerator parameter a and one denominator parameter c. In (3) there are two numerator parameters a and b and one denominator parameter c. It is therefore customary to use for the right member of (2) a notation like that in (3). We write

$$(4) \qquad {}_1F_1(a; c; x) = 1 + \sum_{n=1}^{\infty} \frac{(a)_n x^n}{(c)_n n!},$$

with the subscripts before and after the F denoting the number of numerator and denominator parameters, respectively. When it is thought desirable, the function symbol on the left in (3) is similarly written $_2F_1(a, b; c; x)$. Functions of hypergeometric type with any number of numerator and denominator parameters have been studied for many years.

The subscripts on the F play a useful role when the nature of the function, but not its specific parameters, is under discussion. For instance, we say, "Any $_0F_1$ is essentially a Bessel function of the first kind," and "The Laguerre polynomial is a terminating $_1F_1$." The detailed statements are as follows:

$$(5) \qquad J_n(x) = \frac{(x/2)^n}{\Gamma(n+1)} \, _0F_1\left(-; n+1; -\frac{x^2}{4}\right),$$

$$(6) \qquad L_n(x) = \, _1F_1(-n; 1; x).$$

We have seen that the differential equation (1) has one solution, as indicated in (2),

$$(7) \qquad \qquad y_1 = \, _1F_1(a; c; x).$$

The student can show that another solution, linearly independent of (7), is

$$(8) \qquad y_2 = x^{1-c} \, _1F_1(a+1-c; 2-c; x),$$

so long as c is not an integer.

Again we omit discussion of the logarithmic solutions which may enter if c is integral.

Chapter 21

Additional Topics on
Power Series Solutions

106. Many term recurrence relations, ordinary points. In Chapters 18 and 19 the equations to be solved were chosen carefully to be certain that each led to a recurrence relation involving only two different coefficients. Nothing in the method dictates such a restriction, but those recurrence relations are the only ones for which we know how to obtain a reasonably useful explicit form of solution. As a matter of fact, recurrence relations which cannot be solved explicitly may still be useful and do, indeed, exhibit in an emphatic way the power of the theory behind our work.

Consider the equation

$$(1) \qquad\qquad y'' - y' + xy = 0,$$

which has no singular points in the finite plane. Let us solve the equation in the vicinity of $x = 0$. We know that there is a solution which assumes the form

$$(2) \qquad\qquad y = \sum_{n=0}^{\infty} a_n x^n,$$

with a_0 and a_1 arbitrary, and for which the power series involved converge for all finite x. In order to find the a_n, $n > 1$, we put the y of (2) into equation (1). We thus obtain, after appropriate shifting of the indices of summation,

$$\sum_{n=0}^{\infty} n(n-1)a_n x^{n-2} - \sum_{n=1}^{\infty} (n-1)a_{n-1}x^{n-2} + \sum_{n=3}^{\infty} a_{n-3}x^{n-2} = 0,$$

from which the relations for the determination of the a's are seen to be

$$n = 2: \quad 2a_2 - a_1 = 0,$$
$$n \geq 3: \quad n(n-1)a_n - (n-1)a_{n-1} + a_{n-3} = 0.$$

We cannot obtain an explicit formula for a_n, but we can compute as many coefficients as may be desired and we do know, from the theory not proved here, that the series solutions converge for all finite x. Knowledge of the convergence means much to us this time since we cannot fall back on the ratio test because we do not even have a formula for the general term in the series.

It is frequently desirable to tabulate, or to represent graphically, the solutions of a particular equation. With this in mind let us specialize our constants, a_0 and a_1. So long as the choices made lead to linearly independent solutions, it does not matter what values we use for the constants. Define as y_1 that solution with $a_0 = 1, a_1 = 0$, and y_2 as that solution in which $a_0 = 0, a_1 = 1$; then y_1 and y_2 will be linearly independent.

The complete solution of the differential equation of the present example is $y = Ay_1 + By_2$ where A and B are arbitrary constants, y_1 is given by

$$(3) \qquad y_1 = \sum_{n=0}^{\infty} a_n x^n,$$

in which $a_0 = 1, a_1 = 0, a_2 = 0$, and for

$$n \geq 3: \quad a_n = \frac{(n-1)a_{n-1} - a_{n-3}}{n(n-1)},$$

and y_2 is given by

$$(4) \qquad y_2 = \sum_{n=0}^{\infty} b_n x^n,$$

in which $b_0 = 0, b_1 = 1, b_2 = \frac{1}{2}$, and for

$$n \geq 3: \quad b_n = \frac{(n-1)b_{n-1} - b_{n-3}}{n(n-1)}.$$

It is sometimes interesting and helpful to compute several coefficients in the series solution. For the present example it can be shown that

(5) $\quad y_1 = 1 - \frac{1}{6}x^3 - \frac{1}{24}x^4 - \frac{1}{120}x^5 + \frac{1}{240}x^6 + \frac{1}{630}x^7 + \cdots$

and

(6) $\quad y_2 = x + \frac{1}{2}x^2 + \frac{1}{6}x^3 - \frac{1}{24}x^4 - \frac{1}{30}x^5 - \frac{1}{90}x^6 - \frac{1}{1680}x^7 + \cdots.$

Equations (5) and (6) do not by any means define the functions y_1 and y_2; they contain no indication of the coefficients of higher powers of x. For complete descriptions of the series we must fall back on equations (3) and (4) together with the relations on the a_n and b_n given with those equations.

EXERCISES

Solve each equation about $x = 0$ unless otherwise instructed. State where your solutions are valid.

1. $y'' + (1 + x + x^2)y = 0.$

ANS. $\quad y_1 = \sum_{n=0}^{\infty} a_n x^n$, in which $a_0 = 1$, $a_1 = 0$, $a_2 = -\frac{1}{2}$, $a_3 = -\frac{1}{6}$,

$$n \geqq 4: a_n = \frac{-1}{n(n-1)}(a_{n-2} + a_{n-3} + a_{n-4});$$

$y_2 = \sum_{n=0}^{\infty} b_n x^n$, in which $b_0 = 0$, $b_1 = 1$, $b_2 = 0$, $b_3 = -\frac{1}{6}$,

$$n \geqq 4: b_n = -\frac{1}{n(n-1)}(b_{n-2} + b_{n-3} + b_{n-4}).$$

2. Show that the series in the answers to Ex. 1 start out as follows:

$$y_1 = 1 - \frac{1}{2}x^2 - \frac{1}{6}x^3 - \frac{1}{24}x^4 + \frac{1}{30}x^5 + \frac{17}{720}x^6 + \frac{1}{240}x^7 + \cdots$$

and

$$y_2 = x - \frac{1}{6}x^3 - \frac{1}{12}x^4 - \frac{1}{24}x^5 + \frac{1}{120}x^6 + \frac{1}{144}x^7 + \cdots.$$

3. $(1 - x)y'' + (2 + x)y' - 2y = 0.$

ANS. $y_1 = \displaystyle\sum_{n=0}^{\infty} a_n x^n$, in which $a_0 = 1$, $a_1 = 0$,

$$n \geqq 2: a_n = \frac{(n - 4)}{n(n - 1)}[(n - 1)a_{n-1} - a_{n-2}];$$

$$y_2 = \sum_{n=0}^{\infty} b_n x^n, \text{ in which } b_0 = 0, \ b_1 = 1,$$

$$n \geqq 2: b_n = \frac{(n - 4)}{n(n - 1)}[(n - 1)b_{n-1} - b_{n-2}].$$

4. Show that the answers to Ex. 3 start out as follows:

$$y_1 = 1 + x^2 - \tfrac{1}{3}x^3 + \tfrac{1}{60}x^5 + \tfrac{1}{180}x^6 + \tfrac{1}{840}x^7 + \cdots$$

and

$$y_2 = x - x^2 + \tfrac{1}{2}x^3 - \tfrac{1}{40}x^5 - \tfrac{1}{120}x^6 - \tfrac{1}{560}x^7 + \cdots.$$

5. In Ex. 3 make the choices $a_0 = 3$, $a_1 = 2$, and determine the corresponding solution of the differential equation.

ANS. $y_3 = 3 + 2x + x^2.$

6. $(1 + x)y'' + 2y' - y = 0.$

ANS. $y_1 = \displaystyle\sum_{n=0}^{\infty} a_n x^n$, in which $a_0 = 1$, $a_1 = 0$,

$$n \geqq 2: a_n = -a_{n-1} + a_{n-2}/[n(n - 1)];$$

$$y_2 = \sum_{n=0}^{\infty} b_n x^n, \text{ in which } b_0 = 0, \ b_1 = 1,$$

$$n \geqq 2: b_n = -b_{n-1} + b_{n-2}/[n(n - 1)].$$

7. Show that the series in the answers for Ex. 6 start out as follows:

$$y_1 = 1 + \tfrac{1}{2}x^2 - \tfrac{1}{2}x^3 + \tfrac{13}{24}x^4 - \tfrac{17}{30}x^5 + \tfrac{421}{720}x^6 + \cdots,$$
$$y_2 = x - x^2 + \tfrac{7}{6}x^3 - \tfrac{5}{4}x^4 + \tfrac{157}{120}x^5 - \tfrac{27}{20}x^6 + \cdots.$$

8. In the answers for Ex. 6 prove that the coefficients alternate in sign for $n \geqq 2$. Put $a_n = (-1)^n t_n$ and consider the recurrence relation for t_n.

9. Let $\sigma_n = t_n/t_{n-1}$ where $t_n = |a_n|$ as in Ex. 8. Show that

$$\sigma_n = 1 + \frac{1}{n(n - 1)\sigma_{n-1}}$$

and conclude that for $n > 4$, $1 < \sigma_n < 21/20.$

10. For $0 < x < 1$ the ratio of the absolute values of consecutive terms of the series for y_1 in Ex. 6 is given by

$$\frac{|a_n x^n|}{|a_{n-1} x^{n-1}|} = \sigma_n x$$

with the notation of Ex. 9. Show that for $n > 4$ and $0 < x < 0.95$ it follows that $0 < \sigma_n x < 1$. Hence prove that for these values of x the terms in the y_1 series steadily decrease in numerical value.

11. Use the results of Exs. 8 and 10 to prove that if E_n is the error made in replacing y_1 by the sum of its terms out to and including $a_n x^n$, then for $n > 4$ and $0 < x < 0.95$ it is true that

$$|E_n| < |a_{n+1} x^{n+1}|.$$

12. Follow the procedure of Exs. 9, 10, and 11 and arrive at similar conclusions for the series y_2 in Ex. 6.

13. Compute y_1 and y_2 of Ex. 6 correct to three decimal places when $x = 0.1$. ANS. $y_1(0.1) = 1.005$, $y_2(0.1) = 0.091$.

14. Prove that for any fixed x in the interval $0 < x < 1$ there exists an n_0 such that for $n > n_0$ the terms in the series for y_1 (or for y_2) steadily decrease in numerical value.

15. Prove that for $n > 4$ and $-0.95 < x < 0$, then

$$|E_n| < |a_{n+1} x^{n+1}| \cdot \frac{20}{20 + 21x},$$

where the E_n is as defined in Ex. 11.

16. Compute y_1 and y_2 of Ex. 6 correct to three decimal places for $x = -0.1$.
 ANS. $y_1(-0.1) = 1.006$, $y_2(-0.1) = -0.111$.

17. Solve the equation of Ex. 6 near the regular singular point $x = -1$.

$$\text{ANS.}\quad y_3 = \sum_{n=1}^{\infty} \frac{(x+1)^{n-1}}{n!(n-1)!};$$

$$y_4 = y_3 \ln(x+1) + (x+1)^{-1} - \sum_{n=1}^{\infty} \frac{(H_n + H_{n-1})(x+1)^{n-1}}{n!(n-1)!}.$$

18. $y'' - (1 + x^3)y = 0$.

19. $(1 - x)y'' + xy' + y = 0$.

20. Solve the equation of Ex. 19 about its regular singular point.

107. Many term recurrence relations, regular singular point.
In solving an equation near a regular singular point it will sometimes happen that a many term recurrence relation is encountered. In nonlogarithmic cases the methods developed in Chapter

19 are easily applied and no complications result except that usually no explicit formula will be obtained for the coefficients.

In logarithmic cases the methods introduced in Chapter 19, constructing $y(x, c)$ and $\partial y(x, c)/\partial c$, can become awkward when a many term recurrence relation is present.   There is another attack which has its good points.

Consider the problem of solving the equation

$$(1)\qquad L(y) = x^2y'' + x(3 + x)y' + (1 + x + x^2)y = 0$$

near the origin.   From

$$(2)\qquad y = \sum_{n=0}^{\infty} a_n x^{n+c}$$

it is easily shown that

$$(3)\quad L(y) = \sum_{n=0}^{\infty} (n + c + 1)^2 a_n x^{n+c} + \sum_{n=1}^{\infty} (n + c)a_{n-1}x^{n+c}$$

$$+ \sum_{n=2}^{\infty} a_{n-2}x^{n+c}.$$

Therefore the indicial equation is $(c + 1)^2 = 0$.

Since the roots of the indicial equation are equal, $c = -1, -1$, it follows that there exist the solutions

$$(4)\qquad y_1 = \sum_{n=0}^{\infty} a_n x^{n-1}$$

and

$$(5)\qquad y_2 = y_1 \ln x + \sum_{n=1}^{\infty} b_n x^{n-1},$$

valid for all finite $x \neq 0$.   The region of validity is obtained from the differential equation; the form of the solutions can be seen by the reasoning in Section 92.

We shall determine the a_n, $n > 0$, by requiring that $L(y_1) = 0$. Then the b_n, $n \geq 1$, will be determined in terms of the a_n by requiring that $L(y_2) = 0$.

From $L(y_1) = 0$ it follows that

$$\sum_{n=0}^{\infty} n^2 a_n x^{n-1} + \sum_{n=1}^{\infty} (n-1)a_{n-1}x^{n-1} + \sum_{n=2}^{\infty} a_{n-2}x^{n-1} = 0.$$

Let us choose $a_0 = 1$. Then the rest of the a's are determined by the relations

$$n = 1: \quad a_1 + 0 \cdot a_0 = 0,$$
$$n \geq 2: \quad n^2 a_n + (n-1)a_{n-1} + a_{n-2} = 0.$$

Therefore one solution of the differential equation (1) is

$$(6) \qquad y_1 = \sum_{n=0}^{\infty} a_n x^{n-1},$$

in which $a_0 = 1$, $a_1 = 0$,

$$n \geq 2: \quad a_n = -\frac{(n-1)a_{n-1} + a_{n-2}}{n^2}.$$

Next we wish to require that $L(y_2) = 0$. From

$$(5) \qquad y_2 = y_1 \ln x + \sum_{n=1}^{\infty} b_n x^{n-1}$$

it follows that

$$y_2' = y_1' \ln x + x^{-1}y_1 + \sum_{n=1}^{\infty} (n-1)b_n x^{n-2}$$

and

$$y_2'' = y_1'' \ln x + 2x^{-1}y_1' - x^{-2}y_1 + \sum_{n=1}^{\infty} (n-1)(n-2)b_n x^{n-3}.$$

Now direct computation of $L(y_2)$ yields

$$L(y_2) = L(y_1) \ln x + 2xy_1' - y_1 + xy_1 + 3y_1 + \sum_{n=1}^{\infty} n^2 b_n x^{n-1}$$

$$+ \sum_{n=2}^{\infty} (n-1)b_{n-1}x^{n-1} + \sum_{n=3}^{\infty} b_{n-2}x^{n-1}.$$

Since $L(y_1) = 0$, the requirement $L(y_2) = 0$ leads to the equation

$$(7) \quad \sum_{n=1}^{\infty} n^2 b_n x^{n-1} + \sum_{n=2}^{\infty} (n-1)b_{n-1}x^{n-1} + \sum_{n=3}^{\infty} b_{n-2}x^{n-1}$$

$$= -2xy_1' - 2y_1 - xy_1$$

$$= -\sum_{n=1}^{\infty} 2na_n x^{n-1} - \sum_{n=1}^{\infty} a_{n-1}x^{n-1},$$

in which the right member has been simplified by using equation (6). From the identity (7) relations for the determination of the b_n from the a_n follow. They are

$$n = 1: \qquad\qquad b_1 = -2a_1 - a_0,$$
$$n = 2: \qquad\qquad 4b_2 + b_1 = -4a_2 - a_1,$$
$$n \geqq 3 : n^2 b_n + (n-1)b_{n-1} + b_{n-2} = -2na_n - a_{n-1}.$$

Therefore the original differential equation has the two linearly independent solutions given by the y_1 of equation (6) and

$$(8) \qquad\qquad y_2 = y_1 \ln x + \sum_{n=1}^{\infty} b_n x^{n-1},$$

in which $b_1 = -1$, $b_2 = \frac{1}{2}$,

$$n \geqq 3: \quad b_n = -\frac{(n-1)b_{n-1} + b_{n-2}}{n^2} - \frac{2a_n}{n} - \frac{a_{n-1}}{n^2}.$$

If the indicial equation has roots which differ by a positive integer and if a logarithmic solution is present, then the two solutions will have the form

$$y_1 = \sum_{n=0}^{\infty} a_n x^{n+c_1},$$

$$y_2 = y_1 \ln x + \sum_{n=0}^{\infty} b_n x^{n+c_2},$$

where c_1 is the larger, and c_2 the smaller, root of the indicial equation. The a_n and b_n can again be determined by the procedure used in this section.

108. Bounding the error in computations. If series solutions of a differential equation are to be used in numerical computations, it is highly desirable to have bounds on the error made by stopping with a specified term of the series. If the terms of the series are known explicitly, as in the answers in Chapters 18–20, the problem becomes one usually treated to some extent in calculus. It is the purpose of this section to show that such bounds can be obtained for series whose terms are known only through a many term recurrence relation such as those encountered so far in this chapter.

Suppose that we wish to compute with the series in the solutions $y_1(x)$ and $y_2(x)$ of the example in the preceding section. We had

$$(1) \qquad y_1(x) = \sum_{n=0}^{\infty} a_n x^{n-1}$$

in which $a_0 = 1$, $a_1 = 0$,

$$(2) \qquad n \geqq 2: \quad a_n = -\frac{(n-1)a_{n-1} + a_{n-2}}{n^2}.$$

Let $E_n(x)$ be the error made in computing $y_1(x)$ by using the terms on the right in (1) only out to and including the term $a_n x^{n-1}$. Then $E_n(x)$ is equal to the sum of the remaining terms:

$$(3) \qquad E_n(x) = \sum_{s=n+1}^{\infty} a_s x^{s-1},$$

and

$$(4) \qquad |E_n(x)| \leqq \sum_{s=n+1}^{\infty} |a_s x^{s-1}|.$$

First we need to bound $|a_n|$ where a_n is determined by the recurrence relation (2). We know $a_0 = 1$, $a_1 = 0$. We compute a few more, finding that $a_2 = -\frac{1}{4}$, $a_3 = \frac{1}{18}$, $a_4 = \frac{1}{192}$, etc. Next we search for an inequality on $|a_n|$ which is satisfied by trial for small values of n and which can be proved for all n thereafter by induction based on the recurrence relation (2). This is the only difficult step. Often it takes much experience, some skill, and many trials to obtain an inequality which is strong enough to be useful and weak enough for us to establish it.

Consider the inequality

$$(5) \qquad |a_k| < \frac{2^k}{k!},$$

which is clearly satisfied for $k = 1, 2, 3, 4$. We assume that (5) is satisfied for all k in the range $1 \leqq k < n$ and must prove that it follows from (2) that (5) is also satisfied for $k = n$. From (2) we obtain, for $n \geqq 3$,

$$(6) \qquad |a_n| < \frac{1}{n^2}[(n-1)|a_{n-1}| + |a_{n-2}|].$$

Since (5) is assumed true for $k = n - 1$ and $k = n - 2$, the inequality (6) yields

$$
\begin{aligned}
|a_n| &< \frac{1}{n^2}\left[\frac{2^{n-1}(n-1)}{(n-1)!} + \frac{2^{n-2}}{(n-2)!}\right] \\
&< \frac{2^{n-2}}{n^2}\left[\frac{2}{(n-2)!} + \frac{1}{(n-2)!}\right] \\
&< \frac{3 \cdot 2^{n-2}}{n^2(n-2)!} \\
&< \frac{3(n-1)}{4n} \cdot \frac{2^n}{n!} \\
&< \frac{2^n}{n!},
\end{aligned}
$$

since $3(n - 1) < 4n$. It follows by induction that we have proved that

(7) $$|a_n| < \frac{2^n}{n!}, \quad \text{for } n \geqq 1.$$

We now return to (4) and find that, for $n \geqq 1$,

(8) $$|E_n(x)| < \sum_{s=n+1}^{\infty} \frac{2^s |x|^{s-1}}{s!}.$$

To simplify the series in (8) we shift index from s to $(s + n + 1)$ and obtain

(9) $$|E_n(x)| < \sum_{s=0}^{\infty} \frac{2^{s+n+1} |x|^{s+n}}{(s + n + 1)!}.$$

Since $(s + n + 1)!$ is unwieldy, we replace it by something simpler and smaller, thus making the right member of (9) larger. For positive s and n,

$$(n + 1)! s! < (s + n + 1)!.$$

Hence

$$|E_n(x)| < \sum_{s=0}^{\infty} \frac{2^{s+n+1} |x|^{s+n}}{(n + 1)! s!} = \frac{2^{n+1} |x|^n}{(n + 1)!} \sum_{s=0}^{\infty} \frac{2^s |x|^s}{s!}$$

and finally

(10) $$|E_n(x)| < \frac{2^{n+1} |x|^n e^{2|x|}}{(n + 1)!}.$$

Let us compute $y_1(\tfrac{1}{4})$ to two decimal places. We know that the $y_1(x)$ series starts out

(11) $$y_1(x) = x^{-1} + 0 - \tfrac{1}{4}x + \tfrac{1}{18}x^2 + \tfrac{1}{192}x^3 + \cdots .$$

If we stop with the x^3 term, $n - 1 = 3$, $n = 4$, and we need to bound $E_4(\tfrac{1}{4})$. From (10),

$$|E_4(\tfrac{1}{4})| < \frac{2^5(\tfrac{1}{4})^4 e^{1/2}}{5!} = \frac{e^{1/2}}{960} = 0.0017.$$

Then

$$y_1(\tfrac{1}{4}) = 4 - \tfrac{1}{4}(\tfrac{1}{4}) + \tfrac{1}{18}(\tfrac{1}{4})^2 + \tfrac{1}{192}(\tfrac{1}{4})^3$$
$$= 4 - 0.0625 + 0.0035 + 0.0001$$
$$= 3.9411,$$

with an error less than 0.0017.   We conclude that, to two decimal places, $y_1(\tfrac{1}{4}) = 3.94$.

Turn now to $y_2(x)$ which was found in Section 107 to be given by

$$(12) \qquad y_2(x) = y_1(x) \ln x + \sum_{n=1}^{\infty} b_n x^{n-1},$$

in which $b_1 = -1$, $b_2 = \tfrac{1}{2}$,

$$(13) \quad n \geqq 3: \quad b_n = -\frac{(n-1)b_{n-1} + b_{n-2}}{n^2} - \frac{2a_n}{n} - \frac{a_{n-1}}{n^2}.$$

We show now that $|b_n| < 2^{n+1}/n!$.   From (13) it follows that $b_3 = -\tfrac{1}{108}$, $b_4 = -\tfrac{41}{1152}$, etc.   Let us assume

$$(14) \qquad\qquad |b_k| < \frac{2^{k+1}}{k!}$$

for $1 \leqq k < n$.   We know (14) is satisfied for $k = 1, 2, 3, 4$.   From (13), (14), and (7), it follows that, for $n \geqq 3$,

$$|b_n| < \frac{1}{n^2}\left[\frac{2^n(n-1)}{(n-1)!} + \frac{2^{n-1}}{(n-2)!}\right] + \frac{2^{n+1}}{n \cdot n!} + \frac{2^{n-1}}{n^2(n-1)!}$$

$$< \frac{2^n + 2^{n-1}}{n^2(n-2)!} + \frac{2^{n+1} + 2^{n-1}}{n \cdot n!}$$

$$< \frac{3 \cdot 2^{n-1}}{n^2(n-2)!} + \frac{5 \cdot 2^{n-1}}{n \cdot n!}$$

$$< \frac{2^{n-1}[3(n-1) + 5]}{n \cdot n!}$$

$$< \frac{3n+2}{4n} \cdot \frac{2^{n+1}}{n!}$$

$$< \frac{2^{n+1}}{n!},$$

since $3n + 2 \leqq 4n$ for $n \geqq 2$.   Therefore, by induction,

$$(15) \qquad |b_n| < \frac{2^{n+1}}{n!}, \ n \geqq 1.$$

Now let $E_n{}^*(x)$ be the error made in computing $\sum\limits_{n=1}^{\infty} b_n x^{n-1}$ by using the terms up to and including $b_n x^{n-1}$.   Then

$$E_n{}^*(x) = \sum_{s=n+1}^{\infty} b_s x^{s-1}$$

and by (15), for $n \geqq 1$,

$$|E_n{}^*(x)| < \sum_{s=n+1}^{\infty} \frac{2^{s+1}|x|^{s-1}}{s!}$$

$$< \sum_{s=0}^{\infty} \frac{2^{s+n+2}|x|^{s+n}}{(s+n+1)!}$$

$$< \sum_{s=0}^{\infty} \frac{2^{s+n+2}|x|^{s+n}}{(n+1)!s!},$$

so that

$$(16) \qquad |E_n{}^*(x)| < \frac{2^{n+2}|x|^n e^{2|x|}}{(n+1)!}.$$

The solution $y_2(x)$ starts out as

$$y_2(x) = y_1(x) \ln x - 1 + \tfrac{1}{2}x - \tfrac{1}{108}x^2 - \tfrac{41}{1152}x^3 + \cdots.$$

Let us compute $y_2(\tfrac{1}{4})$ to two decimal places.   First we see that

$$|E_4{}^*(\tfrac{1}{4})| < \frac{2^6(\tfrac{1}{4})^4 e^{1/2}}{5!} = \frac{e^{1/2}}{480} = 0.003.$$

Then

$$y_2(\tfrac{1}{4}) = (3.94)(-1.386) - 1 + \tfrac{1}{8} - \tfrac{1}{108}(\tfrac{1}{4})^2 - \tfrac{41}{1152}(\tfrac{1}{4})^3$$
$$= -5.34.$$

EXERCISES

Solve each equation about $x = 0$ unless otherwise instructed.

1. $x^2y'' + 3xy' + (1 + x + x^3)y = 0$.

ANS. $y_1 = \displaystyle\sum_{n=0}^{\infty} a_n x^{n-1}$, in which $a_0 = 1$, $a_1 = -1$, $a_2 = \frac{1}{4}$,

$$n \geq 3 : a_n = -\frac{a_{n-1} + a_{n-3}}{n^2};$$

$$y_2 = y_1 \ln x + \sum_{n=1}^{\infty} b_n x^{n-1}, \text{ in which } b_1 = 2, \; b_2 = -\frac{3}{4}, \; b_3 = \frac{19}{108},$$

$$n \geq 4 : b_n = -\frac{b_{n-1} + b_{n-3}}{n^2} - \frac{2a_n}{n}.$$

2. $2x(1 - x)y'' + (1 - 2x)y' + (2 + x)y = 0$.

ANS. $y_1 = \displaystyle\sum_{n=0}^{\infty} a_n x^{n+1/2}$, in which $a_0 = 1$, $a_1 = -\frac{1}{2}$,

$$n \geq 2 : a_n = \frac{(2n + 1)(2n - 3)a_{n-1} - 2a_{n-2}}{2n(2n + 1)};$$

$$y_2 = \sum_{n=0}^{\infty} b_n x^n, \text{ in which } b_0 = 1, \; b_1 = -2,$$

$$n \geq 2 : b_n = \frac{2n(n - 2)b_{n-1} - b_{n-2}}{n(2n - 1)}.$$

3. $xy'' + y' + x(1 + x)y = 0$.

ANS. $y_1 = \displaystyle\sum_{n=0}^{\infty} a_n x^n$, in which $a_0 = 1$, $a_1 = 0$, $a_2 = -\frac{1}{4}$,

$$n \geq 3 : a_n = -\frac{a_{n-2} + a_{n-3}}{n^2};$$

$$y_2 = y_1 \ln x + \sum_{n=1}^{\infty} b_n x^n, \text{ in which } b_1 = 0, \; b_2 = \frac{1}{4}, \; b_3 = \frac{2}{27},$$

$$n \geq 4 : b_n = -\frac{b_{n-2} + b_{n-3}}{n^2} - \frac{2a_n}{n}.$$

4. $x^2y'' + x(1 + x)y' - (1 - 3x + 6x^2)y = 0.$

ANS. $y = \sum_{n=0}^{\infty} a_n x^{n-1}$, in which a_0 is arbitrary, $a_1 = 2a_0$, a_2 is arbitrary,

$$n \geq 3: a_n = -\frac{(n + 1)a_{n-1} - 6a_{n-2}}{n(n - 2)}.$$

5. Show that the series in the answer to Ex. 4 start out as follows:

$$y = a_0(x^{-1} + 2 + 4x^2 - \tfrac{5}{2}x^3 + \tfrac{13}{5}x^4 - \tfrac{83}{60}x^5 + \cdots)$$
$$+ a_2(x - \tfrac{4}{3}x^2 + \tfrac{19}{12}x^3 - \tfrac{7}{6}x^4 + \tfrac{53}{72}x^5 + \cdots).$$

6. $xy'' + xy' + (1 + x^4)y = 0.$ Here the indicial equation has roots $c = 0$, $c = 1$, and an attempt to get a complete solution without $\ln x$ fails. Then we put

$$y_1 = \sum_{n=0}^{\infty} a_n x^{n+1}, \qquad y_2 = y_1 \ln x + \sum_{n=0}^{\infty} b_n x^n.$$

The coefficient b_1 ($s = 1$) turns out to be arbitrary and we choose it to be zero. Show that the indicated y_1 and y_2 are solutions if $a_0 = 1$,

$$a_1 = -1, a_2 = \tfrac{1}{2}, a_3 = -\tfrac{1}{6}, a_4 = \tfrac{1}{24},$$
$$n \geq 5: a_n = -\frac{(n + 1)a_{n-1} + a_{n-5}}{n(n + 1)},$$

and the b's are given by

$$b_0 = -1, b_1 = 0 \text{ (so chosen)}, b_2 = 1, b_3 = -\tfrac{3}{4}, b_4 = \tfrac{11}{36},$$
$$n \geq 5: b_n = -\frac{nb_{n-1} + b_{n-5}}{n(n - 1)} - \frac{(2n - 1)a_{n-1} + a_{n-2}}{n(n - 1)}.$$

7. For the y_1 in Ex. 6 prove that the a_n alternate in sign. Also compute the terms of y_1 out to the x^7 term.

ANS. $y_1 = x - x^2 + \tfrac{1}{2}x^3 - \tfrac{1}{6}x^4 + \tfrac{1}{24}x^5 - \tfrac{1}{24}x^6 + \tfrac{31}{1008}x^7 + \cdots.$

8. $x(x - 2)^2y'' - 2(x - 2)y' + 2y = 0.$

ANS. $y_1 = 1 - \tfrac{1}{2}x;$

$$y_2 = y_1 \ln x + \sum_{n=1}^{\infty} b_n x^n, \text{ in which } b_1 = \tfrac{1}{2}, b_2 = -\tfrac{1}{8}, b_3 = -\tfrac{1}{48},$$
$$n \geq 4: b_n = \frac{n - 2}{4n^2}[2(2n - 1)b_{n-1} - (n - 3)b_{n-2}].$$

9. Solve the equation of Ex. 8 about the point $x = 2$.

ANS. $y_1 = (x - 2)$;

$$y_2 = y_1 \ln (x - 2) + \sum_{n=1}^{\infty} \frac{(-1)^n (x - 2)^{n+1}}{2^n n}.$$

10. $2xy'' + (1 - x)y' - (1 + x)y = 0.$

ANS. $y_1 = \sum_{n=0}^{\infty} a_n x^{n+1/2}$ in which $a_0 = 1$, $a_1 = \frac{1}{2}$,

$$n \geq 2 : a_n = \frac{(2n + 1)a_{n-1} + 2a_{n-2}}{2n(2n + 1)};$$

$$y_2 = \sum_{n=0}^{\infty} b_n x^n$$ in which $b_0 = 1$, $b_1 = 1$,

$$n \geq 2 : b_n = \frac{n b_{n-1} + b_{n-2}}{n(2n - 1)}.$$

11. Show that the answers to Ex. 10 are also given by

$$y_2 = e^x, \quad y_1 = e^x \int_0^{\sqrt{x}} e^{-3\beta^2/2} \, d\beta.$$

109. Solution for large x.

The power series solutions which have been studied up to this stage converge in regions surrounding some point $x = x_0$, usually the origin. Such solutions, although they may converge for large values of x, are apt to do so with discouraging slowness. For this reason, and for others of a more theoretical nature, we shall investigate the problem of obtaining solutions particularly useful for large x.

Consider the equation

$$(1) \qquad b_0(x)y'' + b_1(x)y' + b_2(x)y = 0$$

with polynomial coefficients. Let us put

$$(2) \qquad w = \frac{1}{x}.$$

Then

$$\frac{dy}{dx} = \frac{dw}{dx} \frac{dy}{dw} = -\frac{1}{x^2} \frac{dy}{dw} = -w^2 \frac{dy}{dw}$$

and

$$\frac{d^2y}{dx^2} = \frac{dw}{dx}\frac{d}{dw}\left(-w^2\frac{dy}{dw}\right) = -w^2\left(-w^2\frac{d^2y}{dw^2} - 2w\frac{dy}{dw}\right)$$
$$= w^4\frac{d^2y}{dw^2} + 2w^3\frac{dy}{dw}.$$

Thus equation (1) is transformed into the following equation in y and w:

$$(3) \quad b_0\left(\frac{1}{w}\right)w^4\frac{d^2y}{dw^2} + \left[2w^3b_0\left(\frac{1}{w}\right) - w^2b_1\left(\frac{1}{w}\right)\right]\frac{dy}{dw} + b_2\left(\frac{1}{w}\right)y = 0.$$

Since b_0, b_1, and b_2 are polynomials, equation (3) is readily converted into an equation with polynomial coefficients.

If the point $w = 0$ is an ordinary point or a regular singular point of equation (3), then our previous methods of attack will yield solutions valid for small w. But $w = 1/x$, so small w means large x.

As a matter of terminology, whatever is true about equation (3) at $w = 0$ is said to be true about equation (1) "at the point at infinity." For instance, if the transformed equation has $w = 0$ as an ordinary point, then we say that equation (1) has an ordinary point at infinity.

EXAMPLE: Obtain solutions valid for large x for the equation

$$(4) \quad\quad x^2y'' + (3x - 1)y' + y = 0.$$

This equation has an irregular singular point at the origin and has no other singular points in the finite plane. In order to investigate the nature of equation (4) for large x, put $x = 1/w$. We have already found that

$$(5) \quad\quad \frac{dy}{dx} = -w^2\frac{dy}{dw}$$

and

$$(6) \quad\quad \frac{d^2y}{dx^2} = w^4\frac{d^2y}{dw^2} + 2w^3\frac{dy}{dw}.$$

With the aid of (5) and (6) the result of transforming equation (4) is found to be

$$(7) \qquad w^2 \frac{d^2y}{dw^2} - w(1 - w)\frac{dy}{dw} + y = 0,$$

an equation which we wish to solve about $w = 0$.

Since $w = 0$ is a regular singular point of equation (7), the point at infinity is a regular singular point of equation (4).

From the assumed form

$$y = \sum_{n=0}^{\infty} a_n w^{n+c}$$

it follows from equation (7) by our usual methods that

$$L(y) = \sum_{n=0}^{\infty} (n + c - 1)^2 a_n w^{n+c} + \sum_{n=1}^{\infty} (n + c - 1)a_{n-1}w^{n+c},$$

in which $L(y)$ now represents the left member of equation (7). The indicial equation has equal roots, $c = 1, 1$. Let us set up $y(w, c)$ as usual. From the recurrence relation

$$n \geq 1: \quad a_n = -\frac{a_{n-1}}{n + c - 1},$$

it follows that

$$a_n = \frac{(-1)^n a_0}{c(c + 1) \cdots (c + n - 1)}.$$

Hence we choose

$$y(w, c) = w^c + \sum_{n=1}^{\infty} \frac{(-1)^n w^{n+c}}{c(c + 1) \cdots (c + n - 1)},$$

and then find that

$$\frac{\partial y(w, c)}{\partial c} = y(w, c) \ln w$$

$$- \sum_{n=1}^{\infty} \frac{(-1)^n w^{n+c}\left\{\frac{1}{c} + \frac{1}{c + 1} + \cdots + \frac{1}{c + n - 1}\right\}}{c(c + 1) \cdots (c + n - 1)}.$$

Employing the root $c = 1$, we arrive at the solutions

$$y_1 = w + \sum_{n=1}^{\infty} \frac{(-1)^n w^{n+1}}{n!}$$

and

$$y_2 = y_1 \ln w - \sum_{n=1}^{\infty} \frac{(-1)^n H_n w^{n+1}}{n!}.$$

Therefore the original differential equation has the two linearly independent solutions

(8) $$y_1 = \sum_{n=0}^{\infty} \frac{(-1)^n x^{-n-1}}{n!} = x^{-1} e^{-1/x}$$

and

(9) $$y_2 = y_1 \ln (1/x) - \sum_{n=1}^{\infty} \frac{(-1)^n H_n x^{-n-1}}{n!}.$$

These solutions are valid outside a circle centered at the origin and of arbitrarily small radius.

EXERCISES

In each exercise find solutions valid for large x unless otherwise instructed.

1. $x^4 y'' + x(1 + 2x^2)y' + 5y = 0$.

ANS. $$y = a_0 \sum_{k=0}^{\infty} \frac{-15x^{-2k}}{2^k k!(2k - 1)(2k - 3)(2k - 5)}$$
$$+ a_1[x^{-1} - \tfrac{2}{3}x^{-3} + \tfrac{1}{15}x^{-5}]$$

2. $2x^3 y'' - x(2 - 5x)y' + y = 0$.

ANS. $$y_1 = x^{-3/2} + \sum_{n=1}^{\infty} \frac{(-2)^n(n + 1)x^{-n-3/2}}{5 \cdot 7 \cdot 9 \cdots (2n + 3)}.$$
$$y_2 = \sum_{n=0}^{\infty} \frac{(-1)^{n+1}(2n - 1)x^{-n}}{n!}.$$

3. $x(1 - x)y'' - 3y' + 2y = 0$, the equation of Ex. 5, page 298.

$$\text{ANS.} \quad y = a_0(x^2 + 2x + 3) + \tfrac{1}{4}a_3 \sum_{n=0}^{\infty} (n + 4)x^{-n-1}.$$

4. $x^3y'' + x(2 - 3x)y' - (5 - 4x)y = 0$.   See Ex. 5, page 292.

$$\text{ANS.} \quad y_1 = x^2 + \sum_{n=1}^{\infty} \frac{1 \cdot 3 \cdot 5 \cdots (2n - 1)x^{-n+2}}{(n!)^2};$$

$$y_2 = y_1 \ln (1/x) + \sum_{n=1}^{\infty} \frac{1 \cdot 3 \cdot 5 \cdots (2n - 1)(2H_{2n} - 3H_n)x^{-n+2}}{(n!)^2}.$$

5. $2x^2(x - 1)y'' + x(5x - 3)y' + (x + 1)y = 0$.

$$\text{ANS.} \quad y_1 = x^{-1}; \; y_2 = -\sum_{n=0}^{\infty} \frac{x^{-n-1/2}}{2n - 1}.$$

6. Solve the equation of Ex. 5 about the point $x = 0$.

$$\text{ANS.} \quad y_3 = \sum_{n=0}^{\infty} \frac{3x^{n+1/2}}{2n + 3}; \; y_4 = x^{-1}.$$

7. $2x^2(1 - x)y'' - 5x(1 + x)y' + (5 - x)y = 0$.

$$\text{ANS.} \quad y_1 = \tfrac{1}{15} \sum_{n=0}^{\infty} (n + 1)(2n + 3)(2n + 5)x^{-n-1};$$

$$y_2 = \tfrac{1}{2} \sum_{n=0}^{\infty} (n + 1)(n + 2)(2n + 1)x^{-n-1/2}.$$

8. Solve the equation of Ex. 7 about the point $x = 0$.

$$\text{ANS.} \quad y_3 = \tfrac{1}{10} \sum_{n=0}^{\infty} (n + 1)(n + 2)(2n + 5)x^{n+5/2};$$

$$y_4 = -\sum_{n=0}^{\infty} (n + 1)(2n - 1)(2n + 1)x^{n+1}.$$

9. $x(1 + x)y'' + (1 + 5x)y' + 3y = 0$, the equation of Ex. 6, page 292.

ANS. $y_1 = \displaystyle\sum_{n=2}^{\infty} (-1)^{n+1} n(n-1) x^{-n-1};$

$$y_2 = y_1 \ln (1/x) + x^{-1} + x^{-2} + \sum_{n=2}^{\infty} (-1)^{n+1} (n^2 + n - 1) x^{-n-1}.$$

10. $x^2(4 + x^2)y'' + 2x(4 + x^2)y' + y = 0.$

ANS. $y_1 = 1 + \displaystyle\sum_{k=1}^{\infty} \frac{(-1)^k [(-1) \cdot 3 \cdot 7 \cdots (4k-5)]^2 x^{-2k}}{(2k)!};$

$$y_2 = x^{-1} + \sum_{k=1}^{\infty} \frac{(-1)^k [1 \cdot 5 \cdot 9 \cdots (4k-3)]^2 x^{-2k-1}}{(2k+1)!}.$$

11. $x(1 - x)y'' + (1 - 4x)y' - 2y = 0$, the equation of Ex. 18, page 308.

ANS. $y_1 = \displaystyle\sum_{n=1}^{\infty} n x^{-n-1}; \quad y_2 = y_1 \ln (1/x) + \sum_{n=0}^{\infty} x^{-n-1}.$

12. $x(1 + 4x)y'' + (1 + 8x)y' + y = 0$, the equation of Ex. 43, page 309.

ANS. $y_1 = x^{-1/2} + \displaystyle\sum_{n=1}^{\infty} \frac{(-1)^n [1 \cdot 3 \cdot 5 \cdots (2n-1)]^2 x^{-n-1/2}}{2^{4n}(n!)^2};$

$$y_2 = y_1 \ln (1/x) + \sum_{n=1}^{\infty} \frac{(-1)^n [1 \cdot 3 \cdot 5 \cdots (2n-1)]^2 (H_{2n} - H_n) x^{-n-1/2}}{2^{4n-2}(n!)^2}.$$

110. An equation with an irregular singular point.   In the preceding section we solved the equation

(1) $$x^2 y'' + (3x - 1)y' + y = 0$$

for large values of x. Let us now attempt a solution near the irregular singular point $x = 0$.

Proceeding in the manner developed for the treatment of regular singular points, let us put

(2) $$y = \sum_{n=0}^{\infty} a_n x^{n+c}.$$

Then the left member of equation (1) may be found to be

$$L(y) = \sum_{n=0}^{\infty} [(n+c)(n+c-1)+3(n+c)+1]a_n x^{n+c} - \sum_{n=0}^{\infty} (n+c)a_n x^{n+c-1}$$

$$= \sum_{n=0}^{\infty} (n+c+1)^2 a_n x^{n+c} - \sum_{n=0}^{\infty} (n+c)a_n x^{n+c-1}$$

$$= \sum_{n=1}^{\infty} (n+c)^2 a_{n-1} x^{n+c-1} - \sum_{n=0}^{\infty} (n+c)a_n x^{n+c-1}.$$

Therefore the indicial equation is $c = 0$. Already something has happened which could not occur at a regular singular point; the indicial equation has degenerated from a quadratic to a linear equation.

Let us employ this one root $c = 0$ with the hope of obtaining at least one solution of the differential equation. The a_n will be determined from

$$n \geq 1: \quad n^2 a_{n-1} - na_n = 0,$$

or

(3) $$a_n = na_{n-1}.$$

At once it follows that $a_n = n!a_0$, so that the root $c = 0$ has lead us to the tentative solution

(4) $$y_1 = 1 + \sum_{n=1}^{\infty} n!x^n.$$

Since we are dealing with an irregular singular point, the theorems quoted earlier on the convergence of the results do not apply so we turn to the standard ratio test for information. With the ratio test it is easy to show that the series in (4) diverges for $x \neq 0$. Evidently the series converges at $x = 0$. There is therefore no *region* whatever in which the relation (4) is a solution of the differential equation from our elementary standpoint.

Intuitively, we may reason that equation (4) was determined by the differential equation, even though by an unjustified process, and that therefore there *may* be some way in which it will lead us to a proper solution of the differential equation. As a matter of fact, all that is needed here is a bit of advanced mathematics in order to pass from (4) to a solution legitimate in the elementary sense. The theory needed is the expansion of functions in asymptotic series* and it will not be touched upon in this book. We can, however, proceed from the relation (4) to a solution in the formal manner below.

It is simple to show by iterated integration by parts that, for non-negative integral n,

$$\int_0^\infty e^{-t}t^n \, dt = n!.$$

Let us then rewrite equation (4) as

$$(5) \qquad y_1 = \sum_{n=0}^\infty \int_0^\infty e^{-t}t^n \, dt \, x^n.$$

Without regard to justification, we interchange order of integration and summation to get

$$y_1 = \int_0^\infty e^{-t} \sum_{n=0}^\infty (xt)^n \, dt,$$

or

$$(6) \qquad y_1 = \int_0^\infty \frac{e^{-t}}{1 - xt} \, dt.$$

Now the integral on the right in (6) converges for $x \leqq 0$, or for the real part of x nonpositive if x is taken to be complex. It can be shown directly, by constructing $L(y_1)$ and seeing that it vanishes, that equation (6) is a solution of the differential equation (1) in the interval, or region, of convergence. Thus we have obtained a usable solution from the divergent series in equation (4). It must

---

* An introduction to the subject may be found in E. T. Whittaker and G. N. Watson, *Modern Analysis*, Cambridge, Cambridge University Press, 1927, pp. 150–154.

be realized that the validity of the result is not at all affected by the manner in which we arrive at that result. The validity is demonstrated by showing directly that, for the y_1 of equation (6), $L(y_1) = 0$.

The above discussion leaves many questions unanswered. It is intended as a bare introduction to the topic of solutions near an irregular singular point.

111. The solution of certain linear recurrence relations. In the next section we shall encounter some nonhomogeneous linear recurrence relations of the type

$$(1) \qquad\qquad n \geq 1: \quad a_n = f_n a_{n-1} + g_n,$$

in which f_n, g_n, and a_0 are known and a_n, $n > 0$, is to be found.

A special case of the above is easy to solve. Suppose b_0 and t_n are known and

$$(2) \qquad\qquad n \geq 1: \quad b_n = b_{n-1} + t_n.$$

Iteration of the relation yields

$$b_1 = b_0 + t_1,$$
$$b_2 = b_1 + t_2,$$
$$\cdot$$
$$\cdot$$
$$\cdot$$
$$b_n = b_{n-1} + t_n,$$

so that, adding the respective members, we obtain

$$b_n = b_0 + \sum_{k=1}^{n} t_k.$$

All that we need to do to solve the relation (1) is to reduce it to the special case (2). We wish to eliminate f_n. Let us tentatively pass from the unknown a_n to a new unknown b_n by putting

$$(3) \qquad\qquad a_n = \varphi_n b_n$$

where the φ_n will be chosen to eliminate f_n. Using (3) in the relation (1) we are led to

$$\varphi_n b_n = f_n \varphi_{n-1} b_{n-1} + g_n,$$

or

(4) $$b_n = \frac{f_n \varphi_{n-1}}{\varphi_n} b_{n-1} + \frac{g_n}{\varphi_n}.$$

Now we wish to choose φ_n so that $\varphi_n = f_n \varphi_{n-1}$. That we can always do by the methods we have been using right along, as will be exhibited in the examples below. Once φ_n is so chosen, the relation (4) is of the type of (2) and easily solved for b_n. Then a_n is given by equation (3).

Example (a): Let a_0 be arbitrary and find a_n, $n > 0$, from the relation

(5) $$n \geq 1: \quad a_n = n^2 a_{n-1} + n + 1.$$

Let us put $a_n = \varphi_n b_n$ with $\varphi_0 = 1$ so that $a_0 = b_0$. Then (5) leads to

$$n \geq 1: \quad \varphi_n b_n = n^2 \varphi_{n-1} b_{n-1} + (n + 1)$$

so that we wish to choose φ_n to satisfy

(6) $$n \geq 1: \quad \varphi_n = n^2 \varphi_{n-1}.$$

Now

$$\varphi_1 = 1^2 \varphi_0,$$
$$\varphi_2 = 2^2 \varphi_1,$$
$$.$$
$$.$$
$$.$$
$$\varphi_n = n^2 \varphi_{n-1},$$

from which $\varphi_n = (n!)^2 \varphi_0 = (n!)^2$.

The relation for the b's now becomes

$$n \geq 1: \quad (n!)^2 b_n = n^2 [(n - 1)!]^2 b_{n-1} + n + 1,$$

or

(7) $$n \geq 1: \quad b_n = b_{n-1} + \frac{n + 1}{(n!)^2},$$

with $b_0 = a_0$. From (7) it follows at once that

$$b_n = b_0 + \sum_{k=1}^{n} \frac{k + 1}{(k!)^2}.$$

Therefore, for $n \geq 1$,

$$a_n = (n!)^2 a_0 + \sum_{k=1}^{n} \frac{(k+1)(n!)^2}{(k!)^2}.$$

EXAMPLE (b): Solve the relation

(8) $\qquad n \geq 1: \quad (n+3)(n+2)a_n + a_{n-1} = 1.$

At once

$$n \geq 1: \quad a_n = \frac{-a_{n-1}}{(n+3)(n+2)} + \frac{1}{(n+3)(n+2)},$$

so we put $a_n = \varphi_n b_n$, with $\varphi_0 = 1$, and require that

(9) $\qquad n \geq 1: \quad \varphi_n = \frac{-\varphi_{n-1}}{(n+3)(n+2)}.$

Of course

$$\varphi_n = \frac{(-1)^n \varphi_0}{[4 \cdot 5 \cdots (n+3)][3 \cdot 4 \cdots (n+2)]} = \frac{(-1)^n 12}{(n+3)!(n+2)!}.$$

Thus with $a_n = \varphi_n b_n$ the relation for b_n is found to be

$$\frac{(-1)^n 12 b_n}{(n+3)!(n+2)!} = \frac{-(-1)^{n-1} 12 b_{n-1}}{(n+3)!(n+2)!} + \frac{1}{(n+3)(n+2)},$$

or

(10) $\qquad n \geq 1: \quad b_n = b_{n-1} + \frac{1}{12}(-1)^n (n+2)!(n+1)!.$

Hence

$$b_n = b_0 + \frac{1}{12} \sum_{k=1}^{n} (-1)^k (k+2)!(k+1)!$$

and finally,

$$n \geq 1: \quad a_n = \frac{12(-1)^n a_0}{(n+3)!(n+2)!} + \sum_{k=1}^{n} \frac{(-1)^{n+k}(k+2)!(k+1)!}{(n+3)!(n+2)!}.$$

With a little practice the φ_n can often be obtained by inspection.

EXERCISES

For each relation assume that a_0 is arbitrary and solve for a_n, $n > 0$.

1. $n \geq 1 : a_n = -na_{n-1} + 2$.

$$\text{ANS.} \quad n \geq 1 : a_n = (-1)^n n! a_0 + 2 \sum_{k=1}^{n} \frac{(-1)^{n+k} n!}{k!}.$$

2. $n \geq 1 : a_n + 2a_{n-1} = 1$.

$$\text{ANS.} \quad n \geq 1 : a_n = (-2)^n a_0 + (-2)^n \sum_{k=1}^{n} (-\tfrac{1}{2})^k.$$

3. Sum the series in the answer to Ex. 2 and so obtain the solution, $n \geq 1$:
$a_n = (-2)^n a_0 + \frac{1}{3}[1 - (-2)^n]$.

4. $n \geq 1 : (n + 1)a_n - a_{n-1} = n$.

$$\text{ANS.} \quad n \geq 1 : a_n = \frac{a_0}{(n + 1)!} + \sum_{k=1}^{n} \frac{k(k!)}{(n + 1)!}.$$

5. $n \geq 1 : na_n - a_{n-1} = \dfrac{1}{n!}$. $\quad\text{ANS.} \quad n \geq 1 : a_n = (a_0 + H_n)/n!$.

6. $n \geq 1 : n(n + 1)a_n - a_{n-1} = n + 1$.

$$\text{ANS.} \quad n \geq 1 : a_n = \frac{a_0}{n!(n + 1)!} + \sum_{k=1}^{n} \frac{(k - 1)!(k + 1)!}{n!(n + 1)!}.$$

112. Nonhomogeneous equations.

In many instances a non-homogeneous equation

$$L(y) = R(x)$$

can be solved by essentially the same power series methods as we have been using on homogeneous equations. Instead of using the considerable space it would take to develop a thorough treatment of this topic, all that is done here is to illustrate some points in the subject by means of two examples and a few exercises.

EXAMPLE (a): Solve the equation

$$(1) \qquad\qquad xy'' + y = \frac{x^2}{1 - x}$$

near the point $x = 0$.

The corresponding homogeneous equation

(2) $$xy'' + y = 0$$

was solved in Ex. 1, page 303.   Its solutions were found to be

(3) $$y_1 = \sum_{n=1}^{\infty} \frac{(-1)^n x^n}{n!(n-1)!}$$

and

(4) $$y_2 = y_1 \ln x + 1 - \sum_{n=1}^{\infty} \frac{(-1)^n (H_n + H_{n-1}) x^n}{n!(n-1)!}.$$

What we need now is to get a particular solution y_p of equation (1) so that, near $x = 0$, the general solution of (1) can be written

$$y = Ay_1 + By_2 + y_p.$$

The right member of equation (1) can be expanded in a power series near $x = 0$, namely,

$$\frac{x^2}{1-x} = \sum_{n=0}^{\infty} x^{n+2}.$$

Now our differential equation can be rewritten as

(5) $$xy'' + y = \sum_{n=0}^{\infty} x^{n+2},$$

and it is natural to seek a particular solution of the form

(6) $$y = \sum_{n=0}^{\infty} a_n x^{n+\gamma}$$

where the a_n and the γ are yet to be determined.

If the y of equation (6) is to satisfy (5), then we must have

$$\sum_{n=0}^{\infty} (n+\gamma)(n+\gamma-1)a_n x^{n+\gamma-1} + \sum_{n=1}^{\infty} a_{n-1} x^{n+\gamma-1} = \sum_{n=0}^{\infty} x^{n+2}$$

identically in some region surrounding $x = 0$. The lowest degree term on the left is $\gamma(\gamma - 1)a_0 x^{\gamma-1}$ and the lowest degree term on the right is x^2. Therefore we choose* $\gamma = 3$. Then the identity to be satisfied is

$$\sum_{n=0}^{\infty} (n + 3)(n + 2)a_n x^{n+2} + \sum_{n=1}^{\infty} a_{n-1} x^{n+2} = \sum_{n=0}^{\infty} x^{n+2}.$$

For two power series to be identical in a region the corresponding coefficients must be equal. We conclude that the a_n are given by the relations

$$n = 0: \quad 6a_0 = 1,$$
$$n \geqq 1: \quad (n + 3)(n + 2)a_n + a_{n-1} = 1.$$

It is not unreasonable to stop at this stage and to write the general solution of the original differential equation as

$$y = Ay_1 + By_2 + y_p,$$

in which the y_1 and y_2 are given by equations (3) and (4) and

$$(7) \qquad y_p = \sum_{n=0}^{\infty} a_n x^{n+3},$$

where $a_0 = \frac{1}{6}$ and

$$n \geqq 1: \quad a_n = \frac{1 - a_{n-1}}{(n + 3)(n + 2)}.$$

As many a's as are desired may be computed from the recurrence relation above.

By the method of the preceding section an explicit formula for the a_n can be found. Indeed, according to Example (b) of that section,

$$n \geqq 1: \quad a_n = \frac{12(-1)^n a_0}{(n + 3)!(n + 2)!} + \sum_{k=1}^{n} \frac{(-1)^{n+k}(k + 2)!(k + 1)!}{(n + 3)!(n + 2)!}.$$

Therefore, since $a_0 = \frac{1}{6}$, we may write the particular solution indi-

---

* Here complications would enter if the series on the right had started with a term x^k for k zero or a negative integer.

cated in (7) as

$$(8) \quad y_p = \tfrac{1}{6}x^3 + \sum_{n=1}^{\infty} \left[2 + \sum_{k=1}^{n} (-1)^k (k+2)!(k+1)! \right] \frac{(-1)^n x^{n+3}}{(n+3)!(n+2)!}.$$

Further simplification of equation (8) yields

$$(9) \quad y_p = -2y_1 - 2x + x^2 + \sum_{n=1}^{\infty} \sum_{k=1}^{n} \frac{(-1)^{n+k}(k+1)!(k+2)!x^{n+3}}{(n+3)!(n+2)!}$$

and now the term $(-2y_1)$ can be absorbed into the complementary function if so desired.

It is instructive to go through the details of showing directly from (9) that

$$xy_p'' + y_p = \sum_{n=0}^{\infty} x^{n+2}.$$

EXAMPLE (b): Solve the equation

$$(10) \qquad 2x^2 y'' + x(4x - 1)y' + 2(3x - 1)y = x^3 + x^4$$

near $x = 0$.

The corresponding homogeneous equation has the linearly inde . pendent solutions

$$(11) \qquad y_1 = \sum_{n=0}^{\infty} \frac{(-2)^n x^{n+2}}{n!} = x^2 e^{-2x},$$

$$(12) \qquad y_2 = x^{-1/2} + \sum_{n=1}^{\infty} \frac{(-4)^n x^{n-1/2}}{(-3)(-1) \cdot 1 \cdots (2n - 5)},$$

as indicated in Ex. 12, page 282.

If we use

$$y = \sum_{n=0}^{\infty} a_n x^{n+\gamma},$$

then equation (10) becomes

$$\sum_{n=0}^{\infty} (2n + 2\gamma + 1)(n + \gamma - 2)a_n x^{n+\gamma} + \sum_{n=1}^{\infty} 2(2n + 2\gamma + 1)a_{n-1}x^{n+\gamma}$$
$$= x^3 + x^4.$$

It is natural to choose $\gamma = 3$. Then the a's will be determined by the relations

$$n = 0: \quad 7a_0 = 1,$$
$$n = 1: \quad 9(2)a_1 + 2(9)a_0 = 1,$$
$$n \geq 2: \quad (2n + 7)(n + 1)a_n + 2(2n + 7)a_{n-1} = 0.$$

Thus we find that $a_0 = \frac{1}{7}$, $a_1 = -\frac{11}{126}$,

$$n \geq 2: \quad a_n = -\frac{2a_{n-1}}{n + 1}.$$

This recurrence relation has the solution

$$a_n = \frac{(-2)^{n-1}a_1}{3 \cdot 4 \, \cdots \, (n + 1)} = -\frac{11}{126} \cdot \frac{(-1)^{n-1} \cdot 2^n}{(n + 1)!}.$$

Hence a particular solution of the original equation is

$$y = \tfrac{1}{7}x^3 - \tfrac{11}{126}\left[x^4 + \sum_{n=2}^{\infty} \frac{(-1)^{n-1}2^n x^{n+3}}{(n + 1)!} \right],$$

or

$$y = \tfrac{1}{7}x^3 - \tfrac{11}{126} \sum_{n=1}^{\infty} \frac{(-1)^{n-1}2^n x^{n+3}}{(n + 1)!}.$$

This resembles the y_1 of (11) so much that we shift index in the summation to find

$$(13) \qquad y = \tfrac{1}{7}x^3 - \tfrac{11}{126} \sum_{n=2}^{\infty} \frac{(-1)^n 2^{n-1} x^{n+2}}{n!}.$$

The summation involved in equation (13) is the same as that in the expression for y_1 in equation (11) except that two terms are missing and a factor 2^{-1} has been introduced.   We are thus led to rewrite (13) as

$$y = \tfrac{1}{7}x^3 - \tfrac{11}{252}(y_1 - x^2 + 2x^3).$$

But the term proportional to y_1 can be absorbed in the complementary function.   Therefore the differential equation (10) has a particular solution

$$y_p = \tfrac{1}{7}x^3 + \tfrac{11}{252}x^2 - \tfrac{11}{126}x^3,$$

or

(14) $$y_p = \tfrac{11}{252}x^2 + \tfrac{1}{18}x^3,$$

which is easily verified by direct substitution.

If in this example we had chosen $\gamma = 2$, a less apparent choice perhaps, then the a's would have been determined by the relations

$$
\begin{aligned}
n = 0: &\quad 0 \cdot a_0 = 0, \ (a_0 \text{ arbitrary}),\\
n = 1: &\quad 7a_1 + 14a_0 = 1,\\
n = 2: &\quad 18a_2 + 18a_1 = 1,\\
n \geq 3: &\quad na_n + 2a_{n-1} = 0.
\end{aligned}
$$

If we can force a_2 to be zero, then $a_n = 0$ for $n > 2$.   If $a_2 = 0$,

$$
\begin{aligned}
a_1 &= \tfrac{1}{18},\\
a_0 &= \tfrac{1}{14} - \tfrac{1}{2}a_1 = \tfrac{11}{252}.
\end{aligned}
$$

Thus the choices $\gamma = 2$ and $a_0 = \tfrac{11}{252}$ lead to $a_n = 0$ for $n \geq 2$ and so give us again the solution (14).

EXERCISES

For each equation below the corresponding homogeneous differential equation occurs earlier in the book.   Two linearly independent solutions of the homogeneous equation may be found at the reference given. Obtain a particular solution for each equation.

1. $xy'' + (1 - x)y' - y = x/(1 - x)$.   See Ex. 15, page 293.

$$\text{ANS.} \quad y_p = \tfrac{1}{4}x^2 + \sum_{n=1}^{\infty} \left[\tfrac{1}{2} + \sum_{k=1}^{n} \frac{(k + 1)!}{k + 2} \right] \frac{x^{n+2}}{(n + 2)!}.$$

2. Show from the answer to Ex. 1 that another particular solution of the differential equation is

$$y = -\tfrac{1}{2}(1 + x) + \sum_{n=1}^{\infty} \sum_{k=1}^{n} \frac{(k + 1)!x^{n+2}}{(k + 2)(n + 2)!}.$$

3. $xy'' + y = xe^x$. See Ex. 1, page 303.

ANS. $y_p = \tfrac{1}{2}x^2 + \sum_{n=1}^{\infty} \left[1 + \sum_{k=1}^{n} (-1)^k(k + 1)! \right] \frac{(-1)^n x^{n+2}}{(n + 2)!(n + 1)!}.$

4. Show that the answer to Ex. 3 leads also to the particular solution

$$y = x + \sum_{n=1}^{\infty} \sum_{k=1}^{n} \frac{(-1)^{n+k}(k + 1)!x^{n+2}}{(n + 2)!(n + 1)!}.$$

5. $x^2y'' + x(x - 1)y' + (1 - x)y = x^2$. See Ex. 10, page 293.

ANS. $y_p = \sum_{n=0}^{\infty} \frac{(-1)^n x^{n+2}}{(n + 1)(n + 1)!}.$

6. Show that the equation $xy'' + y = e^x$ has a solution of the form

$$y = \sum_{n=0}^{\infty} a_n x^n$$

with a_1 arbitrary. Put $a_1 = 0$ and determine the resultant solution.

ANS. $y = 1 + \sum_{n=2}^{\infty} \sum_{k=2}^{n} \frac{(-1)^{n+k}(k - 2)!x^n}{n!(n - 1)!}.$

7. Show that the equation

$$L(y) = x^2y'' + x(x - 1)y' + (1 - x)y = x$$

has no solution of the form $y = \sum_{n=0}^{\infty} a_n x^{n+\gamma}$.

8. Verify by computing $L(y)$ that the equation of Ex. 7 has the particular solution

$$y = \frac{x}{2} \ln^2 x + \ln x \sum_{n=1}^{\infty} \frac{(-1)^n x^{n+1}}{n \cdot n!} + \sum_{n=1}^{\infty} \frac{(-1)^{n+1}\left(\frac{1}{n} + H_n\right) x^{n+1}}{n \cdot n!}.$$

Chapter 22

Numerical Methods

113. General remarks. There is no general method for obtaining an explicit formula for the solution of a differential equation. Specific equations do arise for which no known attack yields a solution or for which the explicit forms of solution are not well adapted to computation. For these reasons systematic, efficient methods for the numerical approximation to solutions are important. Unfortunately, a clear grasp of good numerical methods requires time-consuming practice and often also the availability of modern computing machines.

This chapter is restricted to a fragmentary discussion of some simple and moderately useful methods. The purpose here is to give the student a concept of the fundamental principles of numerical approximations to solutions. We shall take one problem, which does not yield to the methods developed earlier in this book, and apply to it several simple numerical processes.

114. The increment method. The problem we seek to solve is to obtain that solution of the differential equation

$$(1) \qquad y' = y^2 - x^2$$

for which $y = 1$ when $x = 0$. We wish to know the solution $y = y(x)$ in the range $0 \leq x \leq \frac{1}{2}$.

Equation (1) may be written in differential form as

$$(2) \qquad dy = (y^2 - x^2)dx.$$

Figure 45 shows the geometrical significance of the differential dy and of Δy, the actual change in y, as induced by an increment dx (or Δx) applied to x. In calculus it is shown that, near a point where the derivative exists, dy can be made to approximate Δy as closely as desired by taking Δx sufficiently small.

356

We know the value of y at $x = 0$; we wish to compute y for $0 \leq x \leq \frac{1}{2}$. Suppose we choose $\Delta x = 0.1$, then dy can be computed from

$$dy = (y^2 - x^2)\Delta x.$$

Indeed, $dy = (1 - 0)(0.1) = 0.1$. Thus for $x = 0 + 0.1$, the approximate value of y is $1 + 0.1$. Now we have $x = 0.1$, $y = 1.1$. Let us choose $\Delta x = 0.1$ again. Then

$$dy = [(1.1)^2 - (0.1)^2]\Delta x,$$

so that $dy = 0.12$. Hence at $x = 0.2$ the approximate value of y is 1.22. The complete computation using $\Delta x = 0.1$ is shown in Table 1.

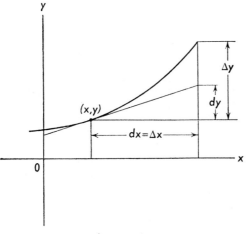

FIGURE 45

The increment Δx need not be constant throughout the interval. Where the slope is larger it pays to take the increment smaller. For simplicity in computations equal increments are used here.

It is helpful to repeat the computation with a smaller increment and to note the changes which result in the approximate values of y. Table 2 shows a computation with $\Delta x = 0.05$ throughout.

In Table 3 the values of y obtained from the computations in Tables 1 and 2 and also the values of y obtained by using $\Delta x = 0.01$ (computation not shown) are exhibited beside the values of y correct to two decimal places. The correct values are obtained by the method of Section 118.   Their availability is in a sense accidental. Frequently, we know of no way to obtain the y value correct to a specified degree of accuracy.   In such instances it is customary to

$$\Delta x = 0.1$$

x	y	y^2	x^2	$(y^2 - x^2)$	dy
0.0	1.00	1.00	0.00	1.00	0.10
0.1	1.10	1.21	0.01	1.20	0.12
0.2	1.22	1.49	0.04	1.45	0.14
0.3	1.36	1.85	0.09	1.76	0.18
0.4	1.54	2.37	0.16	2.21	0.22
0.5	1.76				

Table 1

$$\Delta x = 0.05$$

x	y	y^2	x^2	$(y^2 - x^2)$	dy
0.00	1.000	1.000	0.000	1.000	0.050
0.05	1.050	1.102	0.002	1.100	0.055
0.10	1.105	1.221	0.010	1.211	0.061
0.15	1.166	1.360	0.022	1.338	0.067
0.20	1.233	1.520	0.040	1.480	0.074
0.25	1.307	1.708	0.062	1.646	0.082
0.30	1.389	1.929	0.090	1.839	0.092
0.35	1.481	2.193	0.122	2.071	0.104
0.40	1.585	2.512	0.160	2.352	0.118
0.45	1.703	2.900	0.202	2.698	0.135
0.50	1.838				

Table 2

	$\Delta x = 0.1$	$\Delta x = 0.05$	$\Delta x = 0.01$	correct
x	y	y	y	y
0.0	1.00	1.00	1.00	1.00
0.1	1.10	1.11	1.11	1.11
0.2	1.22	1.23	1.24	1.25
0.3	1.36	1.39	1.41	1.42
0.4	1.54	1.58	1.62	1.64
0.5	1.76	1.84	1.91	1.93

Table 3

resort to decreasing the size of the increment until the y values show changes no larger than the errors we are willing to permit.   Then it is *hoped* that the steadying down of the y values is due to our being

close to the correct solution rather than (as is quite possible) to the
slowness of convergence of the process used.

EXERCISES

1. Use the increment method with $\Delta x = 0.1$ to compute, in the range
$0 \leq x \leq 1$, that solution of the equation

$$y' = x + y$$

for which $y = 1$ when $x = 0$. Also solve the boundary value problem
exactly by elementary methods and compare the y values at intervals of
0.1 in x.

2. Use $\Delta x = 0.05$ in the problem of Ex. 1.

3. Use the method of increments on the boundary value problem

$$y' = e^{-xy}; \quad \text{when } x = 0, \; y = 0,$$

first with $\Delta x = 0.2$ and then with $\Delta x = 0.1$, computing y for the interval
$0 \leq x \leq 2$.

4. Perform the same computations as in Ex. 3 but for the problem

$$y' = (1 + x^2 + y^2)^{-1}; \quad \text{when } x = 0, \; y = 0.$$

115. A method of successive approximation. Next let us
attack the same problem as before,

$$(1) \qquad\qquad y' = y^2 - x^2; \quad x = 0, \quad y = 1,$$

with y desired in the interval $0 \leq x \leq \frac{1}{2}$, by the method suggested
in the discussion of the existence theorem in Chapter 15. Applying
the statements made in that discussion, we conclude that the desired
solution is $y = y(x)$ where

$$y(x) = \operatorname*{Lim}_{n \to \infty} y_n(x)$$

and the sequence of approximations $y_n(x)$ is given by $y_0(x) = 1$ and,
for $n \geq 1$,

$$(2) \qquad\qquad y_n(x) = 1 + \int_0^x [y^2_{n-1}(t) - t^2]dt.$$

For the problem at hand

$$y_1(x) = 1 + \int_0^x (1 - t^2)dt,$$

$$y_1(x) = 1 + x - \tfrac{1}{3}x^3.$$

Next we obtain a second approximation, finding $y_2(x)$ from $y_1(x)$ by means of (2). Thus we find that

$$y_2(x) = 1 + \int_0^x [(1 + t - \tfrac{1}{3}t^3)^2 - t^2]dt,$$

$$y_2(x) = 1 + x + x^2 - \tfrac{1}{6}x^4 - \tfrac{2}{15}x^5 + \tfrac{1}{63}x^7.$$

Then $y_3(x)$, $y_4(x)$, $\cdots$, can be obtained in a similar manner, each from the preceding element of the sequence $y_n(x)$.

In Table 4 the values taken on by $y_1(x)$, $y_2(x)$, and $y_3(x)$ at intervals of 0.1 in x are shown beside the corresponding values of $y(x)$, correct to two decimal places, as obtained in Section 118.

It must be realized that the usefulness of this method is not dependent upon our being able to carry out the integrations in a formal sense.

x	$y_1(x)$	$y_2(x)$	$y_3(x)$	$y(x)$
0.0	1.00	1.00	1.00	1.00
0.1	1.10	1.11	1.11	1.11
0.2	1.20	1.24	1.25	1.25
0.3	1.29	1.39	1.41	1.42
0.4	1.38	1.56	1.62	1.64
0.5	1.46	1.74	1.87	1.93

Table 4

It may be best to perform the integrations mechanically with a planimeter, or by some numerical process such as Simpson's rule.

EXERCISES

1. Apply the method of this section to the problem

$$y' = x + y; \text{ when } x = 0, y = 1,$$

of Ex. 1, Section 114. Obtain $y_1(x)$, $y_2(x)$, and $y_3(x)$.

ANS. $y_1(x) = 1 + x + \tfrac{1}{2}x^2$;
$y_2(x) = 1 + x + x^2 + \tfrac{1}{6}x^3$;
$y_3(x) = 1 + x + x^2 + \tfrac{1}{3}x^3 + \tfrac{1}{24}x^4$.

2. Compute a table of values to two decimal places of y_1, y_2, y_3 of Ex. 1 for $x = 0$ to $x = 1$ at intervals of 0.1. Tabulate also the correct values of y, obtained from the elementary solution to the problem.

116. An improvement on the preceding method. In the method used in Section 115 each of the $y_n(x)$; $n = 0, 1, 2, \cdots$, yields an approximation to the solution $y = y(x)$. It is plausible that usually the more nearly correct a particular approximation $y_k(x)$, the better will be its successor $y_{k+1}(x)$.

The boundary value problem we are treating is

$$y' = y^2 - x^2; \quad x = 0, \quad y = 1$$

and it tells us at once that at $x = 0$, the slope is $y' = 1$. But in Section 115, by blindly following the suggestion in Chapter 15, we started out with $y_0(x) = 1$, a line which does not have the correct slope at $x = 0$.

It is therefore reasonable to alter our initial approximation by choosing $y_0(x)$ to have the correct slope at $x = 0$, still making it also pass through the desired point $x = 0$, $y = 1$. Hence we choose

$$y_0(x) = 1 + x$$

and proceed to compute $y_1(x)$, $y_2(x)$, $\cdots$, as before. The successive stages of approximation to $y(x)$ now become

$$y_1(x) = 1 + \int_0^x [(1 + t)^2 - t^2]dt,$$

$$y_1(x) = 1 + x + x^2,$$

and

$$y_2(x) = 1 + \int_0^x [(1 + t + t^2)^2 - t^2]dt,$$

$$y_2(x) = 1 + x + x^2 + \tfrac{2}{3}x^3 + \tfrac{1}{2}x^4 + \tfrac{1}{5}x^5,$$

and so on.

In Table 5 the values of y_1, y_2, y_3 obtained by this method are shown beside the correct values of y.

x	$y_1(x)$	$y_2(x)$	$y_3(x)$	$y(x)$
0.0	1.00	1.00	1.00	1.00
0.1	1.11	1.11	1.11	1.11
0.2	1.24	1.25	1.25	1.25
0.3	1.39	1.41	1.42	1.42
0.4	1.56	1.62	1.64	1.64
0.5	1.75	1.87	1.92	1.93

Table 5

EXERCISES

1. Apply the method of this section to obtain approximations y_1, y_2, y_3 for the problem of Ex. 1 of Section 114.

        ANS. $y_1(x) = 1 + x + x^2; y_2(x) = 1 + x + x^2 + \frac{1}{3}x^3;$

$$y_3(x) = 1 + x + x^2 + \frac{1}{3}x^3 + \frac{1}{12}x^4.$$

2. Tabulate to two decimal places the y_1, y_2, y_3 of Ex. 1 beside the corresponding values of the exact solution $y(x) = 2e^x - 1 - x$.

117. A purely graphical attack. In treating the boundary value problem

$$(1) \qquad\qquad y' = f(x, y); \quad x = a, \quad y = b,$$

the steps taken in forming the sequence of approximations $y_0(x)$, $y_1(x)$, $y_2(x)$, $\cdots$, are frequently performed graphically.

In such a procedure a curve $y = y_0(x)$, a reasonable first guess, is sketched over the desired interval, taking care to make the curve pass through the point (a, b) and have the proper slope at (a, b) as given by equation (1). Frequently, this starting point, the curve $y = y_0(x)$, can be improved in practical problems by the use of additional information. For instance, it may be known, or strongly suspected, that the desired solution is concave upward in the interval for which it is desired. The use of such a piece of information would permit us to get off to a better start in building our sequence of approximations.

From the initial guess, $y = y_0(x)$, the first approximation would be obtained from

$$y_1(x) = b + \int_a^x f[t, y_0(t)]dt,$$

then $y_2(x)$ from $y_1(x)$ in the same manner, etc. The process would be continued until the graph had settled down; that is, until two successive curves, $y = y_k(x)$ and $y = y_{k+1}(x)$, were not appreciably different.

The method is open to many objections. One danger is that the convergence of the process may be so slow that no appreciable change can be observed graphically between two successive approximations even though a considerable error is still present.

118. Power series. The numerical problem on which we are concentrating in this chapter is that of computing for $0 \leqq x \leqq \frac{1}{2}$ that solution of

$$(1) \qquad\qquad y' = y^2 - x^2$$

for which $y = 1$ when $x = 0$. Let us assume that a power series solution exists. Put

$$(2) \qquad\qquad y = \sum_{n=0}^{\infty} a_n x^n,$$

in which $a_0 = 1$ so that $y = 1$ when $x = 0$. Direct substitution into equation (1) yields

$$\sum_{n=1}^{\infty} n a_n x^{n-1} = \left(\sum_{n=0}^{\infty} a_n x^n \right)^2 - x^2,$$

or

$$\sum_{n=1}^{\infty} n a_n x^{n-1} = -x^2 + \sum_{n=0}^{\infty} \sum_{k=0}^{n} a_k a_{n-k} x^n.$$

A shift of index on the right gives us

$$\sum_{n=1}^{\infty} n a_n x^{n-1} = -x^2 + \sum_{n=1}^{\infty} \sum_{k=0}^{n-1} a_k a_{n-1-k} x^{n-1}.$$

We know $a_0 = 1$. The other a's may be computed one at a time from

$$n = 1: \quad a_1 = a_0 a_0,$$
$$n = 2: \quad 2a_2 = a_0 a_1 + a_1 a_0,$$
$$n = 3: \quad 3a_3 = -1 + (a_0 a_2 + a_1 a_1 + a_2 a_0),$$
$$n \geqq 4: \quad n a_n = a_0 a_{n-1} + a_1 a_{n-2} + \cdots + a_{n-2} a_1 + a_{n-1} a_0.$$

The first few terms of the desired series are found to be as given in

$$y = 1 + x + x^2 + \tfrac{2}{3} x^3 + \tfrac{5}{6} x^4 + \tfrac{4}{5} x^5 + \tfrac{23}{30} x^6 + \tfrac{236}{315} x^7 + \cdots .$$

It is fortunate in this example that convergence of the series solution can be demonstrated by elementary devices.

Direct computation has already yielded $a_0 = 1$, $a_1 = 1$, $a_2 = 1$, $a_3 = \frac{2}{3}$, etc. Let us assume that

$$(3) \qquad\qquad 0 < a_k \leqq 1$$

for each k less than n, i.e., for $0 \leqq k \leqq (n-1)$. Now we know that a_n is determined, for $n \geqq 4$, by

$$(4) \qquad na_n = \sum_{k=0}^{n-1} a_k a_{n-1-k}.$$

Each of the a's on the right in (4) is positive and does not exceed unity. Hence each product $a_k a_{n-1-k}$ is positive and not greater than one,

$$0 < a_k a_{n-1-k} \leqq 1.$$

There are n such terms on the right in equation (4). Therefore from (3) and (4) it follows that $0 < na_n \leqq n$, or

$$(5) \qquad\qquad 0 < a_n \leqq 1.$$

Since we knew that the property (5) held for $n = 0, 1, 2$, and 3, we may now conclude by induction that (5) holds for each integral n.

Because of the inequality (5) it can be seen that the series

$$y(x) = \sum_{n=0}^{\infty} a_n x^n$$

converges at least for $|x| < 1$.

For the range in which we are interested, $0 \leqq x \leqq \frac{1}{2}$, let the error caused by stopping with the term $a_n x^n$ be denoted $E_n(x)$; that is, let

$$E_n(x) = \sum_{k=n+1}^{\infty} a_k x^k.$$

Since $0 < a_n \leqq 1$, it is true for all x in the range $0 \leqq x \leqq \frac{1}{2}$ that

$$|E_n(x)| \leqq \sum_{k=n+1}^{\infty} |a_k x^k| \leqq \sum_{k=n+1}^{\infty} (\tfrac{1}{2})^k = \frac{(\tfrac{1}{2})^{n+1}}{1 - \tfrac{1}{2}} = (\tfrac{1}{2})^n.$$

As a matter of fact it is not difficult to improve upon this bound on the error. But the essential point is that for the range of x in which we are interested we can bound the error made in computing with the power series. Thus we can be certain of two-decimal-point accuracy, something not so readily accomplished with the methods exhibited earlier in this chapter.

Chapter 23

Partial Differential Equations

119. Remarks on partial differential equations. A partial differential equation is an equation which contains one or more partial derivatives. Such equations arise frequently in applications of mathematics. They also enter pure mathematics. The subject of partial differential equations offers sufficient ramifications and difficulties to be of interest for its own sake.

In this book we shall devote the space allotted to partial differential equations almost entirely to the kind of boundary value problem which enters modern applied mathematics at every turn.

Partial differential equations can have solutions involving arbitrary functions and solutions involving an unlimited number of arbitrary constants. In rough language the general solution of a partial differential equation of order n may be defined as a solution involving n arbitrary functions.

The general solution of a partial differential equation is almost never (the wave equation yields one of the few exceptions) of any practical use in solving boundary value problems associated with that differential equation.

120. Some partial differential equations of applied mathematics. Certain partial differential equations enter applied mathematics so frequently and in so many connections that their study is remarkably remunerative. A sufficiently thorough study of these equations would lead the student eventually into every phase of classical mathematics and, in particular, would lead almost at once to contact with special functions which are widely used in modern quantum theory and elsewhere in theoretical physics and engineering.

The derivation of the differential equations to be listed here is beyond the scope of this book. Those derivations can be found (not all in each book) in the books listed for reference at the end of this section.

Some of the ways in which these equations are useful will appear in the detailed applications in Chapter 26.

Let x, y, z be rectangular coordinates in ordinary space. Then, as stated in Chapter 5, the equation

$$(1) \qquad \frac{\partial^2 V}{\partial x^2} + \frac{\partial^2 V}{\partial y^2} + \frac{\partial^2 V}{\partial z^2} = 0$$

is called Laplace's equation. It enters problems in steady-state temperature, electrostatic potential, fluid flow of the steady-state variety, etc.

If a problem involving equation (1) is such that a physical object in the problem is a circular cylinder, then it is possible that cylindrical coordinates will facilitate solution of the problem. We shall encounter such a problem later. It is a matter of advanced calculus to change equation (1) into an equation in which the independent variables are cylindrical coordinates r, θ, z, related to the x, y, z of equation (1) by the equations

$$x = r \cos \theta, \quad y = r \sin \theta, \quad z = z.$$

The resulting equation, Laplace's equation in cylindrical coordinates, is

$$(2) \qquad \frac{\partial^2 V}{\partial r^2} + \frac{1}{r} \frac{\partial V}{\partial r} + \frac{1}{r^2} \frac{\partial^2 V}{\partial \theta^2} + \frac{\partial^2 V}{\partial z^2} = 0.$$

Note that the use of z in both coordinate systems above is safe in making the change of variables only because z is not involved in the equations with other variables. That is, in a change of independent variables such as

$$x = x_1 + y_1 + z_1, \quad y = x_1 - y_1, \quad z = z_1,$$

or its equivalent,

$$x_1 = \tfrac{1}{2}(x + y - z), \quad y_1 = \tfrac{1}{2}(x - y - z), \quad z_1 = z,$$

incorrect conclusions would often result from any attempt to drop the subscript on the z_1, even though $z = z_1$. For instance, from the change of variables under discussion, it follows that

$$\frac{\partial V}{\partial z} = -\tfrac{1}{2}\frac{\partial V}{\partial x_1} - \tfrac{1}{2}\frac{\partial V}{\partial y_1} + \frac{\partial V}{\partial z_1}.$$

Hence $\dfrac{\partial V}{\partial z} \neq \dfrac{\partial V}{\partial z_1}$, even though $z = z_1$.

Let us return to Laplace's equation. In spherical coordinates ρ, θ, φ, related to x, y, z by the equations

$$x = \rho \sin \theta \cos \varphi, \quad y = \rho \sin \theta \sin \varphi, \quad z = \rho \cos \theta,$$

Laplace's equation is

$$(3) \qquad \frac{\partial^2 V}{\partial \rho^2} + \frac{2}{\rho}\frac{\partial V}{\partial \rho} + \frac{1}{\rho^2}\frac{\partial^2 V}{\partial \theta^2} + \frac{\cot \theta}{\rho^2}\frac{\partial V}{\partial \theta} + \frac{\csc^2 \theta}{\rho^2}\frac{\partial^2 V}{\partial \varphi^2} = 0.$$

With an additional independent variable t representing time, and with a constant denoted by a, we can write the wave equation in rectangular coordinates,

$$(4) \qquad \frac{\partial^2 V}{\partial t^2} = a^2\left(\frac{\partial^2 V}{\partial x^2} + \frac{\partial^2 V}{\partial y^2} + \frac{\partial^2 V}{\partial z^2}\right).$$

Equation (4) appears in problems involving wave motions. We shall meet it later in the problem of the vibrating string.

Whenever the physical problem, usually by the shape of the objects involved, suggests a different choice for a coordinate system, the pertinent partial differential equation can be transformed into one with the desired new independent variables. The actual change of variables in partial differential equations is left to advanced calculus; here we use the result.

Suppose that, for some solid under consideration, u represents the temperature at a point with rectangular coordinates x, y, z and at time t. The origin of coordinates and the initial time $t = 0$ may be assigned at our convenience. If there are no heat sources present, then the temperature u must satisfy the heat equation

$$(5) \qquad \frac{\partial u}{\partial t} = h^2\left(\frac{\partial^2 u}{\partial x^2} + \frac{\partial^2 u}{\partial y^2} + \frac{\partial^2 u}{\partial z^2}\right),$$

in which h^2 is a physical constant called thermal diffusivity.   Equation (5) is derived under the assumption that the density, specific heat, and thermal conductivity are constant for the solid being studied.   More comment on the question of the validity of equation (5) will be made in Section 138.

Equation (5) is the equation which pertains in many types of diffusion, not just when heat is being diffused.   It is often called the equation of diffusion.

In the subject of elasticity certain problems in plane stress can be solved with the aid of Airy's stress function φ, which must satisfy the partial differential equation

$$(6) \qquad \frac{\partial^4 \varphi}{\partial x^4} + 2\, \frac{\partial^4 \varphi}{\partial x^2 \partial y^2} + \frac{\partial^4 \varphi}{\partial y^4} = 0.$$

Numerous other partial differential equations arise in applications, though not with the dominating insistency of equations (1), (4), and (5).

REFERENCES

Churchill, R. V., *Fourier Series and Boundary Value Problems*, New York, McGraw-Hill Book Co., 1941.
Hopf, L., *Differential Equations of Physics*, New York, Dover Publications, 1948.

121. Method of separation of variables.   Before attacking an actual boundary value problem in partial differential equations, it is wise to become somewhat proficient in getting solutions of the differential equations.   When we have acquired some facility in obtaining solutions, then we can tackle the tougher problem of fitting them together to satisfy stipulated boundary conditions.

The device to be exhibited here is particularly useful in connection with linear equations, although it does not always apply to such equations.   Of course, it works on those equations of applied mathematics in which we are interested—or we wouldn't be discussing it here.

Consider the equation

$$(1) \qquad \frac{\partial u}{\partial t} = h^2\, \frac{\partial^2 u}{\partial x^2}$$

with h constant.   A solution of equation (1) will in general be a function of the two independent variables t and x and of the parameter h.

Let us seek a solution which is a product of a function of t alone by a function of x alone.   We put

$$u = f(t)v(x)$$

in equation (1) and thus arrive at

(2) $$f'(t)v(x) = h^2 f(t)v''(x),$$

where primes denote derivatives with respect to the indicated argument in the function symbol.

Dividing each member of (2) by the product $f(t)v(x)$, we get

(3) $$\frac{f'(t)}{f(t)} = \frac{h^2 v''(x)}{v(x)}.$$

Now equation (3) is said to have its variables (the independent variables) separated; that is, the left member of equation (3) is a function of t alone and the right member of equation (3) is a function of x alone.

Since x and t are independent variables, the only way in which a function of x alone can equal a function of t alone is for each function to be constant.   Thus from (3) it follows at once that

(4) $$\frac{f'(t)}{f(t)} = k$$

and

(5) $$\frac{h^2 v''(x)}{v(x)} = k,$$

in which k is arbitrary.

Another way of obtaining equations (4) and (5) is this.   Differentiate each member of equation (3) with respect to t (either independent variable could be used) and thus get

$$\frac{d}{dt}\frac{f'(t)}{f(t)} = 0,$$

since the right member of equation (3) is independent of t.   First we obtain equation (4) by integration and then equation (5) follows from (4) and (3).

Equation (4) may be rewritten

$$\frac{df}{dt} = kf,$$

from which its general solution

$$f = c_1 e^{kt}$$

follows immediately.

Before going further into the solution of our problem we attempt to choose a convenient form for the arbitrary constant introduced in equations (4) and (5). Equation (5) suggests that k be taken as a multiple of h^2.

Let us then return to equations (4) and (5) and put $k = h^2\beta^2$, so that we have

(6)
$$\frac{f'(t)}{f(t)} = h^2\beta^2$$

and

(7)
$$\frac{h^2 v''(x)}{v(x)} = h^2\beta^2.$$

Using real β and the choice $k = h^2\beta^2$, we are implying that the constant k is real and positive.* Later we shall obtain solutions corresponding to the choice of a real but negative constant.

From equations (6) and (7) we find at once that

(8)
$$f(t) = c_1 e^{h^2\beta^2 t}$$

and

(9)
$$v(x) = c_2 \cosh \beta x + c_3 \sinh \beta x.$$

Since $u = f(t)v(x)$ we are thus led to the result that the partial differential equation

(1)
$$\frac{\partial u}{\partial t} = h^2 \frac{\partial^2 u}{\partial x^2}$$

has solutions

(10)
$$u = e^{h^2\beta^2 t}[a \cosh \beta x + b \sinh \beta x],$$

---

* The expression "real and positive" is redundant; if something is positive, it must be real. Such redundant phrases do have their places in exposition.

in which β, a, and b are arbitrary constants. The a and b of equation (10) are respectively given by $a = c_1 c_2$ and $b = c_1 c_3$ in terms of the constants of equations (8) and (9).

If we return to equations (4) and (5) with the choice $k = -h^2 \alpha^2$, so that k is taken to be a real negative constant, then we find that the partial differential equation (1) has the solutions

$$(11) \qquad u = e^{-h^2 \alpha^2 t}[A \cos \alpha x + B \sin \alpha x],$$

in which α, A, and B are arbitrary constants.

Finally, let the constant k be zero. It is straightforward to determine that the corresponding solutions of the differential equation (1) are

$$(12) \qquad u = C_1 + C_2 x$$

in which C_1 and C_2 are constants.

Direct verification that equations (10), (11), and (12) are actually solutions of equation (1) is simple.

Since the partial differential equation (1) is linear, we may construct solutions by forming linear combinations of solutions. Thus from (10), (11), and (12) with varying choices of α, β, A, B, a, b, C_1, C_2, we can construct as many solutions of (1) as we wish.

The distinction between equations (10) and (11) is dependent upon the parameters and variables remaining real. Our aim is to develop tools for solving physical problems; hence we do intend to keep things real.

EXERCISES

Except where other instructions are given, use the method of separation of variables to obtain solutions in real form for each differential equation.

1. $\dfrac{\partial^2 u}{\partial t^2} = a^2 \dfrac{\partial^2 u}{\partial x^2}.$

ANS. $u = [A_1 \cos a\beta t + A_2 \sin a\beta t][B_1 \cos \beta x + B_2 \sin \beta x]$,
$u = (A_3 + A_4 t)(B_3 + B_4 x)$,
and
$u = [A_5 \cosh a\beta t + A_6 \sinh a\beta t][B_5 \cosh \beta x + B_6 \sinh \beta x]$,
in which β and the A's and B's are arbitrary constants.

2. $\dfrac{\partial^2 v}{\partial x^2} + \dfrac{\partial^2 v}{\partial y^2} = 0.$

ANS. $v = [A_1 e^{\beta x} + A_2 e^{-\beta x}][B_1 \cos \beta y + B_2 \sin \beta y],$

and $v = (A_3 + A_4 x)(B_3 + B_4 y),$

in which β and the A's and B's are arbitrary constants; the roles played by x and y in the former solution can be interchanged.

3. $\dfrac{\partial^2 u}{\partial t^2} + 2b \dfrac{\partial u}{\partial t} = a^2 \dfrac{\partial^2 u}{\partial x^2}.$ Show that this equation has the solutions:

$$u = g(t)[B_1 \cos kx + B_2 \sin kx],$$

where $g(t)$ can assume any one of the forms:

$$e^{-bt}[A_1 e^{\gamma t} + A_2 e^{-\gamma t}], \ \gamma^2 = b^2 - a^2 k^2, \text{ if } b^2 - a^2 k^2 > 0,$$

or

$$e^{-bt}[A_3 \cos \delta t + A_4 \sin \delta t], \ \delta^2 = a^2 k^2 - b^2, \text{ if } a^2 k^2 - b^2 > 0,$$

or

$$e^{-bt}[A_5 + A_6 t], \text{ if } a^2 k^2 - b^2 = 0,$$

and the solutions

$$u = (A_7 + A_8 e^{-2bt})(B_3 + B_4 x).$$

Find also solutions containing e^{kx} and e^{-kx}.

4. $\dfrac{\partial w}{\partial y} = y \dfrac{\partial w}{\partial x}.$ ANS. $w = A e^{k(2x + y^2)}, \ k$ and A arbitrary.

5. $x \dfrac{\partial w}{\partial x} = w + y \dfrac{\partial w}{\partial y}.$ ANS. $w = A x^k y^{k-1}, \ k$ and A arbitrary.

6. Subject the partial differential equation of Ex. 5 to the change of dependent variable $w = v/y$ and show that the resultant equation for v is

$$x \frac{\partial v}{\partial x} = y \frac{\partial v}{\partial y}.$$

7. Show that the method of separation of variables does not succeed, without modifications, for the equation

$$\frac{\partial^2 u}{\partial x^2} + 4 \frac{\partial^2 u}{\partial x \partial t} + 5 \frac{\partial^2 u}{\partial t^2} = 0.$$

8. For the equation of Ex. 7 seek a solution of the form

$$u = e^{kt} f(x)$$

and thus obtain the solutions

$$u = e^{k(t - 2x)}[A_1 \cos kx + A_2 \sin kx],$$

where k, A_1, A_2 are arbitrary. Show also that the equation of Ex. 7 has the solutions $u = Ax + B$ and $u = Ct + D$, with A, B, C, D arbitrary.

9. For the equation

$$\frac{\partial^2 u}{\partial x^2} + 4x \frac{\partial u}{\partial x} + \frac{\partial^2 u}{\partial y^2} = 0$$

put $u = f(x)g(y)$ and thus obtain solutions

$$u = [A_1 e^{2ky} + A_2 e^{-2ky}][B_1 f_1(x) + B_2 f_2(x)],$$

in which $f_1(x)$ and $f_2(x)$ are any two linearly independent solutions of the equation

$$f'' + 4xf' + 4k^2 f = 0.$$

Obtain also the solutions which correspond to $k = 0$ in the above. For $k \neq 0$, the functions f_1 and f_2 should be obtained by the method of Chapter 18. They may be found in the form

$$f_1(x) = 1 + \sum_{m=1}^{\infty} \frac{(-4)^m (k^2)(k^2 + 2)(k^2 + 4) \cdots (k^2 + 2m - 2)x^{2m}}{(2m)!},$$

$$f_2(x) = x + \sum_{m=1}^{\infty} \frac{(-4)^m (k^2 + 1)(k^2 + 3)(k^2 + 5) \cdots (k^2 + 2m - 1)x^{2m+1}}{(2m + 1)!}.$$

Find similar solutions involving $\cos 2ky$ and $\sin 2ky$.

10. Use the change of variable $u = e^{\beta t}g(x)$ to find solutions of the equation

$$\frac{\partial^2 u}{\partial x^2} + 2 \frac{\partial^2 u}{\partial x \partial t} + \frac{\partial^2 u}{\partial t^2} = 0.$$

ANS. $u = e^{\beta(t-x)}[A_1 + A_2 x]$.

11. Show by direct computation that if $f_1(y)$ and $f_2(y)$ are any functions with continuous second derivatives, $f_1''(y)$ and $f_2''(y)$, then

$$u = f_1(x - at) + f_2(x + at)$$

satisfies the simple wave equation (Ex. 1),

$$\frac{\partial^2 u}{\partial t^2} = a^2 \frac{\partial^2 u}{\partial x^2}.$$

12. Show that $v = f(xy)$ is a solution of the equation of Ex. 6.
13. Show that $w = f(2x + y^2)$ is a solution of the equation of Ex. 4.
14. Show that $u = f_1(t - x) + xf_2(t - x)$ is a solution of the equation of Ex. 10.

122. A problem on the conduction of heat in a slab. Among the equations of applied mathematics already stated is the heat equation in rectangular coordinates,

$$(1) \qquad \frac{\partial u}{\partial t} = h^2 \left(\frac{\partial^2 u}{\partial x^2} + \frac{\partial^2 u}{\partial y^2} + \frac{\partial^2 u}{\partial z^2} \right),$$

in which

$$x, y, z = \text{rectangular space coordinates,}$$
$$t = \text{time coordinate,}$$
$$h^2 = \text{thermal diffusivity,}$$
$$u = \text{temperature.}$$

The constant h^2 and the variables x, y, z, t, u may be in any consistent set of units. For instance, we may measure x, y, z in feet, t in hours, u in degrees Fahrenheit, and h^2 in ft^2 per hour. The thermal diffusivity (assumed constant in our work) can be defined by

$$h^2 = \frac{K}{\sigma \delta},$$

in terms of quantities of elementary physics,

$$K = \text{thermal conductivity,}$$
$$\sigma = \text{specific heat,}$$
$$\delta = \text{density,}$$

all pertaining to the material composing the solid whose temperature we seek.

For our first boundary value problem in partial differential equations it seems wise to set up as simple a problem as possible. We now construct a temperature problem which is set in such a way that the temperature is independent of two space variables, say y and z. For such a problem u will be a function of only two independent variables (x and t), which is the least number of independent variables possible in a partial differential equation.

Consider a huge flat slab of concrete, or some other material reasonably near homogeneity in texture. Let the thickness of the slab be c units of length. Choose the origin of coordinates on a face of the slab as indicated in Figure 46 and assume that the slab extends very far in the y and z directions.

Let the initial ($t = 0$) temperature of the slab be $f(x)$, a function of x alone, and let the surfaces $x = 0$, $x = c$ be kept at zero tempera-

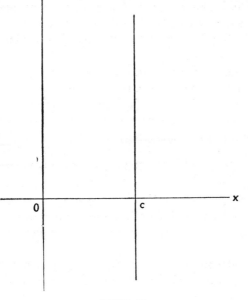

FIGURE 46

ture for all $t > 0$.   If the slab is considered infinite in the y and z directions, or more specifically, if we treat only cross sections nearby (far from the distant surfaces of the slab), then the temperature u at any time t and position x is determined by the boundary value problem:

(2) $$\frac{\partial u}{\partial t} = h^2 \frac{\partial^2 u}{\partial x^2}, \quad \text{for } 0 < t, \ \ 0 < x < c;$$

(3) $\qquad$ As $t \to 0^+$, $\quad u \to f(x)$, $\quad$ for $0 < x < c$;

(4) $\qquad$ As $x \to 0^+$, $\quad u \to 0$, $\qquad$ for $0 < t$;

(5) $\qquad$ As $x \to c^-$, $\quad u \to 0$, $\qquad$ for $0 < t$.

In the boundary value problem (2)–(5), the zero on the temperature scale has been chosen as the temperature at which the surfaces of the slab are held.   Then the $f(x)$ is really the difference between the actual initial temperature and the subsequent constant boundary temperature.

Such a set of symbols as $t \to 0^+$ means that t approaches zero through values above zero. Similarly, $x \to c^-$ means that x approaches c through values less than c, "c minus something" at each stage during the approach. We may say, for instance, that x approaches c from the left.

It is particularly to be noted that we do not require such a condition as that the function $u(x, t)$ be $f(x)$ when $t = 0$. We require only that as $t \to 0^+$, then $u \to f(x)$ for each x in the range $0 < x < c$.

The question of precisely how many boundary conditions, and of what nature, are to be associated with a given partial differential equation in order to assure the existence and uniqueness of a solution is a question of considerable difficulty. In this book we shall use the most popular practical guide, physical intuition. Existence is no problem—we seek a solution; if we find one, we know it exists; if we don't find one, it is hardly balm for our wounds to be told that it exists. To the serious problem of uniqueness we close our eyes entirely.

Let us now attempt to solve the boundary value problem, to find a function $u(x, t)$ which will satisfy the partial differential equation

$$(2) \qquad \frac{\partial u}{\partial t} = h^2 \frac{\partial^2 u}{\partial x^2}, \quad \text{for } 0 < x < c, \quad 0 < t;$$

and which will also satisfy the conditions:

$$(3) \qquad \text{As } t \to 0^+, \quad u \to f(x), \quad \text{for } 0 < x < c;$$
$$(4) \qquad \text{As } x \to 0^+, \quad u \to 0, \qquad \text{for } 0 < t;$$
$$(5) \qquad \text{As } x \to c^-, \quad u \to 0, \qquad \text{for } 0 < t.$$

We already know how to get some solutions of the differential equation (2). Indeed, on pages 369–371 the method of separation of variables was used to arrive at the solutions

$$(6) \qquad u = e^{h^2\beta^2 t}[a \cosh \beta x + b \sinh \beta x],$$

with a, b, β arbitrary constants and the solutions

$$(7) \qquad u = e^{-h^2\alpha^2 t}[A \cos \alpha x + B \sin \alpha x]$$

with A, B, α arbitrary constants.

It is now necessary to attempt to adjust the solutions (6) or (7) so as to satisfy the boundary conditions (3), (4), and (5). Trial shows quickly that it is simpler to satisfy conditions (4) and (5) first and then to tackle (3).

Let us try to satisfy (4) and (5) with solutions in the form of equation (6) above. Now condition (4) requires that when we let $x \to 0^+$, then $u \to 0$ for all positive t. Letting $x \to 0^+$ in equation (6) we conclude that

$$0 = e^{h^2\beta^2 t}[a + 0], \text{ for } 0 < t.$$

Thus we are forced to conclude that $a = 0$, so that the solution (6) becomes

$$(8) \qquad u = be^{h^2\beta^2 t} \sinh \beta x.$$

By condition (5) we must require that as $x \to c^-$, then again $u \to 0$ for all positive t; that is, from equation (8) and condition (5) it follows that

$$be^{h^2\beta^2 t} \sinh \beta c = 0, \text{ for } 0 < t.$$

The exponential $e^{h^2\beta^2 t}$ cannot vanish. For real values of β and c the function $\sinh \beta c$ is zero only when $\beta c = 0$. Hence it follows that $\beta = 0$ or $b = 0$, so that $u \equiv 0$ and we have no chance of satisfying the remaining condition, (3). Let us therefore abandon equation (6) and concentrate upon the solutions

$$(7) \qquad u = e^{-h^2\alpha^2 t}[A \cos \alpha x + B \sin \alpha x].$$

Let us impose conditions (4) and (5) upon the u of equation (7). First we let $x \to 0^+$ and conclude that

$$0 = e^{-h^2\alpha^2 t}[A + 0], \text{ for } 0 < t,$$

so that we must choose $A = 0$. Then (7) reduces to

$$(9) \qquad u = Be^{-h^2\alpha^2 t} \sin \alpha x.$$

Next we impose condition (5), that $u \to 0$ when $x \to c^-$, so that

$$0 = Be^{-h^2\alpha^2 t} \sin \alpha c, \text{ for } 0 < t.$$

We must not choose $B = 0$, if we are to have any success in satisfying the additional condition (3). The function $e^{-h^2\alpha^2 t}$ does not vanish. Therefore, for the u of (9) to satisfy the condition (5) it is necessary that

(10) $\sin \alpha c = 0.$

The sine function is zero when, and only when, its argument is an integral multiple of π; that is, $\sin z$ is zero when $z = 0,\ \pm\pi,\ \pm 2\pi,$ $\cdots,\ \pm n\pi,\ \cdots$. Therefore from (10) it follows that

(11) $\alpha c = n\pi,\ n$ integral.

Since c is given, equation (11) serves to determine the arbitrary parameter α—rather, to restrict the values of α to those given by (11).

With $\alpha = n\pi/c$, the solutions (9) above become

$$u = Be^{-(n\pi h/c)^2 t} \sin (n\pi x/c)$$

with n integral and B arbitrary. Since we need not use the same arbitrary constant B for different values of n, it is wiser to write solutions

(12) $u_n = B_n e^{-(n\pi h/c)^2 t} \sin (n\pi x/c),\ n$ integral.

We lose nothing by restricting the n in equation (12) to the positive integers $1, 2, 3, \cdots$, for $n = 0$ leads to the trivial solution $u \equiv 0$ and the negative integral values for n lead to essentially the same solutions as do the positive integral values.

Let us see where we stand at present. Each of the functions u_n defined by equation (12) is a solution of the differential equation

(2) $\dfrac{\partial u}{\partial t} = h^2 \dfrac{\partial^2 u}{\partial x^2},\quad$ for $0 < x < c,\quad 0 < t,$

and each of those functions satisfies the two conditions

(4)   As $x \to 0^+,\quad u \to 0,\quad$ for $0 < t,$

and

(5)   As $x \to c^-,\quad u \to 0,\quad$ for $0 < t.$

It remains to find from those solutions u_n a solution $u(x, t)$ which will also satisfy the boundary (or initial) condition

(3)   As $t \to 0^+,\quad u \to f(x),\quad$ for $0 < x < c.$

Since the partial differential equation involved is linear and homogeneous in u and its derivatives, a sum of solutions is also a solution.

From the known solutions u_1, u_2, u_3, $\cdots$, u_n, $\cdots$, we may thus construct others. With sufficiently strong convergence conditions it is true that even the infinite series

$$u = \sum_{n=1}^{\infty} u_n,$$

or

(13) $$u(x, t) = \sum_{n=1}^{\infty} B_n e^{-(n\pi h/c)^2 t} \sin (n\pi x/c),$$

is also a solution of the differential equation (2).

The $u(x, t)$ of equation (13) satisfies the equation (2) and the boundary conditions (4) and (5). If $u(x, t)$ is to satisfy the condition (3), then for each x in the interval $0 < x < c$ the right member of equation (13) should approach $f(x)$ as $t \to 0^+$. We assume that we may interchange the order of limit (as $t \to 0^+$) and summation and conclude that the condition (3) formally requires that

(14) $$f(x) = \sum_{n=1}^{\infty} B_n \sin (n\pi x/c), \text{ for } 0 < x < c.$$

Thus we can solve the problem under consideration if we can choose the constants B_n so that the infinite series on the right in (14) has $f(x)$ for its sum for each x in the interval $0 < x < c$. That there exist such coefficients B_n is far from evident. For a large class of functions $f(x)$ an expansion of the type of equation (14) does exist, as will be seen in Chapter 25. Once the B_n are known, they are to be inserted on the right in equation (13), which is then the final solution of the boundary value problem consisting of equation (2) and conditions (3), (4), and (5).

In order to be able to complete the solution of boundary value problems of the kind under consideration here, we need to acquire a knowledge of methods of expansion of functions into trigonometric series. Therefore Chapter 25 is devoted to the development of that type of expansion so that in the final chapter we can solve numerous boundary value problems.

Chapter 24

Orthogonal Sets

123. Orthogonality. A set of functions $f_0(x)$, $f_1(x)$, $f_2(x)$, $\cdots$, $f_n(x)$, $\cdots$, is said to be *an orthogonal set with respect to the weight function* $w(x)$ *over the interval* $a \leqq x \leqq b$ *if*

$$\int_a^b w(x) f_n(x) f_m(x)dx = 0 \text{ for } m \neq n,$$

$$\neq 0 \text{ for } m = n.$$

Orthogonality is a property widely encountered in certain branches of mathematics. Much use is made of the representation of functions in series of the form

$$\sum_{n=0}^{\infty} c_n f_n(x)$$

in which the c_n are numerical coefficients and the $f_n(x)$ is an orthogonal set.

A tremendous literature exists regarding orthogonal sets of functions. A student who wishes to pursue the subject beyond the material in this chapter can get a thorough introduction to it in courses and books on orthogonal polynomials, Fourier series, Fourier analysis, etc. A short list of references is given at the end of Chapter 25.

One simple version of a theorem in the subject of orthogonal functions may be stated as follows:

Given a set of functions

$$\varphi_0(x), \quad \varphi_1(x), \quad \varphi_2(x), \cdots, \quad \varphi_n(x), \cdots,$$

linearly independent (Section 29) and continuous in the interval $a \leqq x \leqq b$, and given a weight function $w(x)$ positive and continuous in that same interval, then a set of functions

$$f_0(x), \quad f_1(x), \quad f_2(x), \cdots, \quad f_n(x), \cdots,$$

exists with the properties that:

(a) Each $f_n(x)$ is a linear combination of φ's;

(b) The $f_n(x)$ are linearly independent on the interval $a \leqq x \leqq b$;

(c) The $f_n(x)$ is an orthogonal set with respect to the weight function $w(x)$ over the interval $a \leqq x \leqq b$.

We already know that the functions $1, x, x^2, \cdots, x^n, \cdots$, are linearly independent and are continuous over any finite interval. Linear combinations of powers of x are polynomials. Hence, given an interval and a proper weight function, there exists in particular a set of polynomials orthogonal with respect to that weight function over that interval. With added conditions on the weight function the restriction to a finite interval can be removed.

124. Simple sets of polynomials. A set of polynomials $f_n(x)$; $n = 0, 1, 2, 3, \cdots$, is called a simple set if $f_n(x)$ is of degree precisely n. The set then contains one polynomial of each degree, $0, 1, 2, \cdots, n \cdots$.

An important property of simple sets is that if $g_m(x)$ is any polynomial of degree m and $f_n(x)$ is a simple set of polynomials, then there exist constants c_k such that

$$(1) \qquad g_m(x) = \sum_{k=0}^{m} c_k f_k(x).$$

PROOF. Let the highest degree term in $g_m(x)$ be $a_m x^m$ and the highest degree term in $f_m(x)$ be $b_m x^m$. Define $c_m = a_m/b_m$, noting that $b_m \neq 0$. Then the polynomial

$$g_m(x) - c_m f_m(x)$$

is of degree at most $(m - 1)$. On this polynomial use the same procedure as was used on $g_m(x)$. It follows that c_{m-1} exists so that

$$g_m(x) - c_m f_m(x) - c_{m-1} f_{m-1}(x)$$

is of degree at most $(m - 2)$. Iteration of the process yields equation (1) in $(m + 1)$ steps. Note that any c_k except c_m may be zero.

125. Orthogonal polynomials. We next obtain for polynomials a condition equivalent to our definition (Section 123) of orthogonality.

THEOREM 1: *If $f_n(x)$ is a simple set of polynomials, a necessary and sufficient condition that $f_n(x)$ be orthogonal with respect to $w(x)$ over the interval $a \leqq x \leqq b$ is that*

$$(1) \qquad \int_a^b w(x)x^k f_n(x)dx = 0, \quad k = 0, 1, 2, \cdots, (n-1),$$

$$\neq 0, \quad k = n.$$

PROOF: Suppose that (1) is satisfied. Since x^k forms a simple set, we can write

$$(2) \qquad f_m(x) = \sum_{k=0}^m a_k x^k.$$

If $m < n$, it follows that

$$\int_a^b w(x)f_m(x)f_n(x)dx = \sum_{k=0}^m a_k \int_a^b w(x)x^k f_n(x)dx = 0$$

by (1), since each k involved is less than n. If $m > n$, interchange the roles of m and n, and repeat the argument. If $m = n$ in (2), then $a_n \neq 0$, and we have

$$\int_a^b w(x)f_n{}^2(x)dx = \sum_{k=0}^n a_k \int_a^b w(x)x^k f_n(x)dx$$

$$= a_n \int_a^b w(x)x^n f_n(x)dx \neq 0.$$

Thus we see that the condition (1) is sufficient for orthogonality of the $f_n(x)$.

Next suppose the $f_n(x)$ satisfy the condition for orthogonality as laid down in Section 123. Since the $f_n(x)$ form a simple set, we can write

$$(3) \qquad x^k = \sum_{m=0}^{k} b_m f_m(x).$$

If $k < n$, it follows that

$$\int_a^b w(x) x^k f_n(x) dx = \sum_{m=0}^{k} b_m \int_a^b w(x) f_m(x) f_n(x) dx = 0,$$

since no m can equal n.   If $k = n$ in (3), then $b_n \neq 0$, and we have

$$\int_a^b w(x) x^n f_n(x) dx = \sum_{m=0}^{n} b_m \int_a^b w(x) f_m(x) f_n(x) dx$$

$$= b_n \int_a^b w(x) f_n^2(x) dx \neq 0.$$

This completes the proof of Theorem 1.

126. Zeros of orthogonal polynomials.   We shall show that real orthogonal polynomials have all their zeros real, distinct, and in the interval of orthogonality.

THEOREM 2:   *If $f_n(x)$ is a simple set of real polynomials orthogonal with respect to $w(x)$ over the interval $a \leqq x \leqq b$, and if $w(x) > 0$ on $a < x < b$, then the zeros of $f_n(x)$ are distinct and all lie in the open interval $a < x < b$.*

PROOF: For $n > 1$, the polynomial $f_n(x)$ does change sign in the interval $a < x < b$ because, by Theorem 1 (with $k = 0$),

$$\int_a^b w(x) f_n(x) dx = 0$$

and $w(x)$ cannot change sign in $a < x < b$.

Let $f_n(x)$ change sign in $a < x < b$ at precisely the distinct points $x = \alpha_1, \alpha_2, \cdots, \alpha_s$.   The α's are precisely the zeros of odd multiplicity of $f_n(x)$ in the interval.   Since $f_n(x)$ is of degree n, it has n zeros, multiplicity counted.   Thus we know that $s \leqq n$.

Form the function

(1) $$\psi(x) = (x - \alpha_1)(x - \alpha_2) \cdots (x - \alpha_s).$$

Then, in $a < x < b$, $\psi(x)$ changes sign at $x = \alpha_1, \alpha_2, \cdots, \alpha_s$. and nowhere else.

If $s < n$, $\psi(x)$ is of degree $< n$, so that

(2) $$\int_a^b w(x)f_n(x)\psi(x)dx = 0$$

by the application of Theorem 1 to each term in the expanded form of $\psi(x)$. But the integrand in (2) does not change sign anywhere in the interval of integration, since $w(x) > 0$ while $f_n(x)$ and $\psi(x)$ change sign at precisely the same points. Therefore the integral in (2) cannot vanish and the assumption $s < n$ has led us to a contradiction.

Thus we have $s = n$. That is, among the n zeros of $f_n(x)$ there are precisely n of odd multiplicity in the open interval $a < x < b$. Therefore each zero is of multiplicity one; the zeros are distinct. The proof of Theorem 2 is complete.

127. Orthogonality of Legendre polynomials. The Legendre polynomials.

(1) $$P_n(x) = F\left(-n, n + 1; 1; \frac{1 - x}{2}\right)$$

of Section 104 were obtained by solving the differential equation

(2) $$(1 - x^2)y'' - 2xy' + n(n + 1)y = 0.$$

The $P_n(x)$ form a simple set of polynomials for which we now obtain an orthogonality property.

From (2) we have

$$(1 - x^2)P_n''(x) - 2xP_n'(x) + n(n + 1)P_n(x) = 0,$$

or

(3) $$D[(1 - x^2)P_n'(x)] + n(n + 1)P_n(x) = 0; \quad D = \frac{d}{dx}.$$

For index m we have

(4) $$D[(1 - x^2)P_m'(x)] + m(m + 1)P_m(x) = 0.$$

We are interested in product $P_m(x)P_n(x)$. Hence we multiply (3) throughout by $P_m(x)$, (4) throughout by $P_n(x)$, and subtract to obtain

$$P_m(x)D[(1 - x^2)P_n'(x)] - P_n(x)D[(1 - x^2)P_m'(x)] \\ + [n(n + 1) - m(m + 1)]P_m(x)P_n(x) = 0.$$

The equation above may be rewritten as

$$(5) \quad (n^2 - m^2 + n - m)P_m(x)P_n(x) \\ = P_n(x)D[(1 - x^2)P_m'(x)] - P_m(x)D[(1 - x^2)P_n'(x)].$$

Now, by the formula for differentiating a product, we get

$$D[(1 - x^2)P_n(x)P_m'(x)] \\ = P_n(x)D[(1 - x^2)P_m'(x)] + (1 - x^2)P_n'(x)P_m'(x)$$

and

$$D[(1 - x^2)P_n'(x)P_m(x)] \\ = P_m(x)D[(1 - x^2)P_n'(x)] + (1 - x^2)P_n'(x)P_m'(x).$$

Hence

$$D[(1 - x^2)\{P_n(x)P_m'(x) - P_n'(x)P_m(x)\}] \\ = P_n(x)D[(1 - x^2)P_m'(x)] - P_m(x)D[(1 - x^2)P_n'(x)].$$

Furthermore, $n^2 - m^2 + n - m = (n - m)(n + m + 1)$. Therefore we can write (5) as

$$(6) \quad (n - m)(n + m + 1)P_m(x)P_n(x) \\ = D[(1 - x^2)\{P_n(x)P_m'(x) - P_n'(x)P_m(x)\}].$$

We have now expressed the product of any two Legendre polynomials as a derivative. Derivatives are easy to integrate. Equation (6) yields

$$(7) \quad (n - m)(n + m + 1) \int_a^b P_m(x)P_n(x)dx \\ = \left[(1 - x^2)\{P_n(x)P_m'(x) - P_n'(x)P_m(x)\} \right]_a^b.$$

We may choose any a and b that we wish. Since $(1 - x^2)$ is zero at $x = -1$ and $x = 1$, we conclude that

(8) $(n - m)(n + m + 1) \int_{-1}^{1} P_m(x)P_n(x)dx = 0.$

Since n and m are to be nonnegative integers, $n + m + 1 \neq 0$. Hence if $m \neq n$, $n - m \neq 0$ and (8) yields

(9) $\int_{-1}^{1} P_m(x)P_n(x)dx = 0.$

The Legendre polynomials are real, so $\int_{-1}^{1} P_n{}^2(x)dx \neq 0.$

We have shown that the Legendre polynomials $P_n(x)$ form an orthogonal set with respect to the weight function $w(x) = 1$ over the interval $-1 < x < 1$. The $P_n(x)$ are a simple set of real polynomials, so the theorems of Sections 125 and 126 apply to them.

Further study of $P_n(x)$ would occupy more space than seems appropriate in an elementary differential equations text. We now list a few of the simplest from among the hundreds of known properties of these interesting polynomials:

(10) $(1 - 2xt + t^2)^{-1/2} = \sum_{n=0}^{\infty} P_n(x)t^n,$

(11) $\int_{-1}^{1} P_n{}^2(x)dx = \dfrac{2}{2n + 1},$

(12) $P_n(x) = \dfrac{1}{2^n n!} D^n(x^2 - 1)^n; \; D = \dfrac{d}{dx},$

(13) $xP'_n = nP_n(x) + P'_{n-1}(x),$

(14) $(x^2 - 1)P'_n(x) = nxP_n(x) - nP_{n-1}(x),$

(15) $nP_n(x) = (2n - 1)xP_{n-1}(x) - (n - 1)P_{n-2}(x).$

128. Other orthogonal sets. In Chapter 20 we solved several differential equations of hypergeometric type. In Section 99 we encountered the Laguerre polynomial

(1) $L_n(x) = \sum_{k=0}^{n} \dfrac{(-n)_k x^k}{(k!)^2} = \sum_{k=0}^{n} \dfrac{(-1)^k n! x^k}{(k!)^2(n - k)!},$

as a solution of the differential equation

(2) $xL_n''(x) + (1 - x)L_n'(x) + nL_n(x) = \mathbf{0}.$

Equation (2) can be put in the form

(3) $D[xe^{-x}L_n'(x)] + ne^{-x}L_n(x) = 0,$

from which the orthogonality of the Laguerre polynomials follows. See Ex. 1 below.

The Hermite polynomial of Section 103,

(4) $$H_n(x) = \sum_{k=0}^{[n/2]} \frac{(-1)^k n! (2x)^{n-2k}}{k!(n - 2k)!}$$

satisfies the differential equation

(5) $H_n''(x) - 2xH_n'(x) + 2nH_n(x) = \mathbf{0}.$

Equation (5) can be put in the form

(6) $D[e^{-x^2}H_n'(x)] + 2ne^{-x^2}H_n(x) = 0,$

from which the orthogonality of the Hermite polynomials follows. See Ex. 3 below.

The Bessel function $J_n(x)$ of Section 102 can be shown to have orthogonality properties also, but they are beyond the scope of this book. See, for example, R. V. Chuichill, *Fourier Series and Boundary Value Problems,* New York, McGraw-Hill Book Co., 1941, Chapter 8.

EXERCISES

1. Use equation (3) above and the method of Section 127 to show that the Laguerre polynomials are orthogonal with respect to the weight function e^{-x} over the interval $0 \leqq x < \infty$.
2. Show, with the aid of Ex. 1, that the zeros of the Laguerre polynomial $L_n(x)$ are distinct and positive.
3. Use equation (6) above and the method of Section 127 to show that the Hermite polynomials are orthogonal with respect to the weight function e^{-x^2} over the interval $-\infty < x < \infty$.
4. Show, with the aid of Ex. 3, that the zeros of the Hermite polynomial $H_n(x)$ are real and distinct.

Chapter 25

Fourier Series

129. Orthogonality of a set of sines and cosines. The functions $\sin \alpha x$ and $\cos \alpha x$ arise in the formal solution of certain boundary value problems in partial differential equations, as was indicated in Chapter 23. We shall now obtain an orthogonality property for a set of such functions with α specified. An interval must be involved; let the origin be chosen at the center of the interval so that the latter appears in the symmetric form: $-c \leqq x \leqq c$.

We shall show that the set of functions,

(A) $\qquad \begin{cases} \sin\,(n\pi x/c), & n = 1, 2, 3, \cdots, \\ \cos\,(n\pi x/c), & n = 0, 1, 2, \cdots, \end{cases}$

or

(A) $\begin{cases} \quad \sin\,(\pi x/c),\ \sin\,(2\pi x/c),\ \sin\,(3\pi x/c),\ \cdots,\ \sin\,(n\pi x/c),\ \cdots, \\ 1,\ \cos\,(\pi x/c),\ \cos\,(2\pi x/c),\ \cos\,(3\pi x/c),\ \cdots,\ \cos\,(n\pi x/c),\ \cdots, \end{cases}$

is orthogonal with respect to the weight function $w(x) = 1$ *over the interval* $-c \leqq x \leqq c$. That is, we shall prove that the integral from $x = -c$ to $x = +c$ of the product of any two different members of the set (A) is zero.

First consider the integral of the product of any of the sine functions in (A) with any of the cosine functions in (A). The result

$$I_1 = \int_{-c}^{c} \sin\,(n\pi x/c)\,\cos\,(k\pi x/c)dx = 0$$

follows at once from the fact that the integrand is an odd function of x; in this instance the result does not depend upon the fact that k and n are integers.

Next consider the integral of the product of two different sine functions from the set (A),

$$I_2 = \int_{-c}^{c} \sin (n\pi x/c) \sin (k\pi x/c) dx, \quad k \neq n.$$

Let us introduce a new variable of integration for simplicity in writing; put

$$\pi x/c = \beta,$$

from which

$$dx = \frac{c}{\pi} d\beta.$$

Then I_2 can be written

$$I_2 = \frac{c}{\pi} \int_{-\pi}^{\pi} \sin n\beta \sin k\beta \, d\beta.$$

Now from trigonometry we get the formula

$$\sin n\beta \sin k\beta = \tfrac{1}{2}[\cos (n-k)\beta - \cos (n+k)\beta]$$

which is useful in performing the desired integration. Thus it follows that

$$I_2 = \frac{c}{2\pi} \int_{-\pi}^{\pi} [\cos (n-k)\beta - \cos (n+k)\beta] d\beta$$

$$= \frac{c}{2\pi} \left[\frac{\sin (n-k)\beta}{n-k} - \frac{\sin (n+k)\beta}{n+k} \right]_{-\pi}^{\pi},$$

since neither $(n-k)$ nor $(n+k)$ can be zero. Because n and k are positive integers, $\sin (n-k)\beta$ and $\sin (n+k)\beta$ each vanish at $\beta = \pi$ and $\beta = -\pi$, then

$$I_2 = 0$$

for $n, k = 1, 2, 3, \cdots$, and $k \neq n$.

Finally, consider the integral of the product of two different cosine functions from the set (A),

$$I_3 = \int_{-c}^{c} \cos (n\pi x/c) \cos (k\pi x/c) dx,$$

where $n, k = 0, 1, 2, 3, \cdots; k \neq n$. The method used on I_2

works equally well here to yield

$$I_3 = \frac{c}{2\pi}\left[\frac{\sin{(n-k)\beta}}{n-k} + \frac{\sin{(n+k)\beta}}{n+k}\right]_{-\pi}^{\pi} = 0.$$

It is easy to see that the integral of the square of any function from the set (A) will not vanish—its integrand is positive except at an occasional point. The values of those integrals are readily obtained. The integral

$$I_4 = \int_{-c}^{c} \sin^2{(n\pi x/c)}dx$$

has an even integrand. Hence it can be written as

$$I_4 = 2\int_0^c \sin^2{(n\pi x/c)}dx.$$

Elementary methods of integration yield

$$I_4 = \int_0^c [1 - \cos{(2n\pi x/c)}]dx$$

$$= \left[x - \frac{c}{2n\pi}\sin{(2n\pi x/c)}\right]_0^c = c.$$

Therefore

$$\int_{-c}^{c} \sin^2{(n\pi x/c)}dx = c \text{ for } n = 1, 2, 3, \cdots.$$

In the same way it follows that, for $n > 0$, n integral,

$$I_5 = \int_{-c}^{c} \cos^2{(n\pi x/c)}dx$$

$$= \left[x + \frac{c}{2n\pi}\sin{(2n\pi x/c)}\right]_0^c = c.$$

For $n = 0$ the integral I_5 becomes

$$I_6 = \int_{-c}^{c} 1 \cdot dx = 2c.$$

Thus

$$\int_{-c}^{c} \cos^2 (n\pi x/c)dx = c \text{ for } n = 1, 2, 3, \cdots ,$$

$$= 2c \text{ for } n = 0.$$

We have shown that the set

(A) $\begin{cases} \sin (n\pi x/c), & n = 1, 2, 3, \cdots , \\ \cos (m\pi x/c), & m = 0, 1, 2, \cdots , \end{cases}$

is orthogonal with respect to the weight function $w(x) = 1$ over the interval $-c \leqq x \leqq c$. We have also evaluated the integrals of the squares of the functions of the set (A).

130. Fourier series: an expansion theorem. With the assumption that there exists a series expansion of the type*

(1) $f(x) = \tfrac{1}{2}a_0 + \sum_{n=1}^{\infty} [a_n \cos (n\pi x/c) + b_n \sin (n\pi x/c)],$

valid in the interval $-c \leqq x \leqq c$, it is a simple matter to determine the coefficients, a_n and b_n. Indeed, disregarding the question of validity of interchange of order of summation and integration, we proceed as follows.

Multiply each term of equation (1) by $\sin (k\pi x/c)dx$, where k is a positive integer, and then integrate each term from $-c$ to $+c$, thus arriving at

(2) $\int_{-c}^{c} f(x) \sin (k\pi x/c)dx = \tfrac{1}{2}a_0 \int_{-c}^{c} \sin (k\pi x/c)dx$

$$+ \sum_{n=1}^{\infty} \left[a_n \int_{-c}^{c} \cos (n\pi x/c) \sin (k\pi x/c)dx \right.$$

$$\left. + b_n \int_{-c}^{c} \sin (n\pi x/c) \sin (k\pi x/c)dx \right].$$

As seen earlier,

* A reason for the apparently peculiar notation, $\tfrac{1}{2}a_0$, for the constant term will be seen quite soon, page 393.

(3) $\displaystyle\int_{-c}^{c} \cos (n\pi x/c) \sin (k\pi x/c)dx = 0$ for all k and n,

and

(4) $\displaystyle\int_{-c}^{c} \sin (n\pi x/c) \sin (k\pi x/c)dx$

$$= 0 \text{ for } k \neq n; \ k, n = 1, 2, 3, \cdots .$$

Therefore each term on the right-hand side of equation (2) is zero except for the term $n = k$. Thus equation (2) reduces to

(5) $\displaystyle\int_{-c}^{c} f(x) \sin (k\pi x/c)dx = b_k \int_{-c}^{c} \sin^2 (k\pi x/c)dx.$

Since

$$\int_{-c}^{c} \sin^2 (k\pi x/c)dx = c,$$

we have

$$b_k = \frac{1}{c} \int_{-c}^{c} f(x) \sin (k\pi x/c)dx, \ k = 1, 2, 3, \cdots ,$$

from which the coefficients b_n in equation (1) follow by merely replacing k by n; that is,

(6) $\displaystyle b_n = \frac{1}{c} \int_{-c}^{c} f(x) \sin (n\pi x/c)dx, \ n = 1, 2, 3, \cdots .$

Let us obtain the a_n in a like manner. Using the multiplier $\cos (k\pi x/c)dx$ throughout equation (1) and then integrating term by term from $x = -c$ to $x = +c$, we get

(7) $\displaystyle\int_{-c}^{c} f(x) \cos (k\pi x/c)dx = \tfrac{1}{2}a_0 \int_{-c}^{c} \cos (k\pi x/c)dx$

$$+ \sum_{n=1}^{\infty} \left[a_n \int_{-c}^{c} \cos (n\pi x/c) \cos (k\pi x/c)dx \right.$$

$$\left. + b_n \int_{-c}^{c} \sin (n\pi x/c) \cos (k\pi x/c)dx \right].$$

The coefficient of b_n in (7) is zero for all n and k.   If $k \neq 0$, then

$$\int_{-c}^{c} \cos{(n\pi x/c)} \cos{(k\pi x/c)}dx = 0 \text{ for } n \neq k,$$
$$= c \text{ for } n = k,$$

and also the coefficient of $\frac{1}{2}a_0$ is zero.   Thus, for $k \neq 0$, equation (7) reduces to

$$\int_{-c}^{c} f(x) \cos{(k\pi x/c)}dx = a_k \int_{-c}^{c} \cos^2{(k\pi x/c)}dx,$$

from which a_k, and therefore a_n, can be found in the way b_k was determined.   Thus we get

$$(8) \qquad a_n = \frac{1}{c} \int_{-c}^{c} f(x) \cos{(n\pi x/c)}dx, \ n = 1, 2, 3, \cdots.$$

Next let us determine a_0.   Suppose $k = 0$ in equation (7) so that we have

$$\int_{-c}^{c} f(x)dx = \frac{1}{2}a_0 \int_{-c}^{c} dx$$
$$+ \sum_{n=1}^{\infty} \left[a_n \int_{-c}^{c} \cos{(n\pi x/c)}dx + b_n \int_{-c}^{c} \sin{(n\pi x/c)}dx \right].$$

The terms involving $n \geq 1$ are each zero.   Hence

$$\int_{-c}^{c} f(x)dx = \frac{1}{2}a_0(2c),$$

$$(9) \qquad a_0 = \frac{1}{c} \int_{-c}^{c} f(x)dx.$$

Equation (9) fits in with equation (8) as the special case $n = 0$. Had the factor $\frac{1}{2}$ not been inserted before as in equation (1), a separate formula would have been needed.   As it is, we may write the formal expansion

$$(10) \qquad f(x) = \tfrac{1}{2}a_0 + \sum_{n=1}^{\infty} [a_n \cos (n\pi x/c) + b_n \sin (n\pi x/c)]$$

with

$$(11) \qquad a_n = \frac{1}{c} \int_{-c}^{c} f(x) \cos (n\pi x/c)dx, \; n = 0, 1, 2, \cdots,$$

$$(12) \qquad b_n = \frac{1}{c} \int_{-c}^{c} f(x) \sin (n\pi x/c)dx, \; n = 1, 2, 3, \cdots.$$

Before proceeding to specific examples and applications it behooves us to state conditions under which the equality in (10) makes sense.

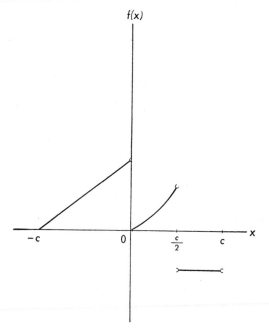

FIGURE 47

When a_n and b_n are given by (11) and (12) above, then the right-hand member of equation (10) is called the *Fourier series, over the interval* $-c \leqq x \leqq c$, *for the function* $f(x)$. A statement of conditions sufficient to insure that the Fourier series in (10) represents the function $f(x)$ in a reasonably meaningful manner follows now.

Let $f(x)$ be continuous and differentiable at every point in the interval $-c \leqq x \leqq c$ except for at most a finite number of points and at those points let $f(x)$ and $f'(x)$ have right- and left-hand limits. Such a function is exhibited in Figure 47.

Under the stipulations of the preceding paragraph the Fourier series for $f(x)$, namely, the series on the right in equation (10) with coefficients given by equations (11) and (12), converges to the value $f(x)$ at each point of continuity of $f(x)$; at each point of discontinuity of $f(x)$ the Fourier series converges to the arithmetic mean of the values approached by $f(x)$ from the right and the left.

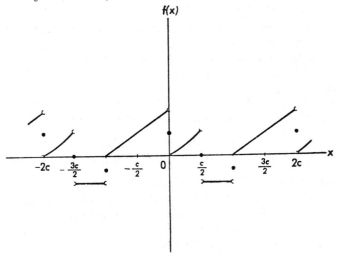

FIGURE 48

Since the Fourier series for $f(x)$ may not converge to the value $f(x)$ everywhere (for instance, at discontinuities of the function), it is customary to replace the equals sign in equation (10) by the symbol $\sim$, which may be read "has for its Fourier series." We write

$$(13) \quad f(x) \sim \tfrac{1}{2}a_0 + \sum_{n=1}^{\infty} \left[a_n \cos (n\pi x/c) + b_n \sin (n\pi x/c) \right]$$

with a_n and b_n given by equations (11) and (12).

An interesting fact and one often useful as a check in numerical problems is that $\frac{1}{2}a_0$ is the average value of $f(x)$ over the interval $-c < x < c$.

The sine and cosine functions are periodic with period 2π, so the terms in the Fourier series (13) for $f(x)$ are periodic with period $2c$. Therefore the series represents (converges to) a function which is as described above for the interval $-c < x < c$ and repeats that structure over and over outside that interval. For the function exhibited in Figure 47 the corresponding Fourier series would converge to the periodic function shown in Figure 48. Note the convergence to the average value at discontinuities, the periodicity, and the way in which the two together determine the value to which the series converges at $x = c$ and $x = -c$.

These statements will be amply illustrated in the numerical examples and exercises of the next section.

131. Numerical examples of Fourier series. We shall now construct the Fourier series for specific functions.

EXAMPLE (a): Construct the Fourier series, over the interval $-2 \leqq x \leqq 2$ for the function defined by

$$(1) \qquad \begin{aligned} f(x) &= 2, \quad -2 < x \leqq 0, \\ &= x, \quad\ \ 0 < x < 2, \end{aligned}$$

and sketch the function to which the series converges.

First we sketch $f(x)$ itself, the result being exhibited in Figure 49. Note that $f(x)$ is undefined except for x between $x = -2$ and $x = +2$.

For the function described in (1),

$$f(x) \sim \tfrac{1}{2}a_0 + \sum_{n=1}^{\infty} [a_n \cos (n\pi x/2) + b_n \sin (n\pi x/2)],$$

in which

$$(2) \qquad a_n = \tfrac{1}{2} \int_{-2}^{2} f(x) \cos (n\pi x/2)dx; n = 0, 1, 2, \cdots,$$

$$(3) \qquad b_n = \tfrac{1}{2} \int_{-2}^{2} f(x) \sin (n\pi x/2)dx; n = 1, 2, 3, \cdots.$$

Since, in the description of $f(x)$, different formulas were used in the two intervals $-2 < x < 0$ and $0 < x < 2$, it is convenient to separate the integrals in (2) and (3) into corresponding parts. Thus inserting the $f(x)$ of (1) into the integral (2) leads us to the form

(4) $a_n = \frac{1}{2} \int_{-2}^{0} 2 \cos (n\pi x/2)dx + \frac{1}{2} \int_{0}^{2} x \cos (n\pi x/2)dx.$

For these integrals, the method of integration will differ according to whether $n = 0$ or $n \neq 0$.

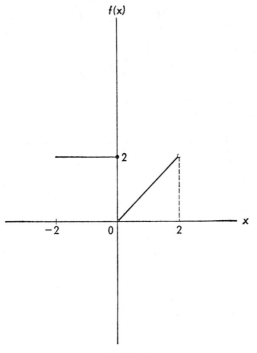

FIGURE 49

If $n \neq 0$, then

$a_n = \frac{2}{n\pi} \left[\sin (n\pi x/2) \right]_{-2}^{0} + \frac{1}{2} \left[\frac{2}{n\pi} x \sin (n\pi x/2) + \left(\frac{2}{n\pi} \right)^2 \cos (n\pi x/2) \right]_{0}^{2},$

or

$$a_n = \frac{2}{n\pi}[0 - 0] + \tfrac{1}{2}\left[0 + \left(\frac{2}{n\pi}\right)^2 \cos n\pi - 0 - \left(\frac{2}{n\pi}\right)^2\right].$$

Hence for $n \neq 0$, the a_n are given by the formula

(5) $$a_n = \frac{-2(1 - \cos n\pi)}{n^2\pi^2}, \quad n = 1, 2, 3, \cdots .$$

For $n = 0$ the above integrations are not valid (division by n), but we return to (4), put $n = 0$, and get

$$a_0 = \tfrac{1}{2}\int_{-2}^{0} 2\,dx + \tfrac{1}{2}\int_{0}^{2} x\,dx,$$

from which

$$a_0 = \left[x\right]_{-2}^{0} + \tfrac{1}{4}\left[x^2\right]_{0}^{2} = 2 + 1 = 3.$$

The b_n may be obtained in a like manner. From (3) and (1) it follows that

$$b_n = \tfrac{1}{2}\int_{-2}^{0} 2 \sin (n\pi x/2)dx + \tfrac{1}{2}\int_{0}^{2} x \sin (n\pi x/2)dx.$$

Thus

$$b_n = \frac{2}{n\pi}\left[-\cos (n\pi x/2)\right]_{-2}^{0}$$
$$+ \tfrac{1}{2}\left[-\left(\frac{2}{n\pi}\right)x \cos (n\pi x/2) + \left(\frac{2}{n\pi}\right)^2 \sin (n\pi x/2)\right]_{0}^{2},$$

from which, since $\cos (-n\pi) = \cos n\pi$,

$$b_n = \frac{2}{n\pi}[-1 + \cos n\pi] + \tfrac{1}{2}\left[-\frac{2}{n\pi}\cdot 2 \cos n\pi + 0 + 0 - 0\right],$$

or

(6) $$b_n = -\frac{2}{n\pi}, \quad n = 1, 2, 3, \cdots .$$

For integral n, $\cos n\pi = (-1)^n$, as is seen by examining both sides for even and odd n. Therefore the formula (5) above can also be written

(7) $\qquad a_n = \dfrac{-2[1 - (-1)^n]}{n^2\pi^2}, \quad n = 1, 2, 3, \cdots .$

We can now write the Fourier series, over the interval $-2 < x < 2$ for the $f(x)$ of this example,

(8) $\quad f(x) \sim \frac{3}{2} - 2 \displaystyle\sum_{n=1}^{\infty} \left[\dfrac{1 - (-1)^n}{n^2\pi^2} \cos (n\pi x/2) + \dfrac{1}{n\pi} \sin (n\pi x/2) \right].$

Several pertinent remarks can be made about (8). The right member of (8) converges to the function shown in the sketch in Figure 50. It converges to $f(x)$ at each point where $f(x)$ is defined

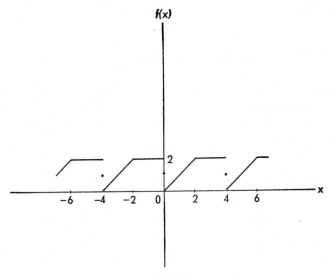

FIGURE 50

except at the discontinuity at $x = 0$. Though $f(0) = 2$, the series converges to unity at $x = 0$.

We may therefore write

(9) $\quad f(x) = \frac{3}{2} - 2 \displaystyle\sum_{n=1}^{\infty} \left[\dfrac{1 - (-1)^n}{n^2\pi^2} \cos (n\pi x/2) + \dfrac{1}{n\pi} \sin (n\pi x/2) \right]$

for $-2 < x < 0$ and for $0 < x < 2$.

It is sometimes desirable to define a new function $\varphi(x)$ as follows:

$$\begin{aligned} \varphi(x) &= f(x), & -2 < x < 0, \\ &= 1, & x = 0, \\ &= f(x), & 0 < x < 2, \end{aligned}$$

and

$$\varphi(x + 4) = \varphi(x).$$

This $\varphi(x)$ is the function exhibited in Figure 50. If $\varphi(x)$ is put in the place of $f(x)$ in (8) above, then the symbol $\sim$ may be replaced by the symbol $=$ for all x.

Because $[1 - (-1)^n]$ is zero for even n, the Fourier series on the right in (8) may be written in the somewhat more compact form

$$(10) \quad f(x) \sim \tfrac{3}{2} - \frac{4}{\pi^2} \sum_{k=0}^{\infty} \frac{\cos\,[(2k+1)\pi x/2]}{(2k+1)^2} - \frac{2}{\pi} \sum_{n=1}^{\infty} \frac{\sin\,(n\pi x/2)}{n}.$$

This is one instance in which an infinite rearrangement in the order of terms, passing from (8) to (10), is easily justified. Consider (10) again after studying the sections on Fourier sine series and Fourier cosine series.

Let us next use the expansion in (8) or (10) to sum two numerical series. For instance, if we put $x = 0$ in (10), then the series has the sum unity as indicated above. Hence

$$1 = \tfrac{3}{2} - \frac{4}{\pi^2} \sum_{k=0}^{\infty} \frac{1}{(2k+1)^2} - \frac{2}{\pi} \sum_{n=1}^{\infty} \frac{0}{n},$$

or

$$(11) \qquad \sum_{k=0}^{\infty} \frac{1}{(2k+1)^2} = \frac{\pi^2}{8}.$$

For $x = 1$, the series in (10) has the sum unity again. Using $x = 1$ in (10) we are led to

$$1 = \tfrac{3}{2} - \frac{4}{\pi^2} \sum_{k=0}^{\infty} \frac{\cos\,[(2k+1)\pi/2]}{(2k+1)^2} - \frac{2}{\pi} \sum_{n=1}^{\infty} \frac{\sin\,(n\pi/2)}{n}.$$

Now $\cos [(2k + 1)\pi/2] = 0$ and $\sin (n\pi/2)$ may be obtained as follows. For even n, $n = 2k$, we get

$$\sin (2k\pi/2) = \sin k\pi = 0.$$

For odd n, $n = 2k + 1$,

$$\sin [(2k + 1)\pi/2] = \sin (k\pi + \tfrac{1}{2}\pi) = \cos k\pi = (-1)^k.$$

Thus we arrive at the equation

$$1 = \tfrac{3}{2} - \frac{2}{\pi} \sum_{k=0}^{\infty} \frac{(-1)^k}{2k + 1},$$

or

$$(12) \qquad \sum_{k=0}^{\infty} \frac{(-1)^k}{2k + 1} = \frac{\pi}{4},$$

which can be verified also by the fact that the left member represents Arctan 1.

EXAMPLE (b): Obtain the Fourier series over the interval $-\pi$ to π for the function x^2. We know that

$$(13) \qquad x^2 \sim \tfrac{1}{2}a_0 + \sum_{n=1}^{\infty} [a_n \cos nx + b_n \sin nx]$$

for $-\pi < x < \pi$, where

$$(14) \qquad a_n = \frac{1}{\pi} \int_{-\pi}^{\pi} x^2 \cos nx \, dx; \quad n = 0, 1, 2, \cdots,$$

and

$$(15) \qquad b_n = \frac{1}{\pi} \int_{-\pi}^{\pi} x^2 \sin nx \, dx; \quad n = 1, 2, 3, \cdots.$$

Now x^2 is an even function* of x and $\sin nx$ is an odd function of x, so that the product $x^2 \sin nx$ is an odd function of x. Therefore $b_n = 0$ for every n. Since $x^2 \cos nx$ is an even function of x,

---

* A review of some properties of even and odd functions of x may be wise at this point. See, for example, C. E. Love and E. D. Rainville, *Differential and Integral Calculus*, fifth ed., The Macmillan Company, New York, 1954, pp. 109–112.

(16) $a_n = \dfrac{2}{\pi} \displaystyle\int_0^{\pi} x^2 \cos nx \, dx; \quad n = 0, 1, 2, \cdots .$

For $n \neq 0$,

$$a_n = \frac{2}{\pi} \left[\frac{x^2 \sin nx}{n} + \frac{2x \cos nx}{n^2} - \frac{2 \sin nx}{n^3} \right]_0^{\pi},$$

from which

$$a_n = \frac{2}{\pi} \left[\frac{2\pi \cos n\pi}{n^2} \right] = \frac{4(-1)^n}{n^2}, \quad n = 1, 2, 3, \cdots .$$

A separate integration is needed for a_0.   We get

$$a_0 = \frac{2}{\pi} \int_0^{\pi} x^2 \, dx = \frac{2}{\pi} \cdot \frac{\pi^3}{3} = \frac{2\pi^2}{3}.$$

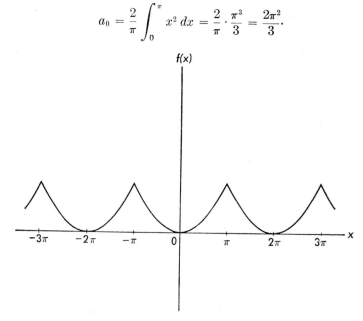

FIGURE 51

Therefore, in the interval $-\pi < x < \pi$,

$$x^2 \sim \frac{\pi^2}{3} + 4 \sum_{n=1}^{\infty} \frac{(-1)^n \cos nx}{n^2}.$$

Indeed, because of continuity of the function involved, we may write

$$(17) \qquad x^2 = \frac{\pi^2}{3} + 4 \sum_{n=1}^{\infty} \frac{(-1)^n \cos nx}{n^2}, \quad \text{for } -\pi \leq x \leq \pi.$$

Beyond the indicated interval the series on the right in equation (17) represents the periodic extension of the original function. The sum of the series is sketched in Figure 51.

EXERCISES

In each exercise obtain the Fourier series, over the indicated interval, for the given function. Always sketch the function which is the sum of the series obtained.

1. Interval, $-c < x < c$; function, $f(x) = 0$, $\qquad -c < x < 0$,
$\qquad\qquad\qquad\qquad\qquad\qquad = c - x$, $\qquad 0 < x < c$.

ANS. $f(x) \sim \dfrac{c}{4} + \dfrac{c}{\pi^2} \displaystyle\sum_{n=1}^{\infty} \dfrac{1}{n^2} [\{1 - (-1)^n\} \cos (n\pi x/c) + n\pi \sin (n\pi x/c)]$.

2. Interval, $-c < x < c$; function, $f(x) = x$.

ANS. $f(x) \sim \dfrac{2c}{\pi} \displaystyle\sum_{n=1}^{\infty} \dfrac{(-1)^{n+1} \sin (n\pi x/c)}{n}$.

3. Interval, $-c < x < c$; function, $f(x) = x^2$. Check your answer with that in Example (b) in the text.

ANS. $f(x) \sim \dfrac{c^2}{3} + \dfrac{4c^2}{\pi^2} \displaystyle\sum_{n=1}^{\infty} \dfrac{(-1)^n \cos (n\pi x/c)}{n^2}$.

4. Interval $-c < x < c$; function, $f(x) = 0$, $\qquad -c < x < 0$,
$\qquad\qquad\qquad\qquad\qquad\qquad = (c - x)^2$, $\qquad 0 < x < c$.

ANS. $f(x) \sim \dfrac{c^2}{6}$

$+ \dfrac{c^2}{\pi^3} \displaystyle\sum_{n=1}^{\infty} \dfrac{1}{n^3} [2n\pi \cos (n\pi x/c) + \{n^2\pi^2 - 2 + 2(-1)^n\} \sin (n\pi x/c)]$.

5. Interval, $-c < x < c$; function, $f(x) = 0$, $\quad -c < x < 0$,
$\qquad\qquad\qquad\qquad\qquad\qquad = 1$, $\qquad 0 < x < c$.

ANS. $f(x) \sim \frac{1}{2} + \sum_{n=1}^{\infty} \dfrac{1 - (-1)^n}{n\pi} \sin (n\pi x/c)$,

or

$$f(x) \sim \frac{1}{2} + \frac{2}{\pi} \sum_{k=0}^{\infty} \dfrac{\sin [(2k + 1)\pi x/c]}{2k + 1}.$$

6. Interval, $-c < x < c$; function, $f(x) = x^3$.

ANS. $f(x) \sim \dfrac{2c^3}{\pi^3} \sum_{n=1}^{\infty} (-1)^{n+1} \dfrac{(n^2\pi^2 - 6) \sin (n\pi x/c)}{n^3}$.

7. Interval $-c < x < c$; function, $f(x) = x(c + x),\quad -c < x < 0$,
$\qquad\qquad\qquad\qquad\qquad\qquad = (c - x)^2,\qquad 0 < x < c$.

ANS. $f(x) \sim$

$$\frac{c^2}{12} + \frac{c^2}{\pi^2} \sum_{n=1}^{\infty} \frac{1}{n^2} [\{3 + (-1)^n\} \cos (n\pi x/c) + n\pi \sin (n\pi x/c)].$$

8. Interval $-2 < x < 2$; function, $f(x) = x + 1,\quad -2 < x < 0$,
$\qquad\qquad\qquad\qquad\qquad\qquad = 1,\qquad\quad 0 \leqq x < 2$.
ANS. $f(x) \sim \frac{1}{2}$

$$+ \frac{2}{\pi^2} \sum_{n=1}^{\infty} \frac{1}{n^2} [\{1 - (-1)^n\} \cos \tfrac{1}{2}n\pi x + n\pi(-1)^{n+1} \sin \tfrac{1}{2}n\pi x].$$

9. Interval, $-1 < x < 1$; function, $f(x) = 0,\quad -1 < x < 0$,
$\qquad\qquad\qquad\qquad\qquad\qquad = 1,\qquad 0 < x < \frac{1}{2}$,
$\qquad\qquad\qquad\qquad\qquad\qquad = 0,\qquad \frac{1}{2} < x < 1$.

ANS.

$$f(x) \sim \tfrac{1}{4} + \frac{1}{\pi} \sum_{n=1}^{\infty} \frac{1}{n} [\sin (n\pi/2) \cos n\pi x + \{1 - \cos (n\pi/2)\} \sin n\pi x].$$

10. Interval, $-\pi < x < \pi$; function, $f(x) = 0,\quad -\pi < x < 0$,
$\qquad\qquad\qquad\qquad\qquad\qquad = x^2,\qquad 0 < x < \pi$.

ANS. $f(x) \sim \dfrac{\pi^2}{6} + 2 \sum_{n=1}^{\infty} \dfrac{(-1)^n \cos nx}{n^2}$

$$+ \frac{1}{\pi} \sum_{n=1}^{\infty} \frac{1}{n^3} [(-1)^{n+1} n^2\pi^2 - 2 + 2(-1)^n] \sin nx.$$

11. Interval, $-\pi < x < \pi$; function, $f(x) = \cos 2x$.   ANS. $f(x) \sim \cos 2x$.

12. Interval, $-\pi < x < \pi$; function, $f(x) = \cos (x/2)$.

$$\text{ANS.}\quad f(x) \sim \frac{2}{\pi} + \frac{4}{\pi} \sum_{n=1}^{\infty} \frac{(-1)^{n+1} \cos nx}{(2n-1)(2n+1)}.$$

13. Interval, $-\pi < x < \pi$; function, $f(x) = \sin^2 x$.

$$\text{ANS.}\quad \sin^2 x \sim \tfrac{1}{2} - \tfrac{1}{2} \cos 2x.$$

14. Interval, $-c < x < c$; function, $f(x) = e^x$.

$$\text{ANS.}\quad f(x) \sim \frac{\sinh c}{c}$$

$$+ \sum_{n=1}^{\infty} \frac{2(-1)^n \sinh c[c \cos (n\pi x/c) - n\pi \sin (n\pi x/c)]}{c^2 + n^2\pi^2}.$$

15. Interval, $-c < x < c$; function, $f(x) = 0,\quad -c < x < 0,$
$$= e^{-x},\quad 0 < x < c.$$

$$\text{ANS.}\quad f(x) \sim \frac{1 - e^{-c}}{2c}$$

$$+ \sum_{n=1}^{\infty} \frac{1 - (-1)^n e^{-c}}{c^2 + n^2\pi^2} [c \cos (n\pi x/c) + n\pi \sin (n\pi x/c)].$$

16. Interval, $-c < x < c$; function, $f(x) = 0,\quad -c < x < \tfrac{1}{2}c,$
$$= 1,\quad \tfrac{1}{2}c < x < c.$$

$$\text{ANS.}\quad f(x) \sim \tfrac{1}{4}$$

$$- \frac{1}{\pi} \sum_{n=1}^{\infty} \frac{1}{n} [\sin \tfrac{1}{2}n\pi \cos (n\pi x/c) + (\cos n\pi - \cos \tfrac{1}{2}n\pi) \sin (n\pi x/c)].$$

17. Interval, $-c < x < c$; function, $f(x) = 0,\quad -c < x < 0.$
$$= x,\quad 0 < x < c.$$

$$\text{ANS.}\quad f(x) \sim \tfrac{1}{4}c$$

$$- \frac{c}{\pi^2} \sum_{n=1}^{\infty} \frac{1}{n^2} [\{1 - (-1)^n\} \cos (n\pi x/c) + n\pi(-1)^n \sin (n\pi x/c)].$$

18. Interval, $-4 < x < 4$, function, $f(x) = 1,\quad -4 < x < 2,$
$$= 0,\quad 2 < x < 4.$$

19. Interval, $-c < x < c$, function, $f(x) = 0,\quad -c < x < 0,$
$$= x(c - x),\quad 0 < x < c.$$

20. Interval, $-c < x < c$, function, $f(x) = c + x,\quad -c < x < 0,$
$$= 0,\qquad\qquad 0 < x < c.$$

21. Use the answer to Ex. 3 to show that $\displaystyle\sum_{n=1}^{\infty} \frac{(-1)^{n+1}}{n^2} = \frac{\pi^2}{12}.$

22. Use the answer to Ex. 7 to show that $\displaystyle\sum_{n=1}^{\infty} \frac{1}{n^2} = \frac{\pi^2}{6}.$

23. Use $x = 0$ in the answer to Ex. 14 to sum the series $\displaystyle\sum_{n=1}^{\infty} \frac{(-1)^n}{c^2 + n^2\pi^2}.$

$$\text{ANS.}\quad \frac{c - \sinh c}{2c^2 \sinh c}.$$

24. Let $c \to 0$ in the result of Ex. 23 and check with Ex. 21.

132. Fourier sine series. On page 379 we found it desirable to have an expansion of a function $f(x)$ in a series involving only sine functions, the expansion to represent the original $f(x)$ in an interval $0 < x < c$. With the notation we have been using, the Fourier series

$$\tfrac{1}{2}a_0 + \sum_{n=1}^{\infty} [a_n \cos (n\pi x/c) + b_n \sin (n\pi x/c)]$$

will reduce to a series with each term containing a sine function if somehow the a_n; $n = 0, 1, 2, \cdots$, can be made to be zero. Examining the formula for a_n, page 394, reveals that the a_n will vanish if the function being expanded is an odd function over the interval $-c < x < c$.

Therefore, in order to get a sine series for $f(x)$ we introduce a new function $g(x)$ defined to equal $f(x)$ in the interval $0 < x < c$ and to be the odd extension of that function in the remaining interval, $-c < x < 0$. That is, we define $g(x)$ by

$$g(x) = f(x),\qquad\ \ 0 < x < c,$$
$$= -f(-x),\quad -c < x < 0.$$

Then $g(x)$ is an odd function over the interval $-c < x < c$. Hence from

$$g(x) \sim \tfrac{1}{2}a_0 + \sum_{n=1}^{\infty} [a_n \cos (n\pi x/c) + b_n \sin (n\pi x/c)]$$

it follows that

$$a_n = \frac{1}{c} \int_{-c}^{c} g(x) \cos (n\pi x/c)dx = 0, \quad n = 0, 1, 2, \cdots,$$

and that

$$b_n = \frac{1}{c} \int_{-c}^{c} g(x) \sin (n\pi x/c)dx = \frac{2}{c} \int_{0}^{c} f(x) \sin (n\pi x/c)dx.$$

The resultant series represents $f(x)$ in the interval $0 < x < c$, since $g(x)$ and $f(x)$ are identical over that portion of the whole interval.

Thus we have

$$(1) \qquad f(x) \sim \sum_{n=1}^{\infty} b_n \sin (n\pi x/c), \quad 0 < x < c,$$

in which

$$(2) \qquad b_n = \frac{2}{c} \int_{0}^{c} f(x) \sin (n\pi x/c)dx, \quad n = 1, 2, 3, \cdots.$$

The representation (1) is called the *Fourier sine series* for $f(x)$ over the interval $0 < x < c$.

It should be realized that the device of introducing the function $g(x)$ was a tool for arriving at (1) and (2); there is no need to repeat it in specific problems. Those we handle by direct use of (1) and (2) above.

EXAMPLE: Expand $f(x) = x^2$ in a Fourier sine series over the interval $0 < x < 1$.

At once we may write, for $0 < x < 1$,

$$(3) \qquad x^2 \sim \sum_{n=1}^{\infty} b_n \sin n\pi x,$$

in which

(4) $b_n = 2 \int_0^1 x^2 \sin n\pi x \, dx$

$$= 2\left[-\frac{x^2 \cos n\pi x}{n\pi} + \frac{2x \sin n\pi x}{(n\pi)^2} + \frac{2 \cos n\pi x}{(n\pi)^3} \right]_0^1$$

$$= 2\left[-\frac{\cos n\pi}{n\pi} + \frac{2 \cos n\pi}{n^3\pi^3} - \frac{2}{n^3\pi^3} \right].$$

FIGURE 52

Hence the Fourier sine series, over $0 < x < 1$, for x^2 is

(5) $$x^2 \sim 2 \sum_{n=1}^{\infty} \left[\frac{(-1)^{n+1}}{n\pi} - \frac{2\{1 - (-1)^n\}}{n^3\pi^3} \right] \sin n\pi x.$$

The series on the right in (5) converges to the function exhibited in Figure 52, that function being called the odd periodic extension, with period 2, of the function

$$f(x) = x^2, \quad 0 < x < 1.$$

EXERCISES

In each exercise obtain the Fourier sine series, over the stipulated interval, for the function given.   Sketch the function which is the sum of the series obtained.

1. Interval, $0 < x < c$; function, $f(x) = 1$.

$$\text{ANS.}\quad f(x) \sim \frac{4}{\pi} \sum_{k=0}^{\infty} \frac{\sin\,[(2k+1)\pi x/c]}{2k+1}.$$

2. Interval, $0 < x < c$; function, $f(x) = x$.   Compare your result with that in Ex. 2, page 403.

3. Interval, $0 < x < c$; function, $f(x) = x^2$.   Check your answer with that for the example in the text.

$$\text{ANS.}\quad f(x) \sim 2c^2 \sum_{n=1}^{\infty} \left[\frac{(-1)^{n+1}}{n\pi} - \frac{2\{1 - (-1)^n\}}{n^3\pi^3} \right] \sin(n\pi x/c).$$

4. Interval, $0 < x < c$; function, $f(x) = c - x$.

$$\text{ANS.}\quad f(x) \sim \frac{2c}{\pi} \sum_{n=1}^{\infty} \frac{1}{n} \sin(n\pi x/c).$$

5. Interval, $0 < x < c$; function, $f(x) = x(c - x)$.

$$\text{ANS.}\quad f(x) \sim \frac{8c^2}{\pi^3} \sum_{k=0}^{\infty} \frac{\sin\,[(2k+1)\pi x/c]}{(2k+1)^3}.$$

6. Interval, $0 < x < 2$; function, $f(x) = x, \quad 0 < x < 1$,
$\qquad\qquad\qquad = 2 - x, \quad 1 < x < 2$.

$$\text{ANS.}\quad f(x) \sim \frac{8}{\pi^2} \sum_{k=0}^{\infty} \frac{(-1)^k}{(2k+1)^2} \sin\,[(2k+1)\pi x/2].$$

7. Interval, $0 < t < t_1$; function, $f(t) = 1, \quad 0 < t < t_0$,
$\qquad\qquad\qquad = 0, \quad t_0 < t < t_1$.

$$\text{ANS.}\quad f(t) \sim \frac{2}{\pi} \sum_{n=1}^{\infty} \frac{1}{n} [1 - \cos\,(n\pi t_0/t_1)] \sin\,(n\pi t/t_1).$$

8. Interval, $0 < x < 1$; function, $f(x) = 0, \quad 0 < x < \frac{1}{2}$,
$\qquad\qquad\qquad = 1, \quad \frac{1}{2} < x < 1$.

$$\text{ANS.}\quad f(x) \sim \frac{2}{\pi} \sum_{n=1}^{\infty} \frac{1}{n} [\cos\,(n\pi/2) - \cos\,n\pi] \sin\,n\pi x.$$

9. Interval, $0 < x < 1$; function, $f(x) = 0,$ $\quad 0 < x < \frac{1}{2},$
$= x - \frac{1}{2}, \quad \frac{1}{2} < x < 1.$

ANS. $f(x) \sim \displaystyle\sum_{n=1}^{\infty} \left[\frac{(-1)^{n+1}}{n\pi} - \frac{2 \sin (n\pi/2)}{n^2\pi^2} \right] \sin n\pi x.$

10. Interval, $0 < x < \pi$; function, $f(x) = \sin 3x.$ ANS. $f(x) \sim \sin 3x.$

11. Interval, $0 < x < \pi$; function, $f(x) = \cos 2x.$ Note the special treatment necessary for the evaluation of b_2.

ANS. $f(x) \sim \dfrac{4}{\pi} \displaystyle\sum_{k=0}^{\infty} \dfrac{(2k+1) \sin [(2k+1)x]}{(2k-1)(2k+3)}.$

12. Interval, $0 < x < \pi$; function, $f(x) = \cos x.$

ANS. $f(x) \sim \dfrac{8}{\pi} \displaystyle\sum_{k=1}^{\infty} \dfrac{k \sin 2kx}{4k^2 - 1}.$

13. Interval, $0 < x < c$; function, $f(x) = e^{-x}.$

ANS. $f(x) \sim \displaystyle\sum_{n=1}^{\infty} \dfrac{2n\pi[1 - (-1)^n e^{-c}] \sin (n\pi x/c)}{c^2 + n^2\pi^2}.$

14. Interval, $0 < x < c$; function, $f(x) = x, \quad 0 < x < \frac{1}{2}c,$
$= 0, \quad \frac{1}{2}c < x < c.$

ANS. $f(x) \sim \dfrac{c}{\pi^2} \displaystyle\sum_{n=1}^{\infty} \left(\dfrac{2}{n^2} \sin \dfrac{n\pi}{2} - \dfrac{\pi}{n} \cos \dfrac{n\pi}{2} \right) \sin \dfrac{n\pi x}{c}.$

15. Interval, $0 < x < 1$; function, $f(x) = (x-1)^2.$

ANS. $f(x) \sim \dfrac{2}{\pi^3} \displaystyle\sum_{n=1}^{\infty} \dfrac{1}{n^3} [n^2\pi^2 - 2 + 2(-1)^n] \sin n\pi x.$

133. Fourier cosine series. In a manner entirely similar to that used to obtain the Fourier sine series, it is possible to obtain for a function defined over the interval $0 < x < c$ a series of cosine terms including a constant term. Indeed, given $f(x)$ defined over the interval $0 < x < c$ and satisfying there the conditions stipulated in Section 130, we may define an auxiliary function $h(x)$ such that

$$h(x) = f(x), \quad 0 < x < c,$$
$$= f(-x), \quad -c < x < 0.$$

Then $h(x)$ is an even function of x and, of course, it is equal to $f(x)$ over the interval where $f(x)$ was defined. Since $h(x)$ is even, it follows that in its ordinary Fourier expansion over the interval $-c < x < c$ the b_n are all zero,

$$b_n = \frac{1}{c} \int_{-c}^{c} h(x) \sin (n\pi x/c)dx = 0,$$

because of the oddness of the integrand. Furthermore, since $h(x)$ is even, $h(x) \cos (n\pi x/c)$ is also even and

$$a_n = \frac{2}{c} \int_{0}^{c} h(x) \cos (n\pi x/c)dx = \frac{2}{c} \int_{0}^{c} f(x) \cos (n\pi x/c)dx.$$

Since $h(x)$ and $f(x)$ are identical over the interval $0 < x < c$, we may write what is customarily called the *Fourier cosine series* for $f(x)$ over that interval, namely,

$$(1) \qquad f(x) \sim \tfrac{1}{2}a_0 + \sum_{n=1}^{\infty} a_n \cos (n\pi x/c), \quad 0 < x < c,$$

in which

$$(2) \qquad a_n = \frac{2}{c} \int_{0}^{c} f(x) \cos (n\pi x/c)dx.$$

EXAMPLE: Find the Fourier cosine series over the interval $0 < x < c$ for the function $f(x) = x$.

At once we have

$$f(x) \sim \tfrac{1}{2}a_0 + \sum_{n=1}^{\infty} a_n \cos (n\pi x/c)$$

in which

$$a_n = \frac{2}{c} \int_{0}^{c} x \cos (n\pi x/c)dx.$$

For $n \neq 0$ the a_n may be evaluated as follows:

$$a_n = \frac{2}{c} \left[\frac{c}{n\pi} x \sin (n\pi x/c) + \left(\frac{c}{n\pi} \right)^2 \cos (n\pi x/c) \right]_0^c$$

$$= \frac{2}{c} \left[\left(\frac{c}{n\pi} \right)^2 \cos n\pi - \left(\frac{c}{n\pi} \right)^2 \right]$$

$$= -\frac{2c}{n^2\pi^2} (1 - \cos n\pi), \quad n \neq 0.$$

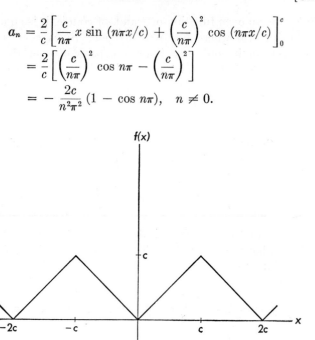

FIGURE 53

The remaining coefficient a_0 is readily obtained;

$$a_0 = \frac{2}{c} \int_0^c x \, dx = \frac{2}{c} \cdot \frac{c^2}{2} = c.$$

Thus the Fourier cosine series, over the interval $0 < x < c$, for the function $f(x) = x$ is

$$f(x) \sim \tfrac{1}{2}c - \frac{2c}{\pi^2} \sum_{n=1}^{\infty} \frac{1 - (-1)^n}{n^2} \cos (n\pi x/c),$$

which may also be written in the form

(3) $$f(x) \sim \tfrac{1}{2}c - \frac{4c}{\pi^2} \sum_{k=0}^{\infty} \frac{\cos\,[(2k+1)\pi x/c]}{(2k+1)^2}.$$

In Figure 53 there is exhibited the sum of the series on the right in (3), often called the even periodic extension of the function x. The sum of the series is, of course, periodic with period $2c$.

EXERCISES

In each exercise obtain the Fourier cosine series for the given function over the stipulated interval and sketch the function to which the series converges.

1. Interval, $0 < x < 2$; function, $f(x) = x$, $0 < x < 1$,
$\qquad\qquad\qquad\qquad\qquad\qquad\; = 2 - x,\quad 1 < x < 2$.

ANS. $f(x) \sim \tfrac{1}{2} + \dfrac{4}{\pi^2} \displaystyle\sum_{n=1}^{\infty} \dfrac{1}{n^2}\,[2\,\cos\,(n\pi/2) - 1 - (-1)^n]\,\cos\,(n\pi x/2)$.

2. Interval, $0 < t < t_1$; function, $f(t) = 1,\quad 0 < t < t_0$,
$\qquad\qquad\qquad\qquad\qquad\qquad\quad = 0,\quad t_0 < t < t_1$.

ANS. $f(t) \sim \dfrac{t_0}{t_1} + \dfrac{2}{\pi} \displaystyle\sum_{n=1}^{\infty} \dfrac{1}{n}\,\sin\,(n\pi t_0/t_1)\,\cos\,(n\pi t/t_1)$.

3. Interval, $0 < x < c$; function, $f(x) = e^{-x}$. Notice how the a_0 term fits in with the others this time so that no separate integration is necessary.

ANS. $f(x) \sim \dfrac{1 - e^{-c}}{c} + 2c \displaystyle\sum_{n=1}^{\infty} \dfrac{1 - (-1)^n e^{-c}}{c^2 + n^2\pi^2}\,\cos\,(n\pi x/c)$.

4. Interval, $0 < x < 1$; function, $f(x) = (x - 1)^2$.

ANS. $f(x) \sim \tfrac{1}{3} + \dfrac{4}{\pi^2} \displaystyle\sum_{n=1}^{\infty} \dfrac{\cos\,n\pi x}{n^2}$.

5. Interval, $0 < x < c$; function, $f(x) = x(c - x)$.

ANS. $f(x) \sim \dfrac{c^2}{6} - \dfrac{c^2}{\pi^2} \displaystyle\sum_{k=1}^{\infty} \dfrac{\cos\,(2k\pi x/c)}{k^2}$.

6. Interval, $0 < x < c$; function, $f(x) = c - x$.

$$\text{ANS.} \quad f(x) \sim \tfrac{1}{2}c + \frac{4c}{\pi^2} \sum_{k=0}^{\infty} \frac{\cos\left[(2k+1)\pi x/c\right]}{(2k+1)^2}.$$

7. Interval, $0 < x < 1$; function, $f(x) = 0, \quad 0 < x < \tfrac{1}{2}$,
$\qquad\qquad\qquad\qquad\qquad\qquad = 1, \quad \tfrac{1}{2} < x < 1$.

$$\text{ANS.} \quad f(x) \sim \tfrac{1}{2} - \frac{2}{\pi} \sum_{k=0}^{\infty} \frac{(-1)^k \cos\left[(2k+1)\pi x\right]}{2k+1}.$$

8. Interval, $0 < x < 1$; function, $f(x) = 0, \qquad 0 < x < \tfrac{1}{2}$,
$\qquad\qquad\qquad\qquad\qquad\qquad = x - \tfrac{1}{2}, \quad \tfrac{1}{2} < x < 1$.

$$\text{ANS.} \quad f(x) \sim \tfrac{1}{8} + \frac{2}{\pi^2} \sum_{n=1}^{\infty} \frac{1}{n^2} \left[\cos n\pi - \cos\left(n\pi/2\right)\right] \cos n\pi x.$$

9. Interval, $0 < x < 1$; function, $f(x) = \tfrac{1}{2} - x, \; 0 < x < \tfrac{1}{2}$,
$\qquad\qquad\qquad\qquad\qquad\qquad = 0, \qquad \tfrac{1}{2} < x < 1$.

$$\text{ANS.} \quad f(x) \sim \tfrac{1}{8} + \frac{2}{\pi^2} \sum_{n=1}^{\infty} \frac{1}{n^2} \left[1 - \cos\left(n\pi/2\right)\right] \cos n\pi x.$$

10. Interval, $0 < x < \pi$; function, $f(x) = \cos 2x$. $\qquad$ ANS. $\; f(x) \sim \cos 2x$.
11. Interval, $0 < x < \pi$; function, $f(x) = \sin 2x$.

$$\text{ANS.} \quad f(x) \sim -\frac{8}{\pi} \sum_{k=0}^{\infty} \frac{\cos\left[(2k+1)x\right]}{(2k-1)(2k+3)}.$$

12. Interval, $0 < x < c$; function, $f(x) = x, \quad 0 < x < \tfrac{1}{2}c$,
$\qquad\qquad\qquad\qquad\qquad\qquad = 0, \quad \tfrac{1}{2}c < x < c$.

$$\text{ANS.} \quad f(x) \sim \frac{c}{8} + \frac{c}{\pi^2} \sum_{n=1}^{\infty} \frac{1}{n^2} \left[n\pi \sin \tfrac{1}{2}n\pi - 2(1 - \cos \tfrac{1}{2}n\pi)\right] \cos\left(n\pi x/c\right).$$

134. Numerical Fourier analysis. In the preceding sections and in the applications in the next chapter the functions for which Fourier series are required are expressed by means of formulas, as for example

$$f(x) = x, \qquad 0 < x < 1,$$
$$ = 2 - x, \quad 1 < x < 2.$$

Then the Fourier coefficients, a_n, b_n, are obtained by formal integrations.

In practice it often happens that a function will in the first place be described only by a graph or by a table of numerical values. Then the Fourier coefficients should be determined by performing the appropriate integrations by some numerical, mechanical, or graphical method. For instance, in the heat conduction problem studied in Section 122, page 374, the initial temperature distribution $f(x)$ might well consist of a table of initial temperature readings for points at various distances from one surface of the slab. At the end of Section 122, on page 379, it is seen that the solution

$$(13) \qquad u(x, t) = \sum_{n=1}^{\infty} B_n e^{-(n\pi h/c)^2 t} \sin (n\pi x/c),$$

of the temperature problem involves the coefficients B_n, which are to be chosen so that

$$(14) \qquad f(x) = \sum_{n=1}^{\infty} B_n \sin (n\pi x/c), \quad \text{for } 0 < x < c.$$

We can see now that (14) is to be the Fourier sine series expansion of $f(x)$. Hence the B_n are given by

$$B_n = \frac{2}{c} \int_0^c f(x) \sin (n\pi x/c) dx$$

from which B_n is to be found numerically and then inserted in (13).

It is natural that in this book there is a marked tendency to consider each topic encountered only in the light of its bearing on differential equations, or even on a particular phase of the subject of differential equations. In all fairness it must be mentioned that Fourier series are involved in many other ways in mathematics and in other sciences. For contact with the subject of curve fitting and the method of least squares see Churchill's *Fourier Series and Boundary Value Problems*, cited earlier. The next section is a brief excursion into an application of Fourier series not dependent upon differential equations.

135. Electrocardiography. Since Fourier series yield a periodic representation for a wide class of functions, it seems reasonable to think of Fourier series in connection with a function which is actually periodic in its natural state.   One kind of such naturally periodic functions is widely used in medical science particularly as an aid in the diagnosis of diseases of the heart.

FIGURE 54

It was found long ago that there is an electric current caused by activity of the heart and that it is possible to record graphically a picture of the voltage involved, the finished product being called an electrocardiogram.   Figures 54 and 55 show portions of electrocardiograms.*

A galvanometer (see any elementary physics text) is an instrument which measures the difference in the electric potential between two specific points, an electric current, or an electromotive force (voltage) associated with the current, depending upon the kind of galvanometer involved.   An electrocardiograph is a particular type of galvanometer, one which records voltage.

When physicians desire to obtain electrocardiograms for a patient, the technicians who are to obtain the desired data follow certain fairly standard procedures which are here outlined without the many finer points of technique.   The machine (electrocardiograph) is connected with the patient at two points—say, at the right arm above the wrist and at the left leg just above the ankle (technically, lead II).   The current generated by the activity of the heart is allowed to pass from the patient's left leg through the galvanometer

* The inclusion of these electrocardiograms is made possible by the generous cooperation of the Collis P. and Howard Huntington Memorial Hospital of Pasadena, California, and in particular the cooperation of Mr. Alden B. Mills, administrator of that institution at the time they were made and released.

to the patient's right arm and proceeds to complete the circuit. The electrocardiograph measures a voltage associated with that current and records it on a graph to a desired scale. The result is an electrocardiogram, lead II, one unit in the numerous collection of pieces of information weighed by the physicians before reaching a diagnosis.

FIGURE 55

A damaged or diseased portion of the heart will resist, totally or partially, the flow of electric current and will thus alter the appearance of the electrocardiogram. The shape, size, and location of the portion causing the deviations from the norm will affect those deviations as will the character of the disease or injury present. Several leads, or combinations of places where the galvanometer and the body are connected, are used.

By means of physical theory, laboratory experiment, and observations on patients, physicians and electrocardiographers have built up a considerable knowledge of the correlation between specific sets of variations from the norm in the electrocardiograms (of various leads) and cardiac injuries and diseases. For details see the excellent exposition by G. E. Burch and Travis Winsor, *A Primer of Electrocardiography*, Philadelphia, Lea and Febiger, second edition, 1949, 245 pages.

Suppose we let t represent time measured in seconds, let $2t_2$ be the duration of a complete period in Figure 54 (a lead II), choose the midpoint of some representative period as the time origin $t = 0$, and let $F_2(t)$ be the ordinate as exhibited in the electrocardiogram for lead II. Then $F_2(t)$ has $2t_2$ as its period,

(1) $$F_2(t + 2t_2) = F_2(t).$$

There will be a Fourier series for $F_2(t)$,

$$(2) \qquad F_2(t) = \tfrac{1}{2}a_0 + \sum_{n=1}^{\infty} [a_n \cos (n\pi t/t_2) + b_n \sin (n\pi t/t_2)],$$

for which the coefficients a_n and b_n can be determined by mechanical means, by a harmonic analyzer, directly from the graphical data.

Assume that the above expansion in Fourier series of the function in the electrocardiogram for lead II has been obtained for normal persons of each sex, weight, and age, at sufficiently close intervals of the latter two to pick up significant changes. Then the $F_2(t)$ for the patient could be expanded in its Fourier series and the coefficients compared with the appropriate normal ones. The same could be done with cardiograms from other leads. In the *Journal of the British Institution of Radio Engineers*, 1949, pages 170–183, W. E. Benham published a Fourier analysis of certain idealized electrocardiograms.

The import of high-frequency peculiarities not revealed by conventional electrocardiograms but noticeably present in those made with a cathode-ray oscillograph with an expanded time scale are being studied by Paul H. Langner, Jr., M. D., Medical Director of the Provident Mutual Life Insurance Company of Philadelphia.

The identification of those changes, in the coefficients in the various Fourier series, which are associated with each cardiac injury, disease, or other phenomenon, could be interesting and even conceivably be useful. It is ultraconservative to state that much remains to be done along these lines.

136. Improvement in rapidity of convergence. In practical problems trigonometric series arise sometimes without the sum function being known in any other form. Computations with such series can be irksome unless the series converge with reasonable rapidity.

Suppose that it is desired to compute, at several points in the interval $0 < x < \pi$, the sum of the series

$$(1) \qquad \sum_{n=1}^{\infty} \frac{(-1)^n n \cos nx}{n^3 + 7}.$$

The series in (1) converges absolutely since its general term is less in absolute value than $1/n^2$ and $\displaystyle\sum_{n=1}^{\infty} 1/n^2$ converges. Let the sum of the series in (1) be denoted by $\varphi(x)$.

For large n the coefficients in the series (1) are well approximated by $(-1)^n/n^2$. But we know the sum of the corresponding series with those coefficients; on pages 401–403 we showed that

$$(2) \qquad x^2 = \frac{\pi^2}{3} + 4 \sum_{n=1}^{\infty} \frac{(-1)^n \cos nx}{n^2}, \quad \text{for } -\pi \leqq x \leqq \pi.$$

Therefore,

$$(3) \qquad \tfrac{1}{4}\left(x^2 - \frac{\pi^2}{3}\right) = \sum_{n=1}^{\infty} \frac{(-1)^n \cos nx}{n^2}, \quad -\pi \leqq x \leqq \pi.$$

Since the coefficients in the series in (3) and those in the series for $\varphi(x)$,

$$(4) \qquad \varphi(x) = \sum_{n=1}^{\infty} \frac{(-1)^n n \cos nx}{n^3 + 7}, \quad 0 < x < \pi$$

are nearly equal for large n, it follows that the difference of those coefficients should be small. So we subtract the members of equation (3) from the corresponding ones of equation (4) and get

$$\varphi(x) - \tfrac{1}{4}\left(x^2 - \frac{\pi^2}{3}\right) = \sum_{n=1}^{\infty} (-1)^n \left[\frac{n}{n^3 + 7} - \frac{1}{n^2}\right] \cos nx$$

$$= \sum_{n=1}^{\infty} \frac{7(-1)^{n+1} \cos nx}{n^2(n^3 + 7)}.$$

Thus we obtain for $\varphi(x)$ the formula

$$(5) \quad \varphi(x) = \tfrac{1}{4}\left(x^2 - \frac{\pi^2}{3}\right) + 7 \sum_{n=1}^{\infty} \frac{(-1)^{n+1} \cos nx}{n^2(n^3 + 7)}, \quad 0 < x < \pi,$$

with which computation of $\varphi(x)$ is simplified, since the coefficients of cos nx in (5) get small more rapidly than those in (4) as n increases.

The device illustrated above is worth keeping in mind when computing with infinite series—whether trigonometric or not. The method is largely dependent upon the presence of a collection of series for which the sum is known.

REFERENCES ON FOURIER SERIES

Churchill, R. V., *Fourier Series and Boundary Value Problems*, New York, McGraw-Hill Book Co., 1941.

Jackson, Dunham, *Fourier Series and Orthogonal Polynomials*, Carus Mathematical Monograph No. 6, Menasha, Mathematical Association of America, 1941.

Langer, R. E., *Fourier Series, The Genesis and Evolution of a Theory*, the first Slaught memorial paper, published as a supplement to the *Amer. Math. Monthly*, **54,** 1947.

Chapter 26

Boundary Value Problems

137. The one-dimensional heat equation. The equation which governs the conduction of heat,

$$(1) \qquad \frac{\partial u}{\partial t} = h^2 \left(\frac{\partial^2 u}{\partial x^2} + \frac{\partial^2 u}{\partial y^2} + \frac{\partial^2 u}{\partial z^2} \right),$$

was introduced on page 367. The symbols in it, together with a set of consistent units often employed in engineering practice, are described below:

$$x, y, z = \text{rectangular space coordinates (ft)},$$
$$t = \text{time (hours)},$$
$$u = \text{temperature (°F)},$$
$$h^2 = \text{thermal diffusivity (ft}^2/\text{hr)}.$$

Another frequently used set of units for the above quantities replaces feet by centimeters, hours by seconds, and degrees Fahrenheit by degrees centigrade.

It has already been indicated in Section 122 that under proper physical conditions it is reasonable to study a certain special case of equation (1), the one-dimensional heat equation

$$\frac{\partial u}{\partial t} = h^2 \frac{\partial^2 u}{\partial x^2}.$$

In Section 122 we obtained from the boundary value problem

$$(2) \qquad \frac{\partial u}{\partial t} = h^2 \frac{\partial^2 u}{\partial x^2}, \quad \text{for } 0 < t, \quad 0 < x < c;$$

$$(3) \qquad \text{As } t \to 0^+, \quad u \to f(x), \quad \text{for } 0 < x < c;$$

$$(4) \qquad \text{As } x \to 0^+, \quad u \to 0, \quad \text{for } 0 < t;$$

$$(5) \qquad \text{As } x \to c^-, \quad u \to 0, \quad \text{for } 0 < t,$$

the relation

(6) $$u(x, t) = \sum_{n=1}^{\infty} B_n e^{-(n\pi h/c)^2 t} \sin (n\pi x/c),$$

where the B_n were to be determined so that

(7) $$f(x) = \sum_{n=1}^{\infty} B_n \sin (n\pi x/c), \quad \text{for } 0 < x < c.$$

Then in Chapter 25 we found that equation (7) above suggests that the series on the right be the Fourier sine series for $f(x)$ over the interval $0 < x < c$, and therefore that

(8) $$B_n = \frac{2}{c} \int_0^c f(x) \sin (n\pi x/c) dx.$$

It is not difficult, but requires material beyond this course, to verify that (6) with coefficients B_n given by (8) is actually a solution; that is, that (6) possesses, for properly chosen $f(x)$, the required convergence properties in addition to its formal satisfaction of the differential equation (2) and the boundary conditions (3), (4), and (5).

The amount of heat which flows across an element of surface in a specified time is proportional to the rate of change of temperature in the direction normal (perpendicular) to that surface. Thus the flux of heat in the x direction (across a surface normal to the x direction) is taken to be

$$-K \frac{\partial u}{\partial x},$$

the constant of proportionality being K, the thermal conductivity of the material involved. The significance of the negative sign can be seen by considering an example in which the temperature increases with increasing x. Then $\partial u/\partial x$ is positive but heat flows toward negative x, from the warmer portion to the colder portion; hence the flux is taken to be negative.

For us the expression for flux of heat will be used most often in forming boundary conditions involving insulation. If there is total insulation at a surface normal to the x direction, then there is no flux of heat across that surface, so

$$\frac{\partial u}{\partial x} = 0$$

at that surface.

EXAMPLE: Find the temperature in a flat slab of unit width such that:

(a) Its initial temperature varies uniformly from zero at one face to u_0 at the other;

(b) The temperature of the face initially at zero remains at zero for $t > 0$; and

(c) The face initially at temperature u_0 is insulated for $t > 0$.

If x is measured from the face at zero temperature, the problem may be written

$$(9) \qquad \frac{\partial u}{\partial t} = h^2 \frac{\partial^2 u}{\partial x^2}, \quad \text{for } 0 < x < 1, \quad 0 < t;$$

$$(10) \qquad \text{As } t \to 0^+, \quad u \to u_0 x, \quad \text{for } 0 < x < 1;$$

$$(11) \qquad \text{As } x \to 0^+, \quad u \to 0, \quad \text{for } 0 < t;$$

$$(12) \qquad \text{As } x \to 1^-, \quad \frac{\partial u}{\partial x} \to 0, \quad \text{for } 0 < t.$$

First we seek functions which satisfy the differential equation (9), using the technique of separating the independent variables. As before we get

$$(13) \qquad u = e^{-h^2\alpha^2 t}[A \cos \alpha x + B \sin \alpha x]$$

with α, A, and B arbitrary. Condition (11) demands that

$$0 = Ae^{-h^2\alpha^2 t}, \quad \text{for } 0 < t,$$

so we must take $A = 0$. We now have

$$(14) \qquad u = Be^{-h^2\alpha^2 t} \sin \alpha x,$$

which satisfies (9) and (11). From (14) it follows that

$$\frac{\partial u}{\partial x} = \alpha Be^{-h^2\alpha^2 t} \cos \alpha x$$

so that condition (12) requires that

$$0 = \alpha B e^{-h^2\alpha^2 t} \cos \alpha, \quad \text{for } 0 < t.$$

We must not choose $\alpha = 0$ or $B = 0$ because then (14) would yield $u = 0$, which cannot satisfy the remaining condition (10). The factor $e^{-h^2\alpha^2 t}$ cannot vanish for any t, to say nothing of doing so for all positive t. Thus we conclude that

(15) $\cos \alpha = 0.$

From (15) it follows that

$$\alpha = (2k + 1)\pi/2; \quad k = 0, 1, 2, \cdots.$$

We now have the functions

$$u = B_k e^{-h^2(2k+1)^2\pi^2 t/4} \sin [(2k + 1)\pi x/2]; \quad k = 0, 1, 2, \cdots,$$

each of which satisfies (9), (11), and (12). To attack the condition (10) we form the series

(16) $$u(x, t) = \sum_{k=0}^{\infty} B_k e^{-h^2(2k+1)^2\pi^2 t/4} \sin [(2k + 1)\pi x/2]$$

and require, because of (10), that

(17) $$u_0 x = \sum_{k=0}^{\infty} B_k \sin [(2k + 1)\pi x/2], \quad \text{for } 0 < x < 1.$$

Comparison of the right member of (17) with the general Fourier sine series expansion for the interval $0 < x < c$, shows that the series in (17) is an expansion over the interval

$$0 < x < 2$$

and that its even terms are missing. That is, we seek a Fourier sine series expansion

(18) $$f(x) \sim \sum_{n=1}^{\infty} b_n \sin (n\pi x/2), \quad \text{for } 0 < x < 2$$

where

$$f(x) = u_0 x, \quad \text{for } 0 < x < 1,$$

and $f(x)$ is so chosen for $1 < x < 2$ that in (18) the terms with even n will drop out.

Physically, it is not difficult to see that we wish to extend the slab its own width beyond $x = 1$ in some way so as to prevent the heat from flowing across the insulated face $x = 1$. Once that fact is realized it soon follows that we need all temperature conditions to be symmetric with respect to that insulated face $x = 1$.

The initial temperature $f(x)$ of our original slab is shown in Figure 56. Let us prescribe $f(x)$ over $1 < x < 2$ to be the reflection through $x = 1$ of the initial temperature, so that in $0 < x < 2$ the initial temperature of the extended slab is as shown in Figure 57.

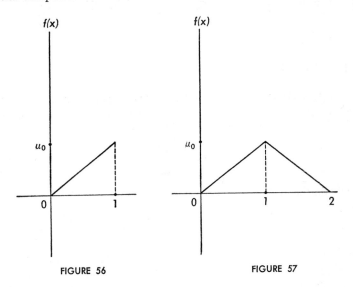

FIGURE 56   FIGURE 57

The boundary value problem (9)–(12) can now be replaced by a new one with slab width 2, initial temperature as exhibited in Figure 57, and with faces $x = 0$ and $x = 2$ held at zero temperature for $t > 0$. The solution to the old problem is the same as that to the new problem except that it is to be used only for $0 < x < 1$.

An alternative procedure is to revert to equation (18) with

$$f(x) = u_0 x, \qquad \text{for } 0 < x < 1,$$
$$= u_0(2 - x), \quad \text{for } 1 < x < 2,$$

and thus to obtain b_n from which the B_k of (16) and (17) follows.

One more method needs mention. After justification, such as in Ex. 10 below, it is permissible to obtain the B_k directly from equation (17) without open recourse to any devices such as the ones above. The student can show in any one or more of these ways that

$$B_k = \frac{8u_0(-1)^k}{\pi^2(2k + 1)^2},$$

so that the problem (9)–(12) has for a solution

$$(19) \quad u(x, t) = \frac{8u_0}{\pi^2} \sum_{k=0}^{\infty} \frac{(-1)^k e^{-h^2(2k+1)^2\pi^2 t/4}}{(2k + 1)^2} \sin\left[(2k + 1)\pi x/2\right].$$

EXERCISES

1. Use the method, not the formulas, of this section to solve the problem of a flat slab initially at a constant temperature u_0 throughout and having its faces $x = 0$ and $x = c$ held at zero temperature for $t > 0$.

     ANS. $u = (4u_0/\pi) \sum_{k=0}^{\infty} \dfrac{e^{-h^2\pi^2(2k+1)^2 t/c^2}}{2k + 1} \sin\left[(2k + 1)\pi x/c\right].$

2. Obtain the average temperature across the slab of Ex. 1 for $t > 0$.

     ANS. $u_m(t) = \dfrac{8u_0}{\pi^2} \sum_{k=0}^{\infty} \dfrac{e^{-h^2\pi^2(2k+1)^2 t/c^2}}{(2k + 1)^2}.$

3. For the one-dimensional heat equation, (2) above, find a solution u such that u is independent of t, $u = A$ for $x = 0$, and $u = 0$ for $x = c$; A is constant.   ANS. $u = A(c - x)/c.$

4. With the aid of the result of Ex. 3 solve the problem of a slab of width c, with initial temperature zero throughout, and with faces $x = 0$ and $x = c$ held at temperatures A and zero respectively, for $t > 0$.

     ANS. $u = A(c - x)/c - \dfrac{2A}{\pi} \sum_{n=1}^{\infty} \dfrac{1}{n} e^{-(hn\pi/c)^2 t} \sin(n\pi x/c).$

5. Combine the result of Ex. 4 with the material of this section to solve the problem of the slab such that

$$
\begin{array}{lll}
\text{As } t \to 0^+, & u \to f(x), & \text{for } 0 < x < c; \\
\text{As } x \to 0^+, & u \to A, & \text{for } 0 < t; \\
\text{As } x \to c^-, & u \to 0, & \text{for } 0 < t.
\end{array}
$$

6. For a particular concrete the thermal diffusivity h^2 is about 0.04 (ft²/hr), so that we may reasonably choose $h^2\pi^2 = 0.4$. A slab 20 feet thick is initially at temperature 130°F and has its surfaces held at 60°F for $t > 0$. Show that the temperature in degrees Fahrenheit at the center of the slab is given by the formula

$$
u = 60 + \frac{280}{\pi} \sum_{k=0}^{\infty} \frac{(-1)^k e^{-(2k+1)^2 t/1000}}{2k+1},
$$

and that, after one month, the temperature correct to the first decimal place is given by

$$
u = 60 + 89.1e^{-t/1000}.
$$

7. Two slabs of the concrete of Ex. 6 (with $h^2\pi^2 = 0.4$ ft²/hr), one slab 15 feet thick and the other 5 feet thick, are placed side by side. The thicker slab is initially at temperature 120°F, the thinner one at 30°F. The outside faces are to be held at 30°F for $t > 0$. Find the temperature throughout the slab for $t > 0$. Measure x from the outer face of the thicker slab.

ANS. $u = 30 + \dfrac{180}{\pi} \displaystyle\sum_{n=1}^{\infty} \dfrac{1 - \cos(3n\pi/4)}{n} e^{-n^2 t/1000} \sin \dfrac{n\pi x}{20}.$

8. Two slabs of the same material, one 2 feet thick and the other 1 foot thick are to be placed side by side. The thicker slab is initially at temperature A, the thinner one initially at zero. The outside faces are to be held at zero temperature for $t > 0$. Find the temperature at the center of the 2-foot slab.

ANS. $\dfrac{4A}{\pi} \displaystyle\sum_{n=1}^{\infty} \dfrac{1}{n} \sin^3(n\pi/3)e^{-(hn\pi/3)^2 t}.$

9. Knowing that the temperature function which is the answer to Ex. 8 has the value A at $t = 0$, show that

$$
\sum_{k=0}^{\infty} \frac{(-1)^k(2k+1)}{(3k+1)(3k+2)} = \frac{2\pi}{9\sqrt{3}}.
$$

10. By extending $f(x)$ in a proper way (see the example of this section) prove that, with an $f(x)$ which is defined in $0 < x < c$ and satisfies the conditions of the convergence theorem stated in Section 130, then the right member in the expansion

$$f(x) \sim \sum_{k=0}^{\infty} B_k \sin [(2k + 1)\pi x/(2c)], \text{ for } 0 < x < c,$$

in which

$$B_k = \frac{2}{c} \int_0^c f(x) \sin [(2k + 1)\pi x/(2c)]dx,$$

represents the extended function in the sense of Section 130.

11. Interpret as a heat conduction problem and solve: equation (2) of this section together with the conditions,

$$\begin{array}{lll}
\text{As } x \to 0^+, & \partial u/\partial x \to 0, & \text{for } 0 < t; \\
\text{As } x \to c^-, & u \to 0, & \text{for } 0 < t; \\
\text{As } t \to 0^+, & u \to f(x), & \text{for } 0 < x < c.
\end{array}$$

12. Interpret and solve the problem consisting of equation (2) and the conditions:

$$\begin{array}{lll}
\text{As } x \to 0^+, & \partial u/\partial x \to 0, & \text{for } 0 < t; \\
\text{As } x \to c^-, & u \to A, & \text{for } 0 < t; \\
\text{As } t \to 0^+, & u \to 0, & \text{for } 0 < x < c.
\end{array}$$

13. Solve the boundary value problem with B a constant,

$$\frac{\partial u}{\partial t} = h^2 \frac{\partial^2 u}{\partial x^2} + B, \text{ for } 0 < x < c, 0 < t;$$

$$\begin{array}{lll}
\text{As } x \to 0^+, & u \to 0, & \text{for } 0 < t; \\
\text{As } x \to c^-, & u \to 0, & \text{for } 0 < t; \\
\text{As } t \to 0^+, & u \to f(x), & \text{for } 0 < x < c.
\end{array}$$

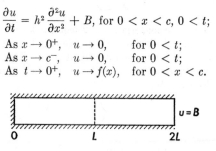

FIGURE 58

14. Two metal rods of the same material, each of length L, have their sides insulated so that heat can flow only longitudinally. One rod is at temperature A, the other at temperature zero. At time $t = 0$ the rods are placed end to end as in Figure 58. The exposed end of the first

rod is then insulated; the exposed end of the second rod is thereafter held at temperature B. Determine the temperature at the juncture of the rods for $t > 0$.

ANS. $u_j = B$

$$+ \frac{1}{\pi} \sum_{k=0}^{\infty} \frac{(-1)^k \{A - 2B \cos [(2k + 1)\pi/4]\}}{2k + 1} e^{-(2k+1)^2 h^2 \pi^2 t/(16 L^2)}.$$

138. Experimental verification of the validity of the heat equation.

It is reassuring to have our mathematical formulas supported in comparison with observed phenomena and pleasant to see those same formulas being of practical* value. Both experiences are encountered in the study of the conduction of heat in concrete dams.

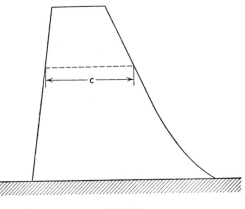

FIGURE 59

When concrete is poured a chemical reaction causes heat to be generated in the material. Exposure to air temperatures cools the concrete, the inner portions cooling more slowly than those near the surface. The temperature differences create stresses and cause

---

* There is a story, perhaps a legend, that H. J. S. Smith, a mathematician of no mean standing, once proposed the toast: "To pure mathematics, may it never be of use to anyone!" Many mathematicians, including the author, regard as pure any part of mathematics which seems to us worthy of study primarily because of its inherent beauty, regardless of applicability to mundane affairs.

expansions and contractions. Because of these facts it is customary when building a large dam to leave contraction joints, openings to facilitate the safe expansion and contraction of the concrete. By the time the concrete has lost most of its heat of setting the dam is grouted (the contraction joints filled) and the dam is ready for use so far as the temperature problem is concerned.

The question of when the dam will be ready for grouting is a serious one for the designer. If it is known that the waiting period would be extremely long, the concrete may be cooled as it is poured. This was done with Boulder Dam (Hoover Dam) which was designed by the United States Bureau of Reclamation. For Boulder Dam the waiting period would have been one and a half centuries; it is a large dam.

FIGURE 60

The temperature problem needs extensive idealization to bring it down to the level for which decently computable solutions are known. Figure 59 shows a typical dam cross section; on it is indicated the thickness c at a random elevation. The designing engineers sometimes proceed to determine the temperatures to be expected at various elevations by replacing the temperature problem for Figure 59 by that for the flat slab in Figure 60. The width c may be varied to approximate the thickness at various elevations.

The designer knows what the initial temperature of the concrete will be (laboratory tests) and he knows what air temperatures to expect (United States Weather Bureau). The solution of the heat problem for Figure 60, with known initial temperature and variable surface temperatures may be handled (see the next section) by superposition of solutions using, for instance, the successive mean monthly anticipated air temperatures. The designer can then predict concrete temperatures across the dam at various elevations and from them conclude when it would be safe to grout the dam.

Replacing Figure 60 by a wedge-shaped cross section to get closer to the appearance of Figure 59 seems to make a negligible difference in the end result, the predicted time for grouting.

During the construction of some large dams thermocouples are installed to permit future readings of temperature at various points in the dam. Years later computations are made by the method described above and the computed temperature curves are compared to the observed ones. The results are pleasant to behold. Frequently, the observed temperature history and the predicted temperature agree within two or three degrees Fahrenheit for years at a time, through the gradual dissipation of the heat of setting and the nearly periodic fluctuations due to seasonal changes in air temperatures.

It is, of course, known that the heat equation is not an exact expression for the relation between temperature, time, the space coordinates, and certain physical constants. Laboratory tests in which small concrete specimens are subjected to temperature changes which are relatively rapid, perhaps 100°F in an hour or two, give clear indication that thermal conductivity and specific heat vary appreciably with the temperature itself. For such tests, comparison of observed temperatures with those predicted by the heat equation with constant thermal diffusivity shows discrepancies which cannot be lightly regarded, as much as 25 per cent of the total change.

Once it is recognized that conductivity and specific heat do change with the temperature, then the mathematical theory can be adapted to the situation. The resulting form of the heat equation is nonlinear. The temperatures obtained by solving that nonlinear equation together with appropriate boundary conditions do agree remarkably well with the observed temperatures; maximum errors involved have an order of magnitude of 2 or 3 per cent of the total temperature change in one instance known to the author.*

139. Surface temperature varying with time. As indicated in the preceding section, a practical problem may well force us to consider variable surface temperatures. A commonly encountered example is that of a slab initially at constant temperature A_0 and

---

* The author engaged in temperature studies for a part of the time, 1933–1937, that he worked at the United States Bureau of Reclamation in Denver, Colorado.

with surfaces maintained thereafter at the variable air temperature $A(t)$. We are thus led to consider the problem of solving the simple heat equation

(1) $$\frac{\partial u}{\partial t} = h^2 \frac{\partial^2 u}{\partial x^2}, \quad \text{for } 0 < t, 0 < x < c,$$

with conditions

(2)   As $t \to 0^+$, $u \to A_0$,   for $0 < x < c$;
(3)   As $x \to 0^+$, $u \to A(t)$,   for $0 < t$;
(4)   As $x \to c^-$, $u \to A(t)$,   for $0 < t$.

Here $A(t)$ represents surface (air) temperature as a function of time. We are concerned only with $A(t)$ of the form exhibited in Figure 61. It may help to think of $A(t)$ as giving mean monthly predicted air temperature, A_1 over the first month $0 < t < t_1$, A_2 over the second month $t_1 < t < t_2$, etc.

FIGURE 61

The function $A(t)$ may be expressed, using $t_0 = 0$, by

(5) $A(t) = A_n$,   for $t_{n-1} < t < t_n$; $n = 1, 2, 3, \cdots$.

For our purpose there is no need for the time intervals to be equal, but it is necessary that $A(t)$ be constant within each time interval.

Since equation (1) is linear and homogeneous in u, any linear combination* of solutions of (1) is also a solution. Since t enters (1) only in $\partial u/\partial t$, any solution remains a solution under a translation of the time origin; that is, if $u(x, t)$ satisfies equation (1), then $u(x, t - t_n)$ satisfies (1) for any constant t_n.

The fundamental solution on which we base our treatment of the problem (1)–(4) is

---

* The method of superposition is more than 200 years old but, so far as is known to the author, its first systematic application to the prediction of temperatures in concrete dams was made around 1930 by R. E. Glover, an engineer at the United States Bureau of Reclamation in Denver, Colorado.

(6) $\qquad F(x,\,t) = 1 - \dfrac{4}{\pi} \displaystyle\sum_{k=0}^{\infty} \dfrac{e^{-(2k+1)^2 h^2 \pi^2 t/c^2}}{2k+1} \sin \dfrac{(2k+1)\pi x}{c},$

for $0 < t,\ 0 < x < c$. Directly, or by comparison with Ex. 1, page 409, the function $F(x,\,t)$ of (6) can be seen to be a solution of the heat equation (1) and to have the properties:

(7) $\qquad$ As $t \to 0^+$, $\quad F(x,\,t) \to 0$, $\quad$ for $0 < x < c$;

(8) $\qquad$ As $x \to 0^+$, $\quad F(x,\,t) \to 1$, $\quad$ for $0 < t$;

(9) $\qquad$ As $x \to c^-$, $\quad F(x,\,t) \to 1$, $\quad$ for $0 < t$.

Since $F(x,\,t)$ in (6) was undefined for $t \leqq 0$, let us take the liberty of defining it as identically zero whenever its second argument t is nonpositive.

(10) $\qquad\qquad\qquad F(x,\,t) \equiv 0, \quad \text{for } t \leqq 0.$

Then the desired solution of the problem (1)–(4) can be written at once as

(11) $\quad u(x,\,t) = A_0 + \displaystyle\sum_{n=1}^{\infty} (A_n - A_{n-1})F(x,\,t - t_{n-1}),$

$$\text{for } 0 < t, \quad 0 < x < c.$$

Note that the series on the right in (11) terminates for any specific t, since sooner or later (as n increases) the argument $(t - t_{n-1})$ becomes and remains negative.

The u of (11) is a linear combination of solutions of (1); it satisfies (2) because of (7). As $x \to 0^+$ or $x \to c^-$, in any range $t_{k-1} < t \leqq t_k$,

$$u \to A_0 + \sum_{n=1}^{k} (A_n - A_{n-1}) = A_k,$$

because of (8) and (9) and the fact that $F(x,\,t - t_{n-1}) \equiv 0$ for $t \leqq t_{n-1}$.

In actual practice computations with the solution (11) are greatly simplified because the $F(x,\,t)$ of (6) is essentially the same for all diffusivities and all slab widths. In equation (6), put $h^2 \pi^2 t/c^2 = \tau$ and $\pi x/c = \zeta$. Then

$$F(x, t) = 1 - \frac{4}{\pi} \sum_{k=0}^{\infty} \frac{e^{-(2k+1)^2\tau} \sin (2k + 1)\zeta}{2k + 1} = \varphi(\zeta, \tau),$$

for $0 < \tau, 0 < \zeta < \pi$. The function φ can be tabulated at intervals of ζ and τ. For a particular slab problem values of h^2, c, t, and x are used to compute the pertinent ζ and τ and the values of φ read from the table.

140. Heat conduction in a sphere. Consider a solid sphere initially at a known temperature which depends only upon distance from the center of the sphere. Let the surface of the sphere be held at zero temperature for $t > 0$. We shall determine the temperature in the sphere for positive t under the assumption that the heat equation

$$(1) \qquad \frac{\partial u}{\partial t} = h^2 \left(\frac{\partial^2 u}{\partial x^2} + \frac{\partial^2 u}{\partial y^2} + \frac{\partial^2 u}{\partial z^2} \right)$$

is valid.

Since the object under study is a sphere, we choose the origin at the center of the sphere and introduce spherical coordinates, related to x, y, z, by

$$x = \rho \sin \theta \cos \varphi, \quad y = \rho \sin \theta \sin \varphi, \quad z = \rho \cos \theta.$$

Then the heat equation (1) becomes

$$(2) \quad \frac{\partial u}{\partial t} = h^2 \left(\frac{\partial^2 u}{\partial \rho^2} + \frac{2}{\rho} \frac{\partial u}{\partial \rho} + \frac{1}{\rho^2} \frac{\partial^2 u}{\partial \theta^2} + \frac{\cot \theta}{\rho^2} \frac{\partial u}{\partial \theta} + \frac{\csc^2 \theta}{\rho^2} \frac{\partial^2 u}{\partial \varphi^2} \right).$$

For the problem we wish to solve the temperature is independent of the coordinates θ and φ, so equation (2) reduces to

$$(3) \qquad \frac{\partial u}{\partial t} = h^2 \left(\frac{\partial^2 u}{\partial \rho^2} + \frac{2}{\rho} \frac{\partial u}{\partial \rho} \right).$$

Let R be the radius of the sphere and $f(\rho)$ be the initial temperature. Then the problem confronting us is

$$(4) \qquad \frac{\partial u}{\partial t} = h^2 \left(\frac{\partial^2 u}{\partial \rho^2} + \frac{2}{\rho} \frac{\partial u}{\partial \rho} \right), \quad \text{for } 0 < t, \quad 0 < \rho < R;$$

$$(5) \qquad \text{As } \rho \to R^-, \quad u \to 0, \quad \text{for } 0 < t;$$

$$(6) \qquad \text{As } t \to 0^+, \quad u \to f(\rho), \quad \text{for } 0 \leqq \rho < R.$$

The student can easily show that the change of dependent variable,

$$(7) \qquad\qquad\qquad u = \frac{v}{\rho}$$

transforms the problem (4)–(6) into the problem

(8) $\qquad\qquad \dfrac{\partial v}{\partial t} = h^2 \dfrac{\partial^2 v}{\partial \rho^2}, \quad$ for $0 < t, \quad 0 < \rho < R$;

(9) $\qquad\qquad$ As $\rho \to R^-, \quad v \to 0, \qquad\qquad$ for $0 < t$;

(10) $\qquad\qquad$ As $\rho \to 0^+, \quad \dfrac{v}{\rho} \to$ a limit, $\quad$ for $0 < t$;

(11) $\qquad\qquad$ As $t \to 0^+, \quad v \to \rho f(\rho), \qquad$ for $0 < \rho < R$.

The added condition (10) is a reflection of the fact that the temperature u is to exist at $\rho = 0$ in spite of relation (7). The new problem (8)–(11) is much like those treated at the beginning of this chapter. Its solution is left as an exercise.

The corresponding problem of finding the temperatures in a solid cylinder is less elementary and involves series of Bessel functions. It may be found worked out in many books.*

EXERCISES

1. Solve the problem (4)–(6) by the method outlined above.

$$\text{ANS.} \quad u = \frac{1}{\rho} \sum_{n=1}^{\infty} b_n e^{-(hn\pi/R)^2 t} \sin (n\pi\rho/R), \text{ in which}$$

$$b_n = \frac{2}{R} \int_0^R \rho f(\rho) \sin (n\pi\rho/R) d\rho.$$

2. A sphere of radius R is initially at a constant temperature u_0 throughout, then has its surface held at temperature u_1 for $t > 0$. Find the temperature throughout the sphere for $t > 0$ and in particular the temperature u_c at the center of the sphere.

---

* See, for example, E. D. Rainville, *Intermediate Differential Equations*, New York, John Wiley & Sons, 1943, pp. 198–206, or R. V. Churchill, *Fourier Series and Boundary Value Problems*, New York, McGraw-Hill Book Co., 1941, pp. 165–167.

ANS. $u = u_1 + \dfrac{2R(u_0 - u_1)}{\rho\pi} \displaystyle\sum_{n=1}^{\infty} \dfrac{(-1)^{n+1}}{n}\, e^{-(hn\pi/R)^2 t} \sin{(n\pi\rho/R)};$

$u_c = u_1 + 2(u_0 - u_1) \displaystyle\sum_{n=1}^{\infty} (-1)^{n+1} e^{-(hn\pi/R)^2 t},\ \text{for } t > 0.$

141. The simple wave equation.

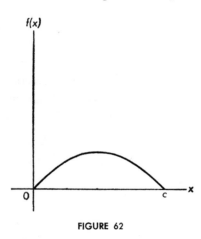

f(x)

0

c

FIGURE 62

If an elastic string held fixed at two points is taut, and then is displaced from its equilibrium position and released, the subsequent displacements from the position of equilibrium may be determined by solving a boundary value problem. Figure 62 shows a representative displacement of the string, which is to be held fixed at $x = 0$ and $x = c$. The displacement y for $0 < x < c$ and $0 < t$ is to be found from the known initial displacement $f(x)$, the initial velocity $\varphi(x)$, and the fact that y must satisfy the one-dimensional wave equation

(1) $$\frac{\partial^2 y}{\partial t^2} = a^2 \frac{\partial^2 y}{\partial x^2},$$

in which the parameter a is a constant which depends upon the physical properties of the string.

The boundary value problem to be solved is

(2) $\dfrac{\partial^2 y}{\partial t^2} = a^2 \dfrac{\partial^2 y}{\partial x^2},\quad$ for $\ 0 < x < c,\ \ 0 < t;$

(3)   As $x \to 0^+,\quad y \to 0,\qquad$ for $0 < t;$

(4)   As $x \to c^-,\quad y \to 0,\qquad$ for $0 < t;$

(5)   As $t \to 0^+,\quad y \to f(x),\qquad$ for $0 < x < c;$

(6)   As $t \to 0^+,\quad \dfrac{\partial y}{\partial t} \to \varphi(x),\quad$ for $0 < x < c.$

It is inherent in the string problem that $f(x)$ be continuous and that $f(0) = f(c) = 0$. Either $f(x)$ or $\varphi(x)$ may be zero throughout the interval. Indeed, the boundary value problem (2)–(6) can always be replaced by two problems, one with $f(x)$ replaced by zero, the other with $\varphi(x)$ replaced by zero. The sum of the solutions of those two problems is the solution of the problem with both an initial velocity and an initial displacement.

The solution of problems such as (2)–(6) with various $f(x)$ and $\varphi(x)$ can be accomplished by the method of separation of variables and use of Fourier series as was done with the heat conduction problems earlier. That work is left for exercises for the student, since it involves no new technique. Note the usefulness of the solutions determined in Ex. 1, page 371.

EXERCISES

In Exs. 1–5 find the displacement for $t > 0$ of the vibrating string problem of this section under the condition that the initial velocity is to be zero and that the initial displacement is given by the $f(x)$ described.

1. $f(x) = x$, for $0 \leqq x \leqq c/2$,
   $= c - x$, for $c/2 \leqq x \leqq c$.

   ANS. $y = \dfrac{4c}{\pi^2} \displaystyle\sum_{k=0}^{\infty} \dfrac{(-1)^k \cos\,[(2k+1)a\pi t/c]\,\sin\,[(2k+1)\pi x/c]}{(2k+1)^2}.$

2. $f(x) = x(c - x)/c.$

   ANS. $y = \dfrac{8c}{\pi^3} \displaystyle\sum_{k=0}^{\infty} \dfrac{\cos\,[(2k+1)a\pi t/c]\,\sin\,[(2k+1)\pi x/c]}{(2k+1)^3}.$

3. $f(x) = x$, for $0 \leqq x \leqq c/4$,
   $= c/4$, for $c/4 \leqq x \leqq 3c/4$,
   $= c - x$, for $3c/4 \leqq x \leqq c$. See Figure 63, page 438.

   ANS. $y = \dfrac{2c}{\pi^2} \displaystyle\sum_{n=1}^{\infty} \dfrac{1}{n^2}\,[\sin\,(n\pi/4) + \sin\,(3n\pi/4)]\,\cos\,(na\pi t/c)\,\sin\,(n\pi x/c),$

   or

   $y = \dfrac{4c}{\pi^2} \displaystyle\sum_{k=0}^{\infty} \dfrac{\sin\,[(2k+1)\pi/4]\,\cos\,[(2k+1)a\pi t/c]\,\sin\,[(2k+1)\pi x/c]}{(2k+1)^2}.$

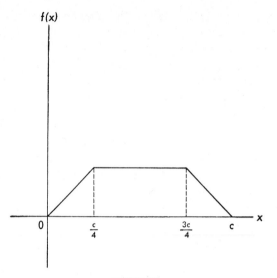

FIGURE 63

4. $f(x) = x$, for $0 \leqq x \leqq \frac{1}{4}c$,
   $= \frac{1}{2}c - x$, for $\frac{1}{4}c \leqq x \leqq 3c/4$,
   $= x - c$, for $3c/4 \leqq x \leqq c$.   See Figure 64.

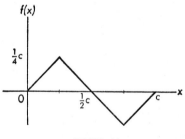

FIGURE 64

ANS. $y = \dfrac{2c}{\pi^2} \displaystyle\sum_{k=0}^{\infty} \dfrac{(-1)^k \cos\,[(4k+2)\pi at/c]\,\sin\,[(4k+2)\pi x/c]}{(2k+1)^2}.$

5. $f(x) = x$, for $0 \leqq x \leqq \frac{1}{4}c$,
   $= \frac{1}{2}c - x$, for $\frac{1}{4}c \leqq x \leqq \frac{1}{2}c$,
   $= 0$, for $\frac{1}{2}c \leqq x \leqq c$.

ANS. $y = \dfrac{2c}{\pi^2} \displaystyle\sum_{n=1}^{\infty} \dfrac{1}{n^2} (2 \sin \tfrac{1}{4} n\pi - \sin \tfrac{1}{2} n\pi) \cos (n\pi a t/c) \sin (n\pi x/c).$

6. Find the displacement of the string of this section if the initial displacement is zero and the initial velocity is given by $\varphi(x) = ax(c - x)/(4c^2)$.

ANS. $y = \dfrac{2c}{\pi^4} \displaystyle\sum_{k=0}^{\infty} \dfrac{\sin [(2k + 1)a\pi t/c] \sin [(2k + 1)\pi x/c]}{(2k + 1)^4}.$

7. Find the displacement of the string of this section if the initial displacement is zero and the initial velocity is given by
$$\varphi(x) = 0, \text{ for } 0 \leqq x \leqq c/3,$$
$$= v_0, \text{ for } c/3 \leqq x \leqq 2c/3,$$
$$= 0, \text{ for } 2c/3 \leqq x \leqq c.$$

ANS. $y = \dfrac{2v_0 c}{\pi^2 a} \displaystyle\sum_{n=1}^{\infty} \dfrac{[\cos (n\pi/3) - \cos (2n\pi/3)] \sin (n\pi a t/c) \sin (n\pi x/c)}{n^2}.$

8. Solve the problem (2)–(6) of this section with the restriction $\varphi(x) = 0$.

ANS. $y = \displaystyle\sum_{n=1}^{\infty} b_n \cos (n\pi a t/c) \sin (n\pi x/c),$

in which $b_n = \dfrac{2}{c} \displaystyle\int_0^c f(x) \sin (n\pi x/c) dx.$

9. Solve the problem (2)–(6) of this section with the restriction $f(x) = 0$.

ANS. $y = \displaystyle\sum_{n=1}^{\infty} B_n \sin (n\pi a t/c) \sin (n\pi x/c),$

in which $B_n = \dfrac{2}{n\pi a} \displaystyle\int_0^c \varphi(x) \sin (n\pi x/c) dx.$

142. Laplace's equation in two dimensions.

On pages 86–92 of Chapter 5 there was some discussion of Laplace's equation, in particular of the two-dimensional case

(1) $$\frac{\partial^2 u}{\partial x^2} + \frac{\partial^2 u}{\partial y^2} = 0.$$

The dependent variable u may represent any one of various quantities, steady-state temperature, electrostatic potential, etc., although in this section we shall use the language of steady-state temperature problems for simplicity in wording and visualization.

The Fourier series method as it is being utilized in this chapter is particularly well adapted to solving steady-state temperature problems for a flat rectangular plate. Let the two faces of the plate be insulated; let no heat flow in the direction normal to them. Then the problem is two-dimensional. Each edge of the plate may be either insulated or held at a known temperature.

Consider a flat rectangular plate with edges of length a and b. Let three edges be kept at zero temperature and the remaining one, one of those of length a, be kept at a specified temperature, a function of distance along that edge. Let us choose a coordinate system and accompanying notation as shown in Figure 65.

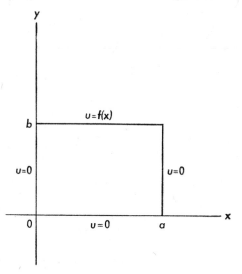

FIGURE 65

The steady-state temperature problem associated with Figure 65 may be written

$$(2) \qquad \frac{\partial^2 u}{\partial x^2} + \frac{\partial^2 u}{\partial y^2} = 0, \quad \text{for } 0 < x < a, \ 0 < y < b;$$

(3)   As $x \to 0^+$, $u \to 0$,   for $0 < y < b$;

(4)   As $x \to a^-$, $u \to 0$,   for $0 < y < b$;

(5)   As $y \to 0^+$, $u \to 0$,   for $0 < x < a$;

(6)   As $y \to b^-$, $u \to f(x)$,   for $0 < x < a$.

The solution of the problem (2)–(6) follows by the same method as was used on boundary value problems for the one-dimensional heat equation. Results appear in the exercises below.

When a rectangular plate problem has nonzero temperatures at more than one edge, the problem can be separated into two or more problems of the type of (2)–(6) above. Insulation of an edge can be treated by doubling the size of the plate with the insulated edge becoming the new center line and then creating temperature conditions symmetric about that center line so that no heat can flow across it. See the methods used in Section 137 at the start of this chapter.

Next let us consider a flat circular plate of radius R subjected to assigned fixed temperatures at its edge and left until it reaches the steady-state condition. Using cylindrical coordinates r, θ, z and conditions that permit no heat flow normal to the faces of the plate, we arrive at a two-dimensional problem,

(7) $$\frac{\partial^2 u}{\partial r^2} + \frac{1}{r}\frac{\partial u}{\partial r} + \frac{1}{r^2}\frac{\partial^2 u}{\partial \theta^2} = 0, \quad \text{for } 0 < r < R, \quad 0 < \theta < 2\pi;$$

(8) $$\text{As } r \to R^-, \quad u \to f(\theta), \quad \text{for } 0 \leqq \theta < 2\pi;$$

(9) $$\operatorname*{Lim}_{r\to 0^+} u \text{ exists}, \qquad \text{for } 0 \leqq \theta < 2\pi;$$

(10) $$\operatorname*{Lim}_{\theta\to 0^+} u = \operatorname*{Lim}_{\theta\to 2\pi^-} u, \quad \text{for } 0 \leqq r < R.$$

If we are willing to define the edge temperature $f(\theta)$ for all θ and make it have the period 2π, then the condition (10) above can be replaced by the requirement that u be a periodic function of θ with period 2π.

The corresponding problems of a wedge, or of a portion of a wedge with concentric circular edges, do not involve any requirement of periodicity in their physical nature.

Separation of variables in equation (7) leads to a need for solving an ordinary equation of Euler-Cauchy type,

(11) $$r^2\,\psi''(r) + r\,\psi'(r) - \alpha^2\,\psi(r) = 0,$$

where α is constant. See Exs. 15–26, page 283.

EXERCISES

Each of Exs. 1–7 below refers to the steady-state temperature problem for the rectangular plate of Figure 65 but with edge conditions as described in the individual exercise.

1. Edges $x = 0$, $x = a$, $y = 0$ held at zero temperature; the edge $y = b$ held at temperature $f(x)$.

$$\text{ANS.} \quad u = \sum_{n=1}^{\infty} c_n \sinh\,(n\pi y/a)\,\sin\,(n\pi x/a),$$

in which

$$c_n \sinh\,(n\pi b/a) = \frac{2}{a} \int_0^a f(x)\,\sin\,(n\pi x/a)dx.$$

2. Edges $x = 0$, $x = a$, $y = 0$ held at zero; the edge $y = b$ held at temperature unity. Solve the problem directly or by using the result of Ex. 1.

$$\text{ANS.} \quad u = \frac{4}{\pi} \sum_{k=0}^{\infty} \frac{\sinh\,[(2k+1)\pi y/a]\,\sin\,[(2k+1)\pi x/a]}{(2k+1)\,\sinh\,[(2k+1)\pi b/a]}.$$

3. Ex. 2 with the change that the edge $y = b$ is to be held at unity for $0 < x < a/2$ and at zero for $a/2 < x < a$.

$$\text{ANS.} \quad u = \frac{2}{\pi} \sum_{n=1}^{\infty} \frac{[1 - \cos\,(n\pi/2)]\,\sinh\,(n\pi y/a)\,\sin\,(n\pi x/a)}{n\,\sinh\,(n\pi b/a)}.$$

4. Edges $x = 0$ and $x = a$ held at zero; edge $y = 0$ insulated; edge $y = b$ held at temperature $f(x)$.

$$\text{ANS.} \quad u = \sum_{n=1}^{\infty} c_n \cosh\,(n\pi y/a)\,\sin\,(n\pi x/a),$$

in which

$$c_n \cosh\,(n\pi b/a) = \frac{2}{a} \int_0^a f(x)\,\sin\,(n\pi x/a)dx.$$

5. Edge $x = 0$ insulated; edges $x = a$ and $y = 0$ held at zero; edge $y = b$ held at unit temperature.

$$\text{ANS.} \quad u = \frac{4}{\pi} \sum_{k=0}^{\infty} \frac{(-1)^k \sinh\,[(2k+1)\pi y/(2a)]\,\cos\,[(2k+1)\pi x/(2a)]}{(2k+1)\,\sinh\,[(2k+1)\pi b/(2a)]}.$$

6. Edges $x = 0$ and $y = 0$ held at zero; edge $x = a$ insulated; edge $y = b$ held at unit temperature.

ANS. $u = \dfrac{4}{\pi} \displaystyle\sum_{k=0}^{\infty} \dfrac{\sinh\,[(2k+1)\pi y/(2a)]\,\sin\,[(2k+1)\pi x/(2a)]}{(2k+1)\,\sinh\,[(2k+1)\pi b/(2a)]}.$

7. Edges $x = 0$ and $y = 0$ insulated; edge $x = a$ held at zero; edge $y = b$ held at unit temperature.

ANS. $u = \dfrac{4}{\pi} \displaystyle\sum_{k=0}^{\infty} \dfrac{(-1)^k\,\cosh\,[(2k+1)\pi y/(2a)]\,\cos\,[(2k+1)\pi x/(2a)]}{(2k+1)\,\cosh\,[(2k+1)\pi b/(2a)]}.$

8. Show that the temperature at the center of the plate of Ex. 2 above is

$$\frac{2}{\pi} \sum_{k=0}^{\infty} \frac{(-1)^k\,\mathrm{sech}\,[(2k+1)\pi b/(2a)]}{2k+1}.$$

9. For a square plate show by superposition of solutions, without obtaining any solution explicitly, that when one face is held at unit temperature and the others are held at zero, then the temperature at the center is $\tfrac{1}{4}$. Then by comparing your result with Ex. 8, using $b = a$, conclude that

$$\sum_{k=0}^{\infty} \frac{(-1)^k\,\mathrm{sech}\,[(2k+1)\pi/2]}{2k+1} = \frac{\pi}{8}.$$

10. A circular plate has radius R. The edge $r = R$ of the plate is held at temperature unity for $0 < \theta < \pi$, at zero temperature for $\pi < \theta < 2\pi$. Find the temperature throughout the plate.

ANS. $u = \tfrac{1}{2} + \dfrac{2}{\pi} \displaystyle\sum_{k=0}^{\infty} \left(\dfrac{r}{R}\right)^{2k+1} \dfrac{\sin\,(2k+1)\theta}{2k+1}.$

11. A plate with concentric circular boundaries $r = a$ and $r = b$, $0 < a < b$, has its inner boundary held at temperature A, its outer one at temperature B. Find the temperature throughout.

ANS. $u = \dfrac{B \ln\,(r/a) - A \ln\,(r/b)}{\ln\,(b/a)}.$

12. The plate of Ex. 11 has its inner edge $r = a$ insulated, its outer edge held at temperature unity for $0 < \theta < \pi$ and held at temperature zero for $\pi < \theta < 2\pi$. Find the temperature throughout.

ANS. $u = \tfrac{1}{2} + \dfrac{2}{\pi} \displaystyle\sum_{k=0}^{\infty} \dfrac{(r/b)^{2k+1} + (a/r)^{2k+1}(a/b)^{2k+1}}{1 + (a/b)^{4k+2}} \cdot \dfrac{\sin\,(2k+1)\theta}{2k+1}.$

13. A flat wedge is defined in polar coordinates by the region $0 < r < R$, $0 < \theta < \beta$. Find the temperature throughout if the edges $\theta = 0$ and $\theta = \beta$ are held at temperature zero and the curved edge $r = R$ is held at unit temperature.

ANS. $u = \dfrac{4}{\pi} \displaystyle\sum_{k=0}^{\infty} \left(\dfrac{r}{R}\right)^{(2k+1)\pi/\beta} \dfrac{\sin\,[(2k+1)\pi\theta/\beta]}{2k+1}$.

14. For the flat wedge of Ex. 13 find the temperature if the edge $\theta = 0$ is held at zero, the edge $\theta = \beta$ is held at unit temperature, and the curved edge $r = R$ is held at temperature $f(\theta)$ for $0 < \theta < \beta$.

ANS. $u = \theta/\beta + \displaystyle\sum_{n=1}^{\infty} A_n \left(\dfrac{r}{R}\right)^{n\pi/\beta} \sin\,(n\pi\theta/\beta)$,

in which

$$A_n = \frac{2}{\beta} \int_0^\beta [f(\theta) - \theta/\beta] \sin\,(n\pi\theta/\beta)d\theta.$$

Index